Dr. Daniel J. Benor

HEALING RESEARCH
Holistic Energy Medicine and Spirituality

VOLUME ONE
Research in Healing

Dr. Daniel J. Benor

HEALING RESEARCH
Holistic Energy Medicine and Spirituality

VOLUME ONE
Research in Healing

British Library Cataloguing-in-Publication Data

A catalogue record for this book is available
from the British Library.
ISBN 1-898271-21-6

Die Deutsche Bibliothek – CIP-Einheitsaufnahme

Benor, Daniel J.:
Healing research : holistic energy medicine
and spirituality / Daniel J. Benor. – München : Helix.

Vol. 1. Research in healing. – 1992
ISBN 3-927930-21-0

First published by Helix Editions Ltd. in the United Kingdom 1993,
under licence from Helix Verlag GmbH, Munich, Federal Republic of Germany.

Helix Editions Ltd.,Centrepoint, Chapel Square, Deddington, Oxfordshire OX15 OSG, United Kingdom
Helix Verlag GmbH, Windeckstrasse 82, D-81375 Munich, Germany

This book was designed and produced in Germany by Helix Verlag GmbH.

House Editor/Designer: Norbert Netzer   House Proof-Reading: Gabi Reiner
Index: Hilary Flenley, Edinburgh   Layout of Tables: Brigitte Eiglmaier

Setting and Page Make-up: Erwin Stummer, Munich, Germany
Filmset in Times New Roman 10.5 pt on 12; titles in Benguiat; mottoes in Snell Roundhand
Jacket Design and Illustration: Tim A. Maunder, Bere Regis, Dorset, U.K.
Printed and bound by Schauenburg Graphische Betriebe GmbH, Schwanau-Allmannsweier, Germany

ISBN 1-898271-21-6
ISBN 3-927930-21-0

HEALING RESEARCH

VOLUME ONE
Research in Healing

CONTENTS

FOREWORD

I have been exploring the realms of healing and parapsychology for more than thirty-five years. My interests have led me to extensive evaluations of clairvoyant diagnosis. The research I have conducted on this subject has thoroughly convinced me of its validity and usefulness.*

Dr. Benor's manuscript goes well beyond anything that I have seen in documenting the abundance of work in the psychic-healing field. Even if one wanted only to have an annotated bibliography of available research in healing and psi phenomena, this book would be worth reading. It would take one several years to accumulate the information if one could find all the references.

As in all such work, this outstanding presentation by Dr. Benor is not likely to sway or appeal the mentally inflexible and those with traditionally closed minds. But for the individual who is truly interested in exploring the amount of information available and who has a concept of that which is not 'known' or is 'uncontrolled', HEALING RESEARCH provides an encyclopedic compilation of material available to this point in time. I am personally delighted to have had an opportunity to review the manuscript prior to its publication. Work such as this needs wide dissemination.

C. Norman Shealy, M.D., Ph.D.

---

* Dr. Shealy's research on clairvoyant diagnosis is reviewed in Chapter I–5. His experiences are detailed in his book, *Occult Medicine Can Save Your Life* (see References).

ACKNOWLEDGEMENTS

My thanks to all the authors and publishers who agreed so generously to permit me to quote their works; to Wayne Norman at the library of the Parapsychology Foundation in New York and to Marian Silverman and her staff at the medical library of Albert Einstein Medical Center in Philadelphia, who helped me track down many of these references.

Grateful acknowledgement is made to the following for permission to quote longer excerpts from copyrighted material:

Curtis Brown Associates, Ltd., for quotations from *Psychic Healers* by David St. Clair, Copyright © David St. Clair;

Paraphysical Laboratory, Downton, Wiltshire, England, for quotations from *Journal of Paraphysics* by Viktor Adamenko;

Harper & Row, Inc., for quotations from *Mystic with the Healing Hands: The Life of Olga Worrall* by Edwina Cerutti, Copyright © by Ambrose A. & Olga N. Worrall, Copyright © 1970 by the Layman's Movement/ Wainwright House;

The Theosophical Publishing House, Wheaton, IL, for quotations from *Five Great Healers Speak Here* by Nancy and Esmond Gardner, Copyright © 1982 by Nancy and Esmond Gardner;

Dean Kraft, for quotations from *Portrait of a Psychic Healer*, published by G.P. Putnam's Sons, Copyright © 1981 by Dean Kraft.

My thanks to all the healers who have given of their time and who have shared openly of themselves, explaining to this initially skeptical scientist about their work and beliefs.

My deepest thanks to the healers who have given me healing. It is through the experience of having healing that I have come to know most about myself, about healing and about what feels important in the world.

INTRODUCTION

Miracles do not happen in contradiction to Nature, but only in contradiction to that which is known to us in Nature.

St. Augustine

Healing brings us to a place of inner peace and harmony.
Photograph by Tony Sleep

Healing in the World Today

Healers practice in every country in the world. They report that they can help to improve nearly every condition known to man. In some instances they find miraculous cures to illnesses which conventional medicine has nothing to offer but a learned diagnosis and a disheartening prognosis. Far more often they provide a modest amelioration of suffering and a healthier perspective.

A wealth of rigorous research literature and a plethora of anecdotal evidence demonstrate that psi healing, biological energy fields and related phenomena exist. There is highly significant evidence for healing effects on enzymes, cells in the laboratory, bacteria, yeasts, plants, animals and humans. More controlled experiments have been conducted on healing than on all the other complementary therapies combined (with the exception of hypnosis and psychoneuroimmunology). [1,2]. In the light of these findings, western medicine will have to make major adjustments in its basic understanding of body functions in health and illness. These are only whiffs of the more general winds of paradigm shifts overtaking western science [3].

The findings reported in this book will be disputed by many scientists. They will state that there must be explanations within conventional science to account for unusual healings. VOLUME II reviews self-healing and energy medicine to clarify how psi healing may transcend ordinary and even extraordinary mind-body interactions. The reader is challenged to join in their criticisms and to suggest theories to explain away the findings and theories considered here. Many body functions are not adequately explained by mechanistic and biochemical models. Psychological and psychosomatic contributions to health and disease can explain aspects of many illnesses, but these concepts have not been integrated fully in western medicine. Excellent research has been conducted, for example, demonstrating that hypnotic and postanesthetic suggestion can dramatically alleviate pain and other postsurgical discomforts and complications (PEARSON; WOLFE; BENSEN). Yet most surgeons are either unaware of these methods or find that these subjects are so alien to their belief systems that they are unwilling even to consider them [4]. With the prevalent emphasis on mechanistic psychological concepts, it is no surprise that the even more revolutionary ideas associated with psi healing research and energy medicine are unwelcomed and often ignored or totally rejected [5].

The reader is also invited to consider new theories to account for phenomena which have been reported from the dawn of recorded history and are alien to Newtonian western scientific thinking, though not to the customs and understanding of many other cultures.

A wide variety of sources was tapped to obtain the psi healing material in this book. I hope that the availability of the literature presented here will excite interest in psi healing, will alert more people to its benefits and will enable further healing research.

Healing means different things to various people. For the purposes of this review psi healing is defined as a systematic, purposeful intervention by one or more persons aiming to help another living being (person, animal, plant or other living system), by means of focused intention, hand contact, or 'passes' to improve their condition. This may involve the invocation of belief systems which include external agents such as God, Christ, other 'higher powers', spirits, universal or cosmic forces or energies; special healing energies or forces residing in the healer; psychokinesis (mind over matter); or self-healing powers or energies latent in the healee.[6]

I prefer the term 'psi healing' or simply 'healing', although others favor such expressions as 'spiritual healing', 'mental healing', 'bio-energo-therapy', or other names[7]. The difficulty in choosing an appropriate term reflects our ignorance of mechanisms involved in the healing process. We must also be careful to set aside our prejudices against aspects of healing which might not suit our backgrounds or experience. A physician who is also a healer tells me, "When I finish my conventional treatments I ask whether patients might let me try a little magic on them which might help. I rarely have anyone refuse. I am surprised myself how pains, even chronic ones, sometimes clear up rapidly with my healing touch. Sometimes a patient catches me out and says, 'Oh! You've given me a healing'. I confess at that point that they

are right. But if I were to mention the word 'healing' at the beginning, I would have fifteen minutes of explaining to them about their notions on what healing isn't or shouldn't be."

Psi healing in the forms of prayer, healing meditation or of laying-on-of-hands, has been practised in virtually every known culture. Prayers and rituals for healing are universally a part of religion. Reports of folk-healers are familiar from legend, the Bible, anthropological studies of 'undeveloped' cultures, the popular press and more recently from scientific research.

There are two broad categories of healing. In the first, prayers or meditation for the ill person's return to health are conducted either by an individual or a group. The healer(s) may be at the side of the healee or may be many miles away. The second form of healing involves some variation of a laying-on-of-hands. The healer places his[8]. hands either on or near the body and may move them (in what may be called 'passes') around the body. Chapter I-1 shares healers' descriptions of their practices.

How healing works is the substance of this book, emphasizing research perspectives. Those experiments meeting rigorous research standards are reviewed in Chapter I-4, each followed by comments on its strengths and weaknesses. Less rigorous studies are presented in Chapter I-5.

I have done my best to present healing as clearly as possible. Detailed reports of original research allow you to decide for yourself whether a belief in healing is warranted. In Chapter IV-1 I share my personal experiences as student healer and healee, my *Weltanschauung* and biases, so you may compare and contrast these with your own in deciding how much credence to give to my discussions and analyses. I have attempted as much as possible to keep summaries of research separate from discussions and speculations. **Discussion** denotes the boundary between literature reviews and discussions. Broader and briefer topical summaries and discussions are in Chapters IV-2 and IV-3.

My own beliefs shifted as I immersed myself in writing this book. I set out intending to clarify whether or not there is a scientific basis for believing that psi healing might be effective. From extensive reading in parapsychology I was receptive to that possibility. Although I had studied healing research, placebo effects, suggestion, hypnosis, biofeedback and other methods by which people can cure themselves, I was still skeptical of psi healing. Subsequent personal experiences and studies have convinced me that that psi healing exists and is a potent therapy.

What is entailed in healing is the subject of these books. In the U.K. the term 'spiritual healing' is used generically for what I label 'psi healing'. Spirituality is a facet to healing which is again alien to much of western science. VOLUME III considers research which begins to confirm that consciousness survives death and that man's spirit may be a vital part of his being. Many healers consider that the spiritual effects of their treatments are more important than the physical ones. After prolonged studies I have overcome my skepticism and agree with them.

I dedicate this book to the researchers who braved their colleagues' skepticism, disapproval and sanctions against psi healing.

They are exploring parts of a world that western society has not only neglected but actually shunned. I take my hat off to those who have chosen to explore and champion subjects that are at best tolerated by much of the establishment and frequently rejected out of hand. They risk their professional standing in the eyes of their peers in search of methods and understanding to help others deal with their physical and emotional disorders. These are modern-day Galileos who dare to question the credos of the established Newtonian scientific community; who dare to suggest that mind and spirit are separable from brain but intimately integrated with the entire body; and who dare to explore the implications and consequences of these beliefs. Although not threatened with burning at the stake, they face inquisitions and ostracism by their peers, curtailment of research funds and even termination of employment.

I dedicate this book equally to the healers who have learned to trust their inner guidance and to provide a service which benefits healees. Individual healers have to brave the censure of disbelievers from scientific and healing communities.

The house of healing is splintered into many fragmentary beliefs and practices. Sadly, many healers are no more tolerant than their critics when it comes to discussing their beliefs and those of others. Hopefully this book may serve as well to open the eyes and ears and hearts of healers to the many rooms in the mansions of healing and to the fact that one may rest in any one room without rejecting the others.

Examining the Evidence

Let me share an anecdotal report of a modest healing.

> A nurse at a hospital where I worked complained of an excruciating headache. "My forehead feels like a truck ran over it!" she moaned. Although previously she had expressed considerable skepticism about psi healing, in her distress she gladly accepted my offer of treatment. I passed my hands a few inches away from her body, scanning tactilely from head to toe. As I did so, I noted a 'sticky' feeling over her forehead, and a generally weak energy field around her entire body.

I then treated her head with a laying-on-of-hands. Within a few minutes she told me the headache was gone. I also picked up a mental image of this woman carrying a burden which was much too heavy for her. I shared this with her and she broke into tears. She told me of her struggles in supporting two children as a single parent; having to work extra hours in order to make ends meet; sorting out a relationship with a man who was having legal difficulties; and not having enough time for meeting her own needs. She was very grateful for the healing and for our discussion on reducing the stresses in her life.

Another instance was related by the late *M. H. TESTER*, a gifted British healer. A wom-

Fig. I-1. M. H. Tester, a healer who wrote one of the clearest books on his healing work. *Photo by courtesy of Psychic News*

an nearing forty came to him for treatment of a duodenal ulcer which had caused severe pain and had not responded to drug or dietary therapy, nor to tranquillizers. Surgery was recommended but she feared this.

> She wanted to know if I could heal her and how she could avoid the dreaded operation... I never give medical advice. It is not my function. I do not have the requisite qualifications. But I do explain the healing process and the philosophy that surrounds it. And somewhere along the line, the questions all answer themselves...

The woman discussed stresses contributing to her ulcer, including being widowed three years earlier and bearing the burden of raising three teenage children.

> ...I put my right hand on the top of her stomach and my left hand on her back. My conscious mind shut itself off as the power flowed through me. At these moments, I lose an appreciation of time. I had no idea if I had been 'out' for a few seconds or for many minutes. Later, I realised it must have been quite a while...
>
> She sat quite still, with her eyes closed. The nervousness had left her. She seemed completely relaxed. When she opened her eyes, she was almost serene. For a while, she said nothing. Then she smiled. It was the first smile I had seen. The lines of tension were gone.
>
> I asked about the pain in her chest. There was none. There was no discomfort, either. She felt fine.

She was scheduled for a barium X-ray ten days later and for a preoperative examination a week after. Tester made an appointment for the next week.

> As she left, she asked me if I thought the operation would now be necessary. I said I did not know. She asked if she should keep to her bland diet. I said it was up to her.
>
> The following Monday, she was a changed woman. She came in smiling and full of good news. She had been completely free of pain and discomfort for a week. She was sleeping right through the night and eating 'like a horse'. For the first time in years, she had eaten fish and chips.

The X-rays showed only scar tissue and the surgeon did not recommend any further treatment. At a final visit, Tester discussed her philosophical views and recommended several books. There were changes on this level as well, which Tester felt would aid her in not having a recurrence.

Science has viewed such anecdotal reports of healers with skepticism. Even reports from physicians who, like myself, are also healers, do little to alter prevalent disbeliefs about healing (ROBERTON; STRAUCH). Skeptics discount our observations. Reports of healing contradict their beliefs too drastically. They also want a theory to explain healing before they would consider it seriously. Because our understanding of psi healing is embryonic, research is essential to explain it and to help it become more generally accepted. Unfortunately, little thorough research has been done with humans. This has fed the skepticism of western scientists, resulting in a vicious circle.

Established institutions are unwilling to invest in studies of healing, so long as respected journals hesitate to publish works on healing. Since only a few medical publications on the subject are available, general ignorance of work in the field of healing is considerable. This, in turn, feeds the skepticism. RICHARD A. PROCTOR relates in *Old and New Astronomy:*

> The aged mathematician Clavius expressed the opinion that the satellites of Jupiter were the children of Galileo's telescope; but the honest Jesuit frankly admitted his mistake when he had himself seen them. Deterred by their backsliding, those of feebler faith declined to look, lest they should be perverted by what they saw.

Skeptics wish to protect the public from charlatanism. They point out that care must be taken in healing research to avoid *Type I research errors*. Treatments that are not sound and effective should not be used and explanations that are unsupported by evidence should not be promoted. This is the primary orientation of western medicine.

Suggestion, hypnosis and other psychological mechanisms can bring about dramatic cures of many illnesses. In essence, these are methods of self-healing. Instances of alleged healings such as of a headache may be no more than self-healings.

Still, anecdotal evidence and logical discussion are insufficient to prove a treatment is effective. A 'controlled' study is the accepted western method for testing a treatment, be it medication, surgical procedure, psychotherapy or any other ministration for illness. This is done in the following way. Individuals with similar problems are divided into two groups. The experimental group is given the treatment while the 'control' group is not. All other variables are kept constant between the two groups as far as possible. If people in the experimental group change more than in the control group, the treatment being studied (hopefully the only variable differentiating the two groups) is given the credit or blame (BENOR/DITMAN).

A check on whether the differences between the groups are meaningful is provided by statistical analysis. These mathematical calculations provide estimates of the level of *probability* (*p*) at which the differences could have occurred by chance. Scientific convention accepts that a difference is reliably demonstrated when it might occur only five times in a hundred; and even better if only one time in a hundred or less (abbreviated, respectively, as 'p less than 0.05 or 0.01' or alternatively 'p < 0.05', etc.).

Statistical analysis is important because we want to be certain that a treatment is effective. A third of any group of people may respond readily to suggestions that they recover from physical ailments. One might thus be fooled into believing that a treatment was worthwhile when actually its effectiveness was due only to the power of suggestion. That is, the suggestion was what led to the observed differences rather than the treatment. Furthermore, if the experimenter is aware of which treatment is being provided to which group, he may give subtle cues to members of the group receiving the experimental treatment that their condition ought to improve. Conversely, he may unintentionally hint to the control group that he does not expect their improvement.

For these reasons it is common to run controlled experiments in 'double-blind' fashion. Neither the experimenters nor the persons treated are aware of which person is receiving the active treatment and which is in the control group. This distributes blatant or latent suggestion effects evenly over experimental and control groups, leaving the experimental variable under study as the one most likely to have caused the differences between the groups.

A variation of the double-blind theme is to use sequential self-controls. In this case each individual receives one form of treatment for a certain period. This is then switched (without clinicians' or patients' knowledge) to an alternative treatment. This is especially appropriate for studies of drug efficacy. Identical active drug and placebo pills can be used in coded fashion. An experimenter other than the examining clinician would distribute experimental and control pills so that blinds are maintained. Each patient's response to the experimental and control treatments can then be studied. This process can be used only in chronic illnesses where treatment alleviates symptoms but doesnot cure the disease. It lessens uncertainty about whether control and experimental groups are comparable.

Western medicine, in its zeal to avoid making *Type I experimental errors* (of accepting as true something that is not), has sometimes gone to the extreme of a *Type II research error* (rejecting as being useless treatments that actually are of value). In this way it has dismissed out-of-hand even consideration of the possibility that psi healing may be effective. Western medicine behaves as PETRARCH admitted, "I am so afraid of error that I keep hurtling myself into the arms of doubt rather than into the arms of truth."

To ensure that we do not reject valuable information as a result of this attitude, anecdotal reports and clinical observations that have not been verified by controlled studies are reviewed in Chapters I-1 and I-5. Healing involves alterations in the body apparently influenced by the minds of the healer and healee, and includes diagnoses by healers which appear based on telepathic or clairsentient perceptions.

Chapter I-3 reviews research from parapsychology which deals with related studies. I am impressed that the peer review given to parapsychological research has been thorough, particularly in view of the high level of skepticism accorded to the field of parapsychology by the western scientific world.

The following parapsychological journals are professionally refereed by a peer review system:
. *The European Journal of Parapsychology;*
The Journal of the American Society for Psychical Research (irregularly since 1957; regularly from 1970);
The Journal of Parapsychology;
The Journal of the Society for Psychical Research;
Research in Parapsychology is the collection of presentation summaries from the annual meeting of the Parapsychological Association, without peer review of the publication, although papers are critiqued as they are presented and the authors have opportunity to revise the papers prior to publication.

Parapsychology is accepted within the American Academy for the Advancement of Science.

Some readers will still criticize the fact that most of the research has been published in parapsychological rather than in medical journals. This is another 'Catch-22' situation. Most medical journals have regularly refused to publish healing research, giving a variety of excuses. They apparently consider it unscientific from the mere fact that it is not within the accepted realms of western medical practice. They point out that such research has not been published previously in medical journals.

The shameful response of JOHN MADDOX, editor of the prestigious journal, *Nature*, to an article on homeopathy which he had approved for publication in his own journal, is a prime example of this process. An entire issue of the *Journal of the American Medical Association (JAMA)* was devoted to such problems (March 9, 1990).

In seeking to comprehend healing we can benefit from the experience of the numerous 'complementary' therapies proliferating today. Chapter II-2 highlights aspects of these which overlap with healing. Changes in the world of matter appear to require energy. This and the descriptions of healing phenomena suggest that the process of psi healing may also involve one or more energies (BENOR 1984). Fields and energies in and near the body are discussed in Chapters II-3, II-4, IV-2 and IV-3.

Healers find that spiritual changes often accompany treatments. Some healers report that spirits help in doing healing and that healings may include aspects of reincarnation. These, along with religious contexts for healing, are considered in VOLUME III. Psychic surgery, combining many aspects of energy medicine and mediumistic phenomena, is reviewed in Chapter III-7.

Some readers will find the evidence sound but will have difficulty accepting the implications of the findings. This is a common problem when one's world view is challenged with new materials which appear to contradict 'common sense'.

There is a great deal, in the most acceptable science of today, that represents a rehabilitation of supposed legends, superstitions, and folklore. Recall Voltaire's incredulity as to fossils, which according to him only a few peasants would believe in... Here was one of the keenest of minds; but it could not accept data, because it rejected explanations of these data.

Charles Fort

We are biased by our materialistic society to believe that anything which is not measurable through our senses is non*sense* or im*material*. Healing suggests that intuitive information may be valid in its own right, outside the laws of the material world. This is similar to modern physics, whose explanations make no sense in terms of classical, Newtonian, physics. Further analogies with modern physics and other hypotheses to explain healing are presented and discussed in VOLUME IV.

Historical Perspectives

Here is a brief history of healing in the West to help put the subject in perspective[9].

From anthropological studies of pre-industrial societies, it is thought that our distant ancestors viewed themselves as close to nature and intimately involved with it. They did not see themselves as distinct from the laws and influences of the environment. The forces of nature, the stars, the spirits and the gods that controlled the cosmos also ruled the people.

Western scientists have pejoratively judged such closeness with nature as a confusion between what is within a person and what is external to him; what he can control by physical methods and what he seeks to influence by 'magical' means. Anthropologists report that shamans or medicine men (the mediators between humans and the world at large) use prayers, chants, talismans, herbs and potions to influence a world that humans in that 'primitive' society could not hope to understand – much less influence to any degree. This presumes that pre-industrial man deludes himself through wishful thinking into believing that he can influence a world which is actually beyond his comprehension and control. Closer, more open scrutiny of modern medicine men such as the native American chief, ROLLING THUNDER, reveals that so-called primitives may know very effective methods of psi healing (BOYD). Personal explorations of healing may lead to greater awareness of and trust in our intuitive modes for knowing.

The dichotomy between physical and psychic approaches to medicine has been prevalent from the dawn of recorded history. The Code of Hammurabi from 2000 B.C. mentions payments to surgeons for successful operations; death for failures. This code also refers to incantations and treatments for demons. Egyptian papyri from several centuries later talk of dual streams of treatment: one involving magical words, charms and incantations; another using scientific approaches of medicines and surgery (ESTES). The Ebers papyrus of 1550 B.C. mentions the laying-on-of-hands for relief of pain.

The Greeks, unlike the Egyptians, did not dichotomize the world. PYTHAGORAS, who lived around the sixth century B.C., was a physician (as well as a mathematician, astronomer and philosopher). He considered healing to be the noblest of his pursuits and integrated healing into his considerations of ethics, mind and soul. He called the energy associated with healing *pneuma*. He felt that this originates in a fire in the center of the universe, which imparts to human beings their vitality and immortal soul. "Pythagoras's central fire was a primordial force, the sparks from which gave life to man." (CODDINGTON) His followers conceived of the pneuma as being visible in a luminous body and held that light could cure illness. They believed that everything is composed of opposites, which is similar to the eastern cosmology of *yin* and *yang*. The opposites are in conflict and need to be balanced in proper proportions to ensure harmony. The condition of the conflicting forces within the individual parallels their relationship in the world.

A century later, *HIPPOCRATES* recognized that the sensations of heat and tingling with a laying-on-of-hands accompanied relief of symptoms. He hypothesized a healing energy, the *vis medicatrix naturae* (the healing power of nature), as the vital force of life. He advised that physicians must identify blocking influences within the individual and between him and the cosmos in order to restore the proper flow of pneuma. Nature (not the doctor) heals the patient. Sadly, he taught that mind and body were separate.

The theory of the greater unity of mind and body which the Pythagoreans had advanced was soon superseded by the Hippocratic beliefs that mind and body are dichotomous. *PLATO* criticized this view: "If the head and the body are to be well, you must begin by curing the soul; that is the first thing ... the great error of our day in the treatment of the human body (is) that physicians separate the soul from the body." The Hippocratic system, which was codified by *GALEN* in the second century A.D., became the standard for medical practices for many centuries thereafter.

JESUS was a great healer. The Bible and Gospels tell of numerous individual and group healings by Christ and the Apostles. They used touch, saliva, mud and cloth *vehicles* for healing, words, prayers, exorcism, faith and compassion[10]. Unfortunately, the church gradually turned away from healing for a variety of reasons (MACMANAWAY; BEK/ PULLAR). It de-emphasized healing in its ministries, sometimes even denying its existence other than in metaphor or mythology.

The Middle Ages saw a stagnation in medicine as in most other areas of intellectual endeavors. Alchemy and witchcraft may have held elements of wisdom concerning healing but these are not readily apparent.

In the seventeenth century, *PARACELSUS* shed the first modern healing light on the fossilized system of medicine of the Middle Ages. He refocused the study of medicine on naturalistic observations and saw human beings as an integral part of nature, reflecting within themselves the larger cosmos without. He apparently saw auras since he reported "a healing energy that radiates within and around man like a luminous sphere" (CODDINGTON). He called this force *archaeus*, believing it could be effective from a distance and could cause as well as cure disease. He also believed that magnets, stars and other heavenly bodies could influence humans via this force. The western notions of *magnetic* or *sympathetic medicine* seemingly came through these observations (later reinforced by *MESMER* and other hypnotists).

Paracelsus further noted that a human being has a second body, which he labeled the *star* or *sidereal body*. He felt that the lower instincts are housed in the animal body, while higher instincts such as wisdom and art are housed in the astral. He believed that the etheric body motivates the physical body under the influence of the mind. He felt that both are integrally related and that both can be subject to disease. For instance, negative thoughts can block flows of archaeus, which could lead to illness. He held that "resolute imagination can accomplish all things".

(CODDINGTON) He also believed in a third body, a soul or eternal spark which is immortal. The energy body is discussed in VOLUME II. Research evidence for survival of the spirit is reviewed in VOLUME III.

Paracelsus was eccentric, irascible and impetuous. Despite his brilliant observations and conceptualizations, he so alienated people that many of his notions produced far less impact than they might have done otherwise. Moreover, his ideas had little chance of competing with those of two other scientists of the seventeenth century, F. Bacon and Descartes.

FRANCIS BACON started the western world along the path of understanding the laws of science in order to *master* nature rather than to become harmonious with nature. *RENÉ DESCARTES* revolutionized western thinking by applying mathematical, logical concepts to an analysis of the world and of humans. His thought is so much a part of current western views that it is hard for many to conceive of a world in which systematic, quantifiable relationships do not exist between objects and between parts of objects.

Descartes' insight had unfortunate consequences. It led to a firm dichotomizing between body (measurable) and mind (intangible) and to the assumption that body could affect mind but not the reverse. These concepts helped to lead us out of the Dark Ages in the physical sciences and to search out physical causes for illness but were detrimental in their denial of the mind as a causal influence on the body. They led science to denigrate everything which was not measurable and explained with scientific theories.

The West was experiencing an industrial revolution at the time Descartes' ideas were spreading. Intoxicated with growing success in comprehension, manipulation and control of the environment, the West focused more and more on a material view of the world. In medicine this extended to a nearly exclusive concentration on physical aspects of disease. This has been productive in the identification of agents of disease, including bacteria, parasites, viruses, vitamines, hormones and genetic anomalies, as well as in discoveries of chemicals and mechanical interventions to treat diseases. It has been counterproductive in producing a lopsided emphasis on *physical* causes and cures of illness.

Only a few scientists dared to question the view that the mind cannot influence the body. Such a voice was that of *GOTTFRIED WILHELM LEIBNIZ*, another contemporary of Descartes. He proposed that centers of force, which he termed *monads*, are the organizing principles in the universe. They reflect in their microcosm the macrocosm of the vaster universe. They express themselves in substance as a force. With their perception, they strive to surpass corporeal limitations. These concepts remain little-recognized even today, although they foreshadow some of the more advanced contemporary ideas on the nature of the universe.

At the end of the eighteenth century, *FRANZ ANTON MESMER* popularized another aspect of healing. He demonstrated that he could improve numerous symptoms with *magnetic passes* of his hands around patients' bodies. At first he held magnets in his hands but soon found he was just as effective without them. He hypothesized that he channelled a *magnetic fluid* into the patient. Although he had staunch followers, the vast majority of the medical community was critical and unaccepting of his findings. A commission, set up in France to study the subject, produced a negative report which effectively sidelined Mesmer's methods.

The *MARQUIS DE PUYSEGUR* introduced a form of healing similar to that of Mesmer. He demonstrated that he could influence patients by an act of will, without the use of magnetic passes and with no recourse to theories of fluids. His work with hypnosis reintroduced an appreciation of the impact of thought on the body. [It is fascinating to learn (M. LONG 1976) that *kahuna* healers in Hawaii were aware of the unconscious mind and of principles of suggestion many centuries before they were discovered in the West.]

In other areas of medical research, *LUIGI GALVANI* and *ALESSANDRO VOLTA* explored the electrical stimulation of animal muscles, puzzling out the nature of the body's electrical activity. Galvani believed this was evidence for a life force in animals.

KARL VON REICHENBACH, a German industrialist, in the middle of the nineteenth century explored a variety of physical properties of living beings, relating them to a universal energy which he believed permeated the body. He called this force *od* or *odyle*.

Scientists seeking to study forces within the body which seemed to be related to health and disease had to fight against the stream of public opinion. Since Cartesian influence had reasoning and research to support its views, scientists with theories which contradicted conventional beliefs were at best ignored and often ridiculed or worse. *WILHELM REICH*, a psychiatrist in the first half of the twentieth century, developed elaborate theories about *orgone* energy. This is a distinct form of universal energy that becomes blocked in the body as a result of emotional problems. He was persecuted and jailed in the United States because of his views. His books were publicly burned. Nevertheless, his adherents, viz. *LOWEN*; *PIERRAKOS*, continued to develop his ideas.

Research in neurology supported the trend against energy medicine. Electrodes inserted in the brain can elicit specific sensations and memories. Here is proof that mind appears to be a product of the physical brain.

At the turn of the century, *SIGMUND FREUD* and *CARL GUSTAV JUNG* clarified that the unconscious mind may be an agent for certain illnesses. This was the birth of modern psychosomatic medicine, which advocates integration of mind with body. *SIR WILLIAM OSLER* recommended that physicians seek to understand the patient who has the disease and not merely the disease the patient has. This element is sorely lacking in most 'efficient', modern medical treatments. The most common complaint against conventional medicine is that the doctor doesn't listen to or talk with the patient.

Modern behavioral psychology demonstrates that learning by reward and punishment, or conditioning of the unconscious mind, may produce illness. This has contributed to our mechanistic view of human beings. Mass-production methods in our hospitals have added to compartmentalization of mind and body. More on these in VOLUME II.

A further element of alienation from self has come with the explosion of medical knowledge, which has produced a need for medical specialization. No single physician today can understand all there is to know about the body. A patient therefore has to parcel out his body among various specialists, who are keepers of the required esoteric knowledge for the diagnosis and treatment of that particular part which is ailing.

The system subtly and insidiously perpetuates itself. Young, idealistic doctors are trained mechanistically, almost exclusively within mass-production facilities, with methods stressing mechanistic efficiency. They learn to treat patients as they themselves were treated and as their superiors treat patients. Deviations from accepted norms meet severe censure from superiors and peers. Students and recent graduates often do not dare to mention interests in complementary therapies, lest their careers be jeopardized.

Economic factors mitigate against the acceptance of psi healing as a legitimate therapy. Drug therapy is a major industry throughout the world. Private health care is another major industry which resists competition.

Intellectual resistance to change is a problem. Western medicine has accepted numerous treatments as worth while with less research evidence to substantiate their validity than is available to support the efficacy of healing. Furthermore, many mechanistic western treatments carry inherent risks, some of them considerable (ROBIN). For example, chemotherapy and radiation therapy for cancer are toxic, noxious and may even be of unproven value if one considers possible sampling errors in much of the research carried out to date (OYE / SHAPIRO).

> We would rather be ruined than changed;
> We would rather die in our dread
> Than climb the cross of the moment
> And let our illusions die.
> *W. H. Auden*

Healing offers at least a non toxic adjunct to conventional therapies for many illnesses and may for this reason alone prove to be a treatment of choice. With further research, it may also become a treatment of first choice in western medicine. Healing aspects of other complementary therapies, in the framework of holistic medicine, are discussed in Chapter II-2.

This book challenges the reader to see the world anew. There is much evidence (not just opinion or speculation) that some individuals can heal themselves and/or others by what have been heretofore termed *paranormal* means. In Chapters I-1, 4 and 5, which deal directly with healing, I have quoted liberally from a wide spread of reports in diverse publications since I feared that in summarizing the ideas of others, sifting their concepts through my understandings of them, I would be presenting my interpretations of these phenomena and not theirs.

Most of the above deals with data of material and energy nature. Psi healing is commonly termed *spiritual healing* in England. Those who give and those who receive healing often have inner experience which they term *spiritual*. Healers frequently note that this may be the most important aspect of their treatments. This is considered in VOLUME III.

The annotated bibliography of research on healing permits readers to arrive at their own conclusions. I hope that this review will challenge the reader's imagination and stimulate pioneers to continue investigating this important frontier, which has barely begun to be explored in a scientific manner.

> Since we have come to the understanding that science is not a description of 'reality' but a metaphysical ordering of experience, the new science does not impugn the old. It is not a question of which view is 'true' in some ultimate sense. Rather, it is a matter of which picture is more useful in guiding human affairs.
> *Willis Harman*

Though the materials in this book are by no means comprehensive, they are as complete a sampling of relevant data as could be reasonably assembled in a single work.

An ancient Chinese proverb observes:

> If you pull at one blade of grass, you get the whole field.

There is a coherent interdigitation which emerges from considerations of the diverse practices and theories considered in HEALING RESEARCH.

The reader may still find a straight reading of these materials overwhelming. Skimming may suit better than plowing directly through. Some may even prefer to start with Chapters I-3 or II-1, which place healing in perspective and make the other chapters more comprehensible. Chapter IV-2 on theories may also be helpful in this regard. Studying the evidence for healing is rather like learning a complex game such as bridge. It is difficult to understand the suit of healing in the game of life until one has some comprehension of other parts, such as the trumps of psychological concomitants of disease. Yet other points cannot be fully understood without an appreciation of the evidence for healing.

At times I have had to insert a word or phrase within a quote in order to smooth the flow of words taken out of context. In such cases, I have placed the inserted words within brackets. The reader's attention is also drawn to the Glossary.

To aid readers in locating names on a page, small capital letters are used for names of authors (e.g. LARISSA VILENSKAYA). Small capitals in italics are used for names and subjects (e.g. *DJUNA DAVITASHVILI*) mentioned by the authors.

I highly recommend the serious reader to the original works reviewed and to the others mentioned in the Footnotes. Many more sources of material are available than could be summarized in this work, large as it is.

CHAPTER I - 1

Healers' Views of Healing

*Sit down before fact like a child, and be prepared
to give up every preconceived notion.
Follow humbly wherever and to whatever abysses
Nature leads, or you shall learn nothing.*

T. H. Huxley

Healers' beliefs and techniques are as varied as human experience and imagination can make them. Without prejudging any of them, let us consider a broad spectrum of anecdotal reports on what they do and believe they do.

Miraculous healings are rare, but marked enhancement of recuperation from a wide variety of disorders is an everyday occurrence. For many of these problems modern medicine can provide only partial treatments or only the questionable solace of a known diagnosis with small hope of palliation. Later chapters include more critical and scientific observations and studies of healing.

JOYCE GOODRICH (1982) lists alternative explanations for healing, which might be kept in mind when reading these descriptions:

1. The 'healee' may heal himself via self-healing mechanisms. The healer's function may be to suggest the possibility of a cure, or to catalyze it in some more active manner.

2. The healer may supply healing energy from his own body or being, perhaps involving dimensions other than those usually employed in everyday, sensory reality (LESHAN 1974a, 1976).

3. The healer may channel energy from outside himself, focusing it or making it available to the healee.

4. The healer may involve the assistance of sentient external agencies such as God, angels, Christ, spirits or others to assist in or to perform the healing.

5. A combination of several of the above is possible, especially the first together with one other, but also the second plus another.

Because of limitations of human sensory and psychological perceptions and understanding of the world, a full comprehension of what constitutes a healing may be beyond our capacities. Perhaps we can expand our means of comprehending the world via altered states of consciousness and extrasensory perceptions. We would then be able to advance the frontiers of understanding of healing, although we might still have difficulties in translating such understandings into linear thought and language.

I invite readers to join me in efforts to determine which of the above possibilities is the most likely. I will present as much evidence, background information and resources as are feasible in one work. I will synthesize my own speculations in Chapters IV-2 and IV-3.

First, let us let the healers and investigators talk for themselves.

Gordon Turner – A Time to Heal: The Autobiography of an Extraordinary Healer

The late GORDON TURNER was one of this century's great English healers. He describes his routines:

> Before attempting to heal the patient, I would stand behind his chair, resting the palms of my hands lightly on his shoulders. I would clear my mind and try to 'sense' the person I was about to treat.
>
> After a few moments, I became aware of his feelings. If he were in pain, I would sense its echo in my own body. With practice the acuteness of my sensitivity made it possible for me to rely on my feelings during these moments of attunement.
>
> I would then let my hands move lightly over the patient's body. As long as I could still my conscious mind they would be

drawn to the exact spot where the treatment was needed. My slowly expanding knowledge of anatomy and physiology was a great help. I would envisage healthy organs in place of those that were diseased. If there was an adjustment of the bones to be made, it was essential that I avoided thinking about what my hands were doing – for that matter even looking at them. Healing had to be a spontaneous rather than an intellectual matter.

Healing involved the transmission of energy – I was sure of that. I could feel this flowing through me. If my attunement had been made too casually, or if I became too personally involved in the healing, it would be my own energy which was drawn upon. But if the attunement was good and my mind clear, I could feel the healing power flowing through me from some apparently inexhaustible source. On such occasions I could heal for hours without tiring.

Discussion   TURNER believed that energies flowed both through and from himself. He was one of the most astute observers and reporters on healing. He also saw spirits. He kept an open mind regarding the questions we are examining in this book.

Larissa Vilenskaya – Parapsychology in the USSR

LARISSA VILENSKAYA studied bioelectronics and healing in the U.S.S.R. After moving to the West she was editor of the journal, Psi Research. In the following section she reports on aspects of healing research in the Soviet Union.

1. DJUNA DAVITASHVILI, a healer, reports that she can diagnose which parts of the body are diseased because different illnesses elicit different sensations in her hands as she passes them over the patient. These include 'prickling, warmth or other sensations not easy to define'. She can *charge* a plant with healing energy, which ordinary people can subsequently sense as a prickling feeling when passing a hand near the plant.

Vilenskaya refers to an investigation of Davitashvili's diagnostic ability:

Preliminary statement about the results of experimental work conducted by Evgenia Yuvashevna (Juna) Davitashvili at the Consultative and Diagnostics Center of ... Moscow, affiliated with the City Polyclinic ... during the period of November 17 through December 31, 1980: "During the course of the six-week period, 43 people who previously underwent examinaions in various medical institutions, were examined by J. Davitashvili with the intention of diagnosing their conditions. Concurrence of the clinical diagnoses and the diagnoses made by J. Davitashvili yielded 97.3%. It should be noted that in 49.7% of the cases she diagnosed additional concomitant diseases (which were confirmed in 86.9% of the cases during further polyclinic examination)."

In another study, a sensitive thermographic (temperature measuring) device was used to demonstrate posttraumatic arterial blockage in the right arm of the healee.

Before the session, the right hand was not visible on the photograph because its temperature was equal to the room temperature, due to the circulation disorder. In the middle of his forearm, a place of sharp decrease in temperature was visible – a manifestation of the mal-functions of body thermoproduction because of cicatrix (scar) changes as a result of the wound.

After the recording of this condition, a session for correction of the biofield of the right arm of the patient was conducted. J. Davitashvili carried out characteristic passes by her right hand along the patient's arm, and he felt clearly several specific sensations: heaviness in his hand, later in the whole arm, developing almost to slight pain, then the patient could not ball his hand into a fist because of the sensation of 'pushing away' between his fingers, as if they were 'the same poles of magnet'. In 8-10 minutes all these sensations disappeared and only the increasing warmth remained, which disappeared after the session. After the end of the session the thermograms of the patient's arm were recorded every 15 minutes. The thermograms showed the increasing temperature, widening of the area of higher temperature, with the hand becoming visible. First, blood volume in the smaller vessels increased and then in the larger vessels. In spite of the tissue changes due to the scar in the middle part of the forearm, the area of the 'cold' zone decreased. In 45 minutes after the session, the patient's hand was clearly visible at the thermovisor; its temperature increased, comparing with that before the session, at 2.5 – 3.0 degrees Celsius, although subjective sensation of warmth was lacking.

It should be noted that the right ('working') hand of the inductor became apparently cooler. The thermograms showed the difference in temperatures of the right and the left hands of the inductor, despite her doing intensive passes by the right hand. In a few minutes the equality in temperatures was reestablished after the inductor's autogenic suggestion.

2. *VITALY YAKOVLEV* is a healer who frequently treats headaches. Healees report that the pain seems to move with his hands as he passes them over their heads. In this way, Yakovlev 'gathers' the pain at the back of the head, and with a rapid movement of his hands from beside the temples to the chin, 'throws down' the pain. Healees say that at that moment the pain disappears.

3. *VLADIMIR SAFONOV*, engineer and former free-lance newspaper correspondent, has psi healing abilities. He recommends the following:

* Those aspiring to heal should, in the author's opinion, have the following attributes:
– a desire to overcome the inner barrier of disbelief in the possiblity of radiating the bioenergy from one's body;
– good health and no hereditary disease; age ranging from 30 to 50 years;
– lack of blind respect for an 'opposing' authority;
– some knowledge of medicine and human physiology;
– altruism and humanity; and
– the desire to research and share observations and findings.
* Distant healing requires the following:
… the ability of a healer to concentrate on the person for whom the energy is intended; to be able to imagine (without closing his eyes) the basic features of the person (face, tone of voice, clothes), remembering the last visual encounter with him. Of real assistance is a photograph of the person looking directly into the camera. The

maximum length of a distant healing session is 5-8 minutes. This duration is connected with specific features of one's thought processes, which does not allow prolonged concentration on one thought or image.

An interesting phenomenon that sometimes accompanies the transmission of energy from a distance is the appearance (involuntary) of a picture of the surrounding circumstances, in which the person receiving the energy is situated.

*   Distant diagnosis is possible from photographs.
... any photograph, even one taken in childhood carries information about the state of health of the person on the day when the diagnosis is made. In trying to learn this method of diagnostics, the following points are of great importance:
    Imagine clearly and in detail that the person whose conditions a healer is to determine is sitting on an empty chair near the healer.
    Having imagined as if it were the real person on the empty chair, the healer can begin the diagnostics with his hands. It is advisable at the beginning of training for the actual person to be present in the room.
    An essential condition is to forget for the moment that you are diagnosing an empty space in which you are imagining the object, but rather to think that you are diagnosing the actual person.
    The diagnosing of the imagined 'double' gives the same feeling as during ordinary diagnostics of a patient, only in the former case the sensations are weaker and less easily felt; the healer has to concentrate to the maximum degree possible.

Safonov can also identify the illness that caused the death of a person from a post-mortem photograph.
*   There is also another method of diagnostics. Sometimes a healer can, without analyzing his sensations, simply know that there is a diseased part of the body under his hand. Knowledge outstrips the observation.
*   Distant diagnosis is possible via the telephone.
    Quite by chance the author found that he was able to diagnose a person while talking to him by phone. Hearing the voice of the person, he could obtain in his mind an impression of the appearance of the person and of his disease.
*   Rejuvenation is possible via visualization.
    Throughout the ages, mankind has been seeking an explanation for the process of aging of the organism, trying to preserve the body through the most diverse ways and means. However, each of us can direct the 'biological clocks' within us, i.e. we can turn the hands of the clock backwards without the aid of any other force or action outside ourselves. In order to do this one has to restore in his memory one day of his life (hour by hour) when he was young, healthy and happy. This means to live again in the past. It may be for an hour or two, or for a day. Having spent one hour in the past, the organism 'charges' an enormous supply of bioenergy.

Discussion SAFONOV makes helpful suggestions for applications of healing. However, he does not explain why good health in the healer is required. This contradicts the experience of at least two healers I know who had serious illnesses from which they were cured prior to becoming healers themselves (LOM-BARDI; SHUBENTSOV). The suggestion that the healer lack 'blind respect for an opposing authority' is couched in negative terms. This would presumably mean the healer is confident of his own abilities, which has been noted by others to be important. Safonov's recommendation of visualizations for rejuvenation is unique. Many reports state that visualization is beneficial in several other ways.[1]

4. BARBARA IVANOVA, a Moscow parapsychologist, developed a "method for increasing perception of 'intuitive information' ". These are her instructions:

* Imagine some pleasant event or any picture or image which pleases you.
* Try to understand and remember how you have imagined this – what 'place' this mental image occupied in your mind.
* 'Wipe off' from your 'inner screen' everything that you imagined and create a 'vacuum' in your mind.
* When an experimenter gives a task-program (e.g. to identify the location of a scar on the body of a person situated in another room), wait passively 'filling the vacuum' by a programmed image. In other words, wait for the appearance of 'quasi-visual' or 'quasi-auditory' images in the same way and in the same 'place' of your mind where you had previously a conscious image.

VILENSKAYA states:

Using, along with the aforestated procedure, group relaxation and various exercises on visualization of spontaneous and 'programmed' images, Barbara Ivanova indicated that many of her students after several training sessions were able to perform remote diagnostics, successfully determining the nature and location of diseases, as well as locations of pains, scars, tumors, etc. The most gifted students sometimes could receive the name of a disease in medical terms, as 'quasi-auditory' information, while not possessing knowledge in medicine and in some cases not even understanding what this name meant. More often students gave some features and locations of disorders on the human body, without giving the exact name of a disease.

According to Ivanova, the same method also leads to development in students of the ability to perceive general intuitive (i.e. clairvoyant, including precognitive) information, not connected with medical problems. Having possessed these abilities herself, she observed that the results of the training group were much higher when training sessions were conducted by a 'psychic' person. Thus, it appears that not only the training method itself is important but rather some kind of 'psychic' (wordless) influence of a group leader.

Vilenskaya compares the healing work of Ivanova, who trained herself deliberately for this ability, with that of *BROTHER MACEDO*, a gifted natural healer in Brazil.

Both of them are able to perform mass sessions of healing (Barbara Ivanova – during her lectures, and Brother Macedo – during mutual meditations of participants); neither need to know the exact medical diagnosis to perform healing, believing that their radiations will 'find' the diseased organ or system ('weak spots') in the patient's body.
… 'telergy' applied by the Brazilian healer (as he coined it), and 'bioenergy' applied

by Soviet healers, are, in my opinion, manifestations of the same process of interactions of human beings which is as yet not understood by science.

Several testimonials by patients for Ivanova's healing ability are presented. A letter from Ivanova describes a series of controlled experiments in which some of Russia's best healers were studied. No measurable changes were noted. Ivanova notes that the officials reporting the results of these experiments omitted many important details.

Ivanova adds:

... if one has the ability to radiate bioenergy, it is not enough to give one the right to heal. First of all, a harmonization of both, patient and healer, is necessary, and only afterwards one may try to send his energy. There can be no lasting results without a certain ethical and moral level.

MARIA MIR visited the Soviet Union and obtained a number of writings by and about IVANOVA, which she and VILENSKAYA have put together in *The Golden Chalicet*. In this work, Ivanova expands upon her experiences in carrying out and teaching psi diagnosis and healing. She reports that she always uses either direct contact or, for distant healings, a link-up with the ill person via the telephone.

She teaches healing very cautiously to a select group of students, who must be ethical and moral people. She feels that otherwise healing energies could potentially 'boomerang' and affect the healer negatively, or be misused in unethical ways.

Student healers are led by very gradual steps to longer and longer periods of healing. Ivanova also utilizes a psychic induction procedure to enhance the healing abilities of her students. Of special interest are her precau-

tions to healers against dissipating their own energies in healing, instead of transmitting a cosmic energy. She notes that the following negative reactions have been observed in the healers (not in people they treat) when proper caution has not been employed:

* tingling, which can be so strong as to be 'exceedingly tormenting,' often associated with sensations of heat;
* muscular contractions, which are occasionally quite strong;
* giddiness, which may even proceed to complete loss of consciousness;
* perspiration;
* exhaustion, which can reach proportions of total weakness and depletion, especially when the healer exceeds his capacities and engages in healing beyond the time limits commensurate with his level of skill;
* feeling of fever, which can include shivering, cold, and weakness, again associated with excessive energy depletion;
* loss of weight, 'sometimes 800 – 1,000 grams after thirty minutes of work';
* high concentration of sugar in the blood, even to levels seen in diabetes;
* blood pressure changes, occasionally to dangerous levels;
* stress-like brainwaves, similar to those seen under strong emotional excitement;
* heart dysfunctions with pulse rates increasing or decreasing, and electrocardiograms demonstrating arrhythmias;
* loss of coordination, a rare occurrence;
* temporary loss of taste, smell, or other senses, with hypersensitivity or even sensory hallucinations;
* disturbance of endocrine system functioning on rare occasions;
* pains, especially in the extremities, but

also in other body parts;

* respiration disorder (not described specifically);

* loss or disturbance of sleep – a frequent occurrence;

* general depression, 'irritability or other signs of exhaustion of the nervous system, as well as many other symptoms of malfunction'.

* All of these disorders can be felt for minutes, hours or days, and some of them even for months, if necessary measures are not taken... We can view these disorders as a stress-response...

We can avoid these negative responses of mind and body by gradually training the psychic and exposing the body to the influence of our psi energies or that of other psychics only to a degree compatible with the psychic's potential.

IVANOVA reports on a variety of uncontrolled studies with success in diagnosis and relief of a range of symptoms and illnesses. She states that a negative governmental attitude in the Soviet Union, with censorship of reports of healing research activities, led to great difficulties for healers during the last decade.

In personal communication during a visit to the U.K., Ivanova mentioned an intercontinental healing experiment. A group of Americans visiting in Moscow videotaped her giving group healing. When the video tape was played to an audience in the U.S., the audience experienced healing effects.

Ivanova also shared her feeling that reincarnation is one of the most important concepts she teaches.

It is not that the same person passes from one physical life to another. Rather, it is a part, or facet, of a much more profound entity which expresses itself in physical existence to work out lessons of love and understanding for relationships with itself, with fellow beings and with its place is the cosmos. (In the West you might say 'With God', but this is against the beliefs currently acceptable in the Soviet Union.)

I myself have clear memories of previous lives as a German naval officer in the last century; as a courtesan in Spain; as a man in Brazil; and more. It is because of these lives that it was easy for me to learn Spanish, Portuguese and Italian. I apparently never had a previous life in an English speaking country or in Czechoslovakia, because these languages have been extremely difficult for me to learn. After only eight months' study, I was doing simultaneous translations in Portuguese. After three years' studies I still could barely translate a Czech newspaper, though Czech is very close to Russian which I have spoken all of my life.

We must also be aware that groups of people, nations and even the planet as a whole have group karma. This can explain some of the trends and events in history. After nations have swung to the dark side, as with Germany in this century, there is a challenge for its citizens to learn karmic lessons and to work out ways to compensate and make amends for their wrongs.

Ivanova has clairaudient perceptions for diagnosis and also for information she channels from sources suggesting discarnate entities, the collective unconscious and higher intelligences.

Discussion   Ivanova's methods for teaching clairsentience resemble those of SILVA MIND

CONTROL. Though they seem reasonable, they still require validation studies.

Ivanova's letter on the unsuccessful experiments implies that the negative attitudes of the observers may have influenced the process or the reporting.

The transmission of healing simultaneously to large numbers of patients has been reported by OLGA WORRALL and others. This might involve the healer making healing energies available, while the healees are the ones who draw the energy to themselves. This is even clearer in the case of ESTEBANY, described below.

It is encouraging that relations between the West and the East now permit increased sharing of information.

I am unsure what to conclude from the long list of symptoms Ivanova reports her student healers may experience. She speculates that they may be related to stress. Perhaps the negative atmosphere in the Soviet Union placed healers under pressures, which were expressed in these symptoms. In the West it is common for healers to report temporary sensations ('telesomatic reactions') which appear to correspond with the patient's symptoms, but it is unusual for such symptoms to persist or to be taken as dangerous.[2] In fact, some healers use these sensations to diagnose patients' problems.

Healers can often diagnose illness instantly, and could be a tremendous asset if their abilities could be integrated into mainstream medicine.

There are numerous healer techniques which seem idiosyncratic to particular practitioners. We have no idea as yet which of these may be essential to healing and which are merely magical beliefs, purely coincidental or necessary healing practices.

Nancy Gardner and Esmond Gardner – Five Great Healers Speak Here

The authors posed a standard set of questions to five gifted healers.

The following is noteworthy:

1. GURUDER SHREE CHITRABHANA, a Jain healer in India, states:

> . . . a true religious leader . . .[is] the small boat which takes the spiritual pilgrim from the shore to the deep-water vessel of spirituality out in the harbor.
>
> The limitations [to healing] are karma. Karma is an all-important factor in a healing or a blessing. If the karma is heavy, the efforts of the healer cannot succeed. Karma is the sum to date of your past actions in this life and in your previous lifetimes. It is the reaction and boomerang return of your deeds and thoughts and is constantly being modified by your present actions and thoughts. It is an absolute law, as forceful as an invisible wind that bends us with its power like so many trees, uprooting some and, when we die, blowing our souls into new situations like so many seeds.
>
> During your lifetime, your karma can be recorded in four ways.
> * It is writen on the water and is gone before you can read it.
> * It is written with pencil and can be erased.
> * It is written with ink. A special substance is needed to erase it.
> * It is carved in stone and written in blood. It can only be expiated with deeply carved suffering and understanding.
>
> The first two types of recording are gener-

ally acts of light-hearted carelessness, some little wound, an unkind joke, a thoughtless bit of character assassination. You feel sorry and – it is gone. The third is done with intention and is erased with difficulty. A special soul substance is needed such as deep, true compassion.

The fourth karma is cold sin, done without compunction. It is carved so deep in stone that no master, healer, or saint can help to remove this in one lifetime. The patient should understand that if his karma is caused by something that is written in blood, only a counterbalance through good karma accumulated in the passage of time can cure it. An enlightened healer can only point the way to awareness and the building of a clean future.

No healer can take complete responsibility on his head and say, "I am going to heal you." That disturbs the law of the universe, which is not governed by one healer or one person. If he claims that he is able to heal any kind of disease, that is ignorance of the law, or he is on an ego trip, setting himself above the laws of the universe.

However, instead of saying to sick people as so many do who accept the law of reincarnation, "It is your fate, you have earned it, endure it", the healer should point the way out of this condition. With the present disorder of the body, he should point out that it is important to keep a strong spiritual level. When we are negative, we are below our level and then illness comes. We have gone out of nature, out of balance, and we have not lived a life in tune with the natural laws of love, compassion, and humanity. We must know constantly that our thoughts are living things with vibrations that can bless or harm us. Send out only thoughts that will come back to you with high vibrations bearing interest. Interest is the extra compassion we give.

2. The authors asked BROTHER MANDUS of England, "What is the most cooperative and ideal behavior on the part of the patient?" He answered:

> ... love ... is the central flame of life ...
> ... So many miracles of healing take place when we turn our attention away from ourselves and seek an objective for living joyously so that others may be prospered and blessed because we pass their way.
> ... in this whole area of spiritual experience must lie the prevention of so much human disease and disaster, and that, in the end prevention was even better than miraculous cure.

3. MAMA MONA NDZEKELI, president of the African Spiritual Church of South Africa, blends African tribal traditions with Christianity in her healings.

Mama Mona feels she need not diagnose problems in order to cure them, though demonstrating her diagnostic skills to a skeptic may provide confidence in her ability to help. She reports that shaking hands casually in social settings is a drain on her healing powers.

A lot of her healing has been done by a special handshake.

> ... healers ... project a light, the quality of which depends upon the giver... Mama Mona has seen and described balls of fire falling upon the heads of the persons being helped, even upon her own head.

4. Oh SHINNAH, an American Indian, has been instructed in the Native American ways of healing and holds a master's degree in experimental psychology. She uses crystals in healing.

The crystals that are used for healing have their own power and energy, and do their work by just being in the proximity of the one in need of healing. When held in the hands, they can be programmed to specific ills. They will magnify the intentions of the healer, and through their purity, combine the forces of nature and spirit to channel healing vibration, promote clarity, help one to be less emotionally reactive, refract disharmonious energies, release negative ions, collect positive ions, and work with one's dreams, without any help from the two-legged. They have memory and attract the spirits of light.

When asked, "... can the healer use any method at will?" she answered:

We too often become more attached to method than to the actual healing. Many years ago, I asked Dr. Karl Menninger if he had one lesson to give me to guide the rest of my life, what would it be. He very quickly answered, "If it works, do it, and do it Now".

On other topics she observes:

Healing is innate within most of our natures. It is society that closes us off to inborn abilities.

Anyone who wishes to help 'make better' must develop a deep sense of love and compassion, which is a reflection of one's spiritual self in union with the nature and Source. One must be willing to explore his own illnesses and loneliness and welcome change. Through the looking within, we may become truly empty, leaving space to be filled by That which is Above. We attach to and personalize our illnesses, claiming them as our own – my

migraine, my cancer, my broken life. It seems the two-legged has a propensity for suffering. We cling to our psychosis and disease. If we give over our pain, what then will take its place?

We must practice surrender in our every moment, in our everyday lives. If we develop the quality of balance and emptiness, we will be working in harmony with the forces of nature and spirit all the time, therefore having a stronger effect for good in the world.

5. HARRY EDWARDS is the last healer interviewed. His views are summarized later in this chapter.

Discussion The GARDNER'S, in a more modest way, approach a few of the same questions that are addressed in this book. They identify some of the common denominators of healing and many of the individual, idiosyncratic and personal methods and views of these healers.

The sceptic will point out that it is hard to prove whether the theory of karmic influences provides a valid explanation or is merely a *hedge* used by healers against disappointment or losing face in unsuccessful treatments.

Crystals are reported by many to facilitate healing. We do not yet know whether this is a magical belief or whether they might prove valid with more careful scrutiny. Sensitives who see auras report that the crystals augment healing effects. My personal impression is that they do interact with healing energies.

Love, acceptance and compassion are repeatedly mentioned by healers and healees as vital components of healing. Love is felt as an active force during healings, not merely experienced as a positive bedside manner. The Gardners' book is highly recommended for its rich descriptions of healers views.

Oszkar Estebany – Personal communications (1982)

OSZKAR ESTEBANY[3] was a healer who was studied in well-controlled studies on enzymes, animals and people, producing very significant results.

His life and work have received little attention in healing literature. In telephone discussions and correspondence I found him to be warm, compassionate and eager to discuss his healing gifts.

He was a major in a Hungarian army artillery unit. He reports:

> Like my fellow soldiers, I massaged my horse when he was exhausted. After my massage my horse was frisky while the others' horses were hardly rested. I began experiments on the garrison horses, then on dogs and cats. Next, I found that pains of people would go away when I laid my hands on them.
>
> Once I had grown convinced I could heal with my hands I turned more and more to healing. After the Second World War when I left the army I devoted myself entirely to this. During the first years I turned no one away. I could work twelve to fourteen hours a day and treat up to twenty people in a day's work.

DOUGLAS DEAN (1985) adds a few snippets on the disovery and development of Estebany's healing gifts:

> He found that if he put his hands around a bottle of water the power passed into the water and the member of the family could drink the water and the pain would go away, or also he could pass his hands around a wad of cotton wool and the power would go into the cotton wool; he could package this up and send it through the mail to distant relatives. They would strap it to their backs, go to bed, and if they had a backache the backache was supposed to have gone in 10 minutes.

Fig. I-2. Oszkar Estebany, one of the most studied Healers in the U. S. and Canada.
Courtesy of "Human Dimensions"

ESTEBANY states (1982):

> The term 'healer' in my opinion is completely incorrect, because we healers only give energy to the patient (call it electromagnetic, spiritual, or, if you like psychic energy), while the actual healing comes from God, or from nature, depending on the faith and spiritual disposition of the healer. I choose God because – during my long years of practice – I received so much help from above that I would not dare to credit nature, or Nature with it.
>
> You ask me what I do, and how I do it? With the ... laying-on-of-hands (LH) I try to help patients by relieving pain and diagnosing ailments, often ending in prompt recovery. Studying myself I have the feeling that I am like a magnet, naturally not

with all the properties of a magnet ... I feel as if I were surrounded by a magnetic field. I do not think that I myself radiate the energy directly or indirectly because I was able to treat at least 20 patients daily, sometimes even 40, without feeling tired or exhausted, and the last person under my hands felt the same 'sensation' as the first one. So the magnetic field around me – perhaps combined with my touch – affects the patients the same as a magnet affects a piece of soft iron. The iron approached by a magnet becomes magnetic without the magnet losing any of its magnetic power. All this looks simple and easily understandable, but what happens when the healing is a distant healing, when I can't touch my patient and can't stretch my magnet to thousands of kilometers?

ESTEBANY often uses intermediary substances, such as pieces of paper, as *vehicles* for distant healings. He shared:

Really I didn't do anything special, just cut an ordinary sheet of paper into small pieces and sign each piece, but even the signing is unnecessary. I learned that everything I take in my hands picks up my energy, even radiates it and becomes surrounded by a sort of magnetic field. The energy is invisible, but its heat can be felt. Every material has this property to a certain degree, but the most responsive are: water, fibrous material, wood, plant, human or animal body and so forth. One day even the 'soul', 'spirit', – though not matter – may take this energy, which would be an interesting topic for you as a psychiatrist. With all this energized material, no matter how far from me, I remain in contact for a long time. I believe this is the reason that I

can do successful distant healing only on a person treated by me personally before, or on a person who is in possession of material energized previously by me.

The pieces of paper radiate heat as if they were alive. My friends in Hungary use my letters (typewritten too), by putting them under their pillows in order to relieve pain, and they write incredible stories about this. This is not autosuggestion because it was tried on babies and sick people who were not aware that my letter was smuggled under their pillows.

I want to emphasize that it makes a great difference how long I hold it in my hands. Sister Justa in Buffalo during experiments handed me for LH treatment a test-tube containing enzyme called trypsin, damaged by ultraviolet radiation which reduced its activity to 68–70%. We got the best results when I held the test-tubes in my hands for 70 minutes. I do the same now when treating water or cotton-wool.

A treated object can pass energy to another nearby object. To prove this, here is another story: A patient of mine, suffering from cystic fibrosis, had a wood-carving, Dürer's 'praying hands', carved by myself. He kept this carving in his hospital bed, hidden in a towel, because it gave him strength when choking; it was his talisman. One day the nurse, by mistake, instead of the hospital towel, put my patient's towel on the chest of some children suffering from the same disease. The children during the treatment uniformly asked: "Why is the towel so nice and warm today? What a good feeling spreads from it." So the wood-carving passed the energy to the towel it was wrapped in.

I use distant healing more and more often

recently. I have patients with cancer, gall-stones, kidney stones, bladder trouble and so forth, who are exposed to sudden, ex-cruciating pain, so they call me up by tel-ephone, even in the dead of night, asking for help. These patients, relieved from pain, usually fall asleep during my heal-ing.

Even if we don't see each other, or don't think of each other for years, I remain in contact with my distant patients, provided – as mentioned before – they were treated by me at least once personally before, or possess treated objects. If this is the case, the result of the distant healing is usually positive. Regarding the distant healing, as far as I am concerned, with intensive con-centration I would imagine the patient in my presence as if he were before my eyes, then I would use the LH methods over the patient's body in thought, believing that I can awake his dormant energy – which is present in everyone – and believing also that I can even strengthen his energy with the still unknown energy I possess. Since the energy, as a result of continued expen-diture, is used up to a certain degree, the treatment in most cases has to be repeated. I believe that traces of the energy remain in the human organism for a long time af-ter the last treatment. It cannot be felt, but when required, it can be activated by both the patient and healer: the former by strengthening his dormant energy, or re-collection; the latter by trying to make connection for absent healing. This I wanted to achieve by sending small pieces of treated paper to the patient. Thus, the contact between healer and patient is not constant, just a faint memory, which has to be activated.

There are no set rules for healing. People are different according to their physical and mental capacity and spiritual constitu-tion. So every person has to be treated in-dividually.

In answer to the question, "Do you teach healing?" ESTEBANY answers, "No!" Asked, "How do people become healers?" he says:

I could not explain how anyone could de-velop this energy in question, or pass it on to somebody else by learning. Healing is a gift of God, a talent according to the Bible. True, everybody can relieve some little pain, but this is not considered healing. One cannot develop healing by study, as is done in other physical arts and sciences. Either you have it inside you, or you don't.

He commented on healing energy:

I don't feel that I get the energy from out-side sources. I feel as if I were a magnet myself with a magnetic field around me, which enables me to give energy... The bearer of this energy is the body, not the soul (spirit). In my opinion, when a healer dies, the magnetic energy remains with the corpse.

Beside the body's magnetism, the spirit also works, directs and differentiates. A painter (artist), or sculptor works with the body, but is influenced by spirit. When de-pressed, he uses different colors than in a happy, balanced state. But soul, spirit can-not be sick. When, for example, a sick per-son, suffering from schizophrenia, dies, the departing spirit stays whole and healthy. Otherwise, it would remain sick for ever, which does not make any sense.

Estebany does not feel he is guided by any spir-its. He is powerless to help himself if he is ill.

Discussion   ESTEBANY uses intermediary materials as vehicles to make connections between himself and his healees during distant healing. It is not clear whether these substances actually store energy or serve as a means for the sick person to draw energy from Estebany or perhaps from the same source from which Estebany obtains his power. Alternatively, Estebany may constantly be sending energy through these sensitized objects.[4]

Research in parapsychology on clairsentience has shown that psychically perceptible imprints can be left in objects by people who hold them. This supports Estebany's observations. Of course, the objects in addition may be placebos – aids to the healer and ill persons to believe more fully in the healing process and to activate self-healing in the healee.

There is a rich lore on healing through saints' relics (GORRES) and numerous reports of healings effected through handkerchiefs by JESUS and the APOSTLES (Appendix A). Many other modern day healers report they can convey healing in this way.

Yefim Shubentsov – Healing Seminar, Philadelphia (July 1982)

YEFIM SHUBENTSOV is a Russian healer who emigrated to the United States in 1980. Raised in an orphanage from about the age of two (his parents disappeared and he does not know what happened to them), he says, "I had to be tough to survive!" He grew up with the mixed careers of boxing instructor, painter and free-lance illustrator and artist. In 1969 he was hospitalized because of a large tumor on his right leg. A bone graft was necessary after its removal as the wound healed poorly. A friend introduced him to some people who were exploring healing. He was told that he had healing ability and could probably help himself. Though initially skeptical, he successfully healed his leg wound.

He soon proved to himself he could relieve pain and improve some health conditions. He joined a group of investigators, initially as a hobby, but soon became convinced that this should be his life's work.

Shubentsov studied aspects of medicine and practised many techniques of concentration, visualization and methods of activating diagnostic and therapeutic bioenergetic skills. From 1972 to 1980 he was head of a research group at a bioelectronics laboratory.

Today he lives in Boston, practising *bioenergetic therapy*. He teaches his methods to physicians and others interested in healing. Here are some of Shubentsov's comments on healing:

1. There are positive and negative biological fields of two types.

*   People sometimes find that they have a natural aversion to others. This is because of differences in their biofields. It is easy to test this. Two people need only hold up their palms towards each other (as though about to push each other away). At a distance of an inch or two between the palms it is possible to detect a sensation of warmth or cold. If warmth is felt there is a positive interaction between their fields; if cold, the interaction is negative. Positive and negative social/ psychological interactions are anticipated in accordance with these sensations. These qualities are permanent characteristics and cannot be changed.

*   A person can make his fields positive

or negative in another sense. By positive or negative thoughts or with variations in health and disease, a person's field acquires positive or negative characteristics. The positive feels cool to a healer's hands; the negative warm and prickly. These can affect others positively and negatively, producing relaxation, relief of pain, and healing, or the opposite. In extreme cases, such as when a person who had a disease makes a present of a piece of jewelry she wore to someone dear to her, she may actually be doing her dear one a grave disservice. The jewelry may transmit negative effects to the next wearer. Such fields can be cleansed from the object by a healer simply through appropriate passes of his hands over the object.

The healer protects himself and the sick persons from negative effects of such fields with the mental affirmation: "Nothing negative from me to you or from you to me."

These negative effects are the basis for the 'evil eye'. In small towns it is easy to identify the person who emanates negative 'vibes' when he visits. Everyone knows everyone else. When three neighbors each notice separately that one person's visit is associated with negative vibrations, he is identified as the source of these feelings and accused of the 'evil eye'.

2. Shubentsov believes healing can be taught to everyone. This involves no miracles. It is a physiological process, unrelated to the belief systems of the person being healed. The steps in healing include the following:

*   Through practice, hands can be sensitized to various emanations from inani-

mate and animate objects. This provides sensitivity to the biofield for diagnosis. Practice in sensing the biofield leads to a 'vocabulary' of sensations associated with various physiological conditions. By repetition the healer can learn which sensations are correlated with which conditions.

A broken, green twig can provide practice in the sensation of injury.

*   Healing energy is emitted by one of a healer's hands more than by the other. With experience one discovers which it is. This is then used as the active hand, which is held over the point of pain or illness and moved with a clockwise motion (facing the patient). The other hand is held immobile on the opposite side of the body to enhance the healing effect.

*   The optimal time of day for healing powers can be identified. Very advanced healers who have learned to control their energies can heal equally well at any time of day or night. The beginning healer should take a series of containers with earth and seeds in them and, keeping light and watering constant, give healing to each container at different times of day. The plants growing best will reveal the healer's most potent time of day for healing.

3. Distant healing is performed with a visualization of the subject. The healer makes his usual passes over the visualized body. This can also be used by the healer for self-healing. In this case, he visualizes himself and gives his visualized-self the healing. The healee can make contact with the healer from a distance, via a picture of the healer. This may be a basis for the efficacy of religious objects such as a cross or pictures of saints.

4. Healing energy directed with a probe at acupuncture points is many times more effective than insertion of needles at those points. Touch healing is more powerful than auric healing. Healing energy applied to medications can markedly enhance their potency.

5. One must be careful not to treat a pain, which may be caused by an illness of acute nature, for which the pain is a danger signal.

6. SHUBENTSOV prefers to treat specific illnesses, where he has demonstrated success in healing.

These include (according to my seminar notes):

* headaches, including migraines;
* high or low blood pressure;
* myopia (nearsightedness, which can be markedly reduced with healing in some cases and only slightly in others; the progressive deterioration of vision with myopia can be halted in most cases);
* nystagmus (tremors of the eye muscles) of various etiologies;
* arthritic pains (not deformities);
* muscle pains of all sorts;
* circulatory insufficiency due to atherosclerotic disease;
* heart disease, including atherosclerotic problems, angina, postmyocardial infarction (heart attack) recuperation; (cardiac arrhythmias may be exacerbated unless proper [unstated] techniques are used);
* ulcer-pains, not bleeding;
* constipation;
* hemorrhoids;
* impotence;
* menopausal hot flashes;
* allergies of all sorts (these are Shubentsov's specialty; he holds the subject in his therapeutic biofield while having him smell, touch or taste minute quantities of the allergen for increasingly long periods of time.

This desensitization while undergoing healing treatment can produce total cessation of allergic reactions for ever with a single treatment per allergy of about 15 minutes. Shubentsov includes Raynaud's and Buerger's diseases within his category of 'allergy to cold');

* phobias, habits (overeating, smoking), and obsessions; which respond to a particular healing technique within 10 seconds. Shubentsov asks the healee to vividly visualize himself enjoying his habit or experiencing his phobia or obsession. Shubentsov then visualizes a situation himself, which is extremely negative, while making powerful passes in front of the patient. He claims that single sessions produce cures in the desires or negative thoughts, if the patients do not go back to experience them in the next fewweeks.

7. Shubentsov prefers to treat problems that respond readily and rapidly to healing. A marked subjective or objective response within the first session is a good sign. If no response is obtained after an hour's effort, prospects are generally poor for marked benefit from his healing (without prolonged efforts). This is not to say that his healing cannot help in difficult cases. Moderate improvement is possible with daily treatments of an hour or more for problems such as paralyses following strokes or trauma, or polio-related neuromuscular problems. Shubentsov feels such investments in time and effort are inordinate and draining on the healer.

8. Shubentsov says that aging processes are arrested when people are exposed over long periods to healers' fields. "In the years I worked in my institute in Russia, those who worked within a 16-meter radius of myself did not develop wrinkles!"

9. Shubentsov feels that healing energy comes either directly from the healer's body or is channeled through the healer from an unidentified outside source.

He himself is a tireless person. He literally has never known what it means to be tired and has had to question others in order to gather some concept of what this means. He can work for many hours not only without subjective tiredness but also with equal effectiveness at the end of his work as at the beginning. He sleeps only about five hours nightly.

10. Attitudes toward healing research in the U.S.S.R. in the 1970's are of interest. Soviet scientists sought to demonstrate the efficacy of a new therapy in 100 cases. No controls were required. Healing is an elective subject in some Russian medical schools. Shubentsov taught 400 doctors in his last years there. The government was taking a very serious interest in these phenomena, not only for health reasons but also for potential military applications. For this reason Shubentsov alerts that any information released from the U.S.S.R. regarding healing was likely to be of minimal value or possibly even deliberately misleading.[5]

11. The U.S.S.R. took the biorhythm theory seriously (THOMMEN). Workers whose jobs could entail danger if they were not functioning at maximum capacity were given days off when their biorhythm charts indicated a bad day.

12. Shubentsov suffers from limitations to his practice imposed by the American medical system. He may not diagnose or touch a patient for fear of prosecution. In the Soviet Union, where doctors were all salaried, they were often happy to have a healer help their patients. He was often encouraged to help in any and every way he could. There was no competition for patients' business to produce restrictive legislation on the help of a healer.

Discussion   SHUBENTSOV'S orientation is extremely pragmatic. He wants to be sure that his treatments are effective and therefore chooses illnesses that will rapidly demonstrate a response to healing which is observable and preferably measurable. Having learned healing by arduous and exacting practice of techniques of observation and sensing/ treating with his hands, he is extremely clear on how to teach others these skills.

For this reason, Shubentsov has little appreciation for controlled studies. His observations are likely to include Type I errors. I am skeptical regarding the effectiveness of his treatments for phobias, obsessions and habits.

Many healers report sensations of heat and cold but do not interpret them as more than indications that healing is occuring.

The caution against removing pains is logical but I have never heard of a person endangered or harmed through removal of pains by healing.

His views on teaching healing, diametrically opposite to Estebany's, suggest that healers' opinions may be strongly colored by their life experiences and beliefs. Alternatively, perhaps the healing of gifted natural healers differs from that of those who develop their gifts intentionally.

Since the policies of Perestroika have been introduced, healing has been freed of much of the previous governmental constraint. Healers are flourishing in private practice and in collaboration with doctors and other complementary therapists. Some even have popular TV programs, with reports that healing can be received through video transmission.

Mieczyslaw Wirkus – Personal communication (1987)

MIECZYSLAW WIRKUS was born in Poland and now lives near Washington, D.C. He discovered his healing ability as a child when he was able to relieve his sister's asthma attacks by placing his hands on her shoulders. Healing is called *bioenergotherapy* (BET) in Poland, where it has been officially approved as a paramedical treatment. Wirkus was officially licensed there to practise biodiagnosis and BET following completion of practical and theoretical courses and examinations under the commission of the Psychotronics Society of Warsaw.

Wirkus can identify the present and future states of health of a person by passing his hands through the biofield, noting

> . . . cold, warm, tingling, pressure and/or pain vibrations.
> . . . Occasionally I also feel stabbing pains. At times it even seems to me as though an invisible force were tearing pieces of flesh from my palm. In order not to feel the patient's illness and deplete my own energy, I prevent his negative currents from entering my body by dint of mental effort. I imagine that I've created a kind of barrier to them in my wrist. Then I 'shake them off' or 'rub them off' on the wall.
>
> Recently I find it less and less necessary to bring my hands near the patient in order to discover what's wrong with him. I am developing an ability to perceive diseased organs. I 'see' them in very different ways. When I close my eyes they appear to me as if on negatives. At times I perceive something like golden flashes. There are also precise pictures, as exact as those in an anatomical atlas. Once, when I approached a

> patient, I felt a pain in my kidney. The next moment I caught a clear 'glimpse' of his diseased suprarenal gland. However the rest of the kidney I was 'viewing' was blurred. It turned out later than the patient really did have problems with his suprarenal gland. Another time, in the right lower part of a patient's stomach, I 'glimpsed' a sort of needle pointing into her body. Surprised, I asked the patient whether she had pains in that area. She said yes. It turned out that it was ovarian pain radiating into her body.

Sessions usually last 20 – 30 minutes.

> After examining an individual I begin transmitting my energy to him . . . I generally place my palms on his head, on the spot where the brain center regulating the function of the diseased organ is located. In this manner, by means of the nervous system, I balance the energy levels in the diseased organ and in the surrounding area.
> . . . I even sense the organ in my hands as if I were holding it. I transfer my energy to it, eliminate the blockage, and make the 'disoriented cells' return to their right proportion sand right place.
> . . . it seems as if the organ were blocked by a ring that prevents the proper bioenergetic information from entering it. My job is to eliminate this ring and correct the 'mistakes' in the patient's biofield by means of my own energy. . .

Wirkus finds that people often report warmth or heat in the area addressed either during or after sessions. Some report general relaxation and/or sleepiness. Others report no sensation. "In cases of severe pain a temporary increase (12 to 48 hours) in discomfort can occasionally occur but is soon followed by marked decrease in pain." Sometimes one visit suffices. At other times several sessions are needed. BET does not require patients to participate and has been helpful to infants and comatose patients.

WIRKUS believes, as do his colleagues in Poland, that BET restores exhausted energies to an organism from the body of the bioenergotherapist. He finds support for his theory in Kirlian photography, which shows that BET therapists have a wider and stronger biofield than the average person.

In addition to the laying-on-of-hands, Wirkus feels

> ... there is one more condition: You must love people, you cannot have any rancor, malice or hatred in you. Concentrating on kindness and love raises the energy level; it is a source of strength...

Sessions with Wirkus have been especially helpful in healing diseases of the nervous system, asthma, gastric ulcers, ovarian cysts, sterility, nervous illness, psychosomatic diseases, childhood deafness, allergies and pains of all sorts (including migraine, arthritis, and cancer).

He believes that most people possess a modicum of healing ability and that, with a strong desire to help and with practice, most can significantly develop this gift.

Wirkus objects to the term *psychic,* feeling that these are natural abilities present in most people, whereas *psychic* seems to connote unusual or esoteric abilities.

Discussion   It is encouraging to learn that in Poland *bioenergy* diagnosis and healing are being integrated actively and enthusiastically with conventional medical treatment. I hope that medicine in the West may soon follow this example.

Bruce MacManaway with Johanna Turcan – Healing: The Energy That Can Restore Health

The late BRUCE MACMANAWAY, a British healer, shares a treasure trove of healing experiences from 40 years of clinical practice.

The following points are especially noteworthy:

1. MacManaway often used a dowser's pendulum to diagnose illnesses and to seek treatments. This may be done close to or at a great distance from the healee.

2. In *surrogate* healing, MacManaway gave laying-on-of-hands treatment by proxy through the healee's friend or relative, who performed the treatments under the healer's direction. This method proved effective in cases where the sick person was unable to avail himself directly of the treatments because of the severity of illness or distance from MacManaway.

3. Group healings, with several healers treating the same patient, seemed to produce superior results. The authors briefly cite experiments of MAXWELL CADE which support this contention, demonstrating enhanced effects on electroencephalograms (EEGs) in healees as increasing numbers of healers participated (CADE/COXHEAD).

4. MacManaway found that focusing his healing on the spine was especially helpful in a wide spectrum of illnesses, even when the sickness did not appear to be related to the spine in western concepts of physiological and anatomical processes. He noted, for instance, that healing directed to the levels of thoracic vertebrae numbers four and five were helpful in cases of severe psychiatric problems.

5. MacManaway saw energy flows corresponding to eastern theories of chakras. He found that changes occurred in these areas during healing.

6. MACMANAWAY described an instance in which out-of-body healing occurred:

> There was a small girl in Perthshire whom I knew purely on account of my spare-time hobby which was teaching show jumping to members of the Pony Club. She fell ill and as she was not responding to treatment, her mother (whom I did not really know at all) rang up a mutual friend to see if I would be prepared to help. Unfortunately, I was away and could not be contacted. The friend, having talked to me about telepathy in the past, endeavoured to send me a telepathic message stressing the severity of the child's illness. The rest of the story came from the child. She was sitting up in bed the next morning, her fever symptoms gone and loudly demanding breakfast. Her mother expressed surprise and delight. "Don't be silly, Mummy", came the response. "You know that man from the Pony Club, Major MacManaway, came to see me last night." Her mother looked blank. "Yes, he held his hands over my tummy and it was very hot and then he told me I'd be all right in the morning. And I am."

Discussion   This excellent book shares numerous healing techniques and a wealth of healing experience. Surrogate healers/healees are described by other healers and by kinesiologists. Their intervention raises several questions. Is the surrogate person merely a telepathic link? Does he contribute in any other way to the healing process? Is he transformed temporarily into a healer?

Edgar Chase – Personal communication (1988)

EDGAR CHASE, a surprisingly spry and alert octogenarian, has been a healer for close to two decades. He worked as an industrial scientist, head of a management consulting group, and university lecturer. He discovered his healing abilities while taking his wife to another healer[6] for treatment of her painfully deformed spine. Edgar (as he prefers to be called) studied anatomy and radionics and still uses a pendulum in his work.

Retired from active participation in sports and from coaching England's hockey team, Edgar is still an avid spectator sportsman. He is understandably proud of his track record in healing, with a national reputation for treating severe sports injuries. Athletes whose doctors predicted they would be sidelined for the rest of the season were back on the field at the end of a week after Edgar treated their injuries. During the past few years he has had considerable success treating more difficult diseases, such as cancer, multiple sclerosis and posttraumatic coma. People in coma for weeks and months have returned to consciousness after Edgar's treatments.

His methods are noteworthy in several respects:

1. In scanning people's bodies diagnostically with his hands, he notes sensations associated with particular dysfunctions: "A fracture feels like a toothache; muscle problems are a dull ache; a trapped sciatic nerve can feel like a serious electric shock in my hands; depression and nervousness like a prickle; cancer like worms moving under the skin; asthma like mites under the skin; and pituitary gland imbalance like an irregular vibrating moped engine."

2. With knowledge of anatomy and physiology, EDGAR CHASE states he is able to do the following:

> I can visualise the structure of each part of the body and diagnose from imbalanced radiations which emerge from the body, and by treating at this location the healing energy has a direct route to the centre of the root cause of the problem.

3. Edgar finds that pebbles which he has held for a while (particularly from Iona, known as an earth 'power point'), seem to carry curative powers for his patients.

4. In distant healings (which he feels are effective when touch healings are not possible) Edgar connects best with the healee if he has a lock of hair and a photograph. He feels he has greatest success if he tunes into the patient's mind by rotating the photograph to a particular orientation indicated by a dowsing pendulum. He feels it is important for the healee to be in a quiet, receptive state when healing is being sent. He also sends distant healing by placing the photograph and hair on a medium-sized stone which he has held in his hands for many hours, saturating it with healing.

5. He finds he can markedly reduce anxiety if he directs healing through his fingers to particular points on the shoulders and neck which are related to anxiety (according to instructions he received from a Japanese acupuncturist). He also treats hormonal and emotional problems by directing healing to the pituitary, allowing patients to heal themselves.

6. When imparting healing to a person or an object, Edgar's thumb, forefinger and the intervening web of muscles will twitch for the duration of treatment. When sufficient healing has been transmitted the twitching ceases automatically along with the treatment.

7. Edgar believes healing works by restoring life force to atoms which have been depleted of this energy.

8. Edgar is able to treat himself effectively for many problems. Partial loss of vision in his right eye, which developed four years ago, is now fully restored as a result of self-treatment. He has had no colds for decades. He subsequently developed arthritis in the hip. He says he is unable to heal himself of this problem mainly because of the physical restrictions in orienting his hands to the correct position.

9. Kirlian photographs of his fingers made at Birmingham University demonstrated a flare between three and four inches long around his index fingers during healing. The Kirlian aura was only a quarter of an inch long when Edgar was not visualizing healing.

Edgar does not know how his healing works, even in many cases where conventional therapies have failed.

> There could be a psychological explanation. Since a treatment session seldom lasts less than one hour, there is a unique opportunity to get to know the patient and his problems in life. The total problem is identified, and it is possible to treat 'wholeness'. Patients are encouraged to talk about the problems they face and in doing so they defuse their difficulties. Objectives can then be created to optimize the resources available and to identify additional resources that have to be acquired if the objectives are to be achieved. This is 'The Cybernetics of Wholeness'.
>
> ... those patients who recover from 'terminal' illness or illnesses classed as incurable by medical technology do so when their own body healing powers are stimulated or regenerated by a gifted healer who

can reverse despair and despondency to genuine hope as a result of experiencing positive responses to the healing energy which complements and makes effective the treatment given by the orthodox medical consultant...

It is important that patients in hospital should not be treated by a healer without the knowledge and consent of the doctor. If a change results from the treatment, positive or negative, the doctor would be confused and could draw wrong conclusions as to the effectiveness of his own treatment.

Discussion   Edgar's spectrum of healing practices is broad. His potency may be enhanced by his understanding of anatomy and also may be a measure of his dedication to being a good healer. His graduation from many of the practices of radionics to healing without needing in every case to use intermediary devices is again typical of some of the better healers. I was unable to obtain a satisfactory explanation from him as to why he couldn't heal his own hip by absent healing.

Dean Kraft – Portrait of a Psychic Healer

DEAN KRAFT, a gifted natural healer, describes a number of loosely controlled experiments in which he participated. In those that were conducted carefully he was able to achieve the following:

1. Influencing cancer cells in a laboratory. HeLa cancer-cell cultures are standardized cell preparations that grow tenaciously on the walls of the laboratory culture flasks. Few cancer cells are dislodged even if the flasks are vigorously shaken. In five trials (once at the Livermore Laboratories in Califoria and four times at the Science Unlimited Research Foundation in San Antonio, Texas) Kraft was able to loosen many more cancer cells than were dislodged in control flasks. Cells were visually counted in a hemacytometer. Four trials lasted 20 minutes each. In the fifth trial, lasting 60 minutes (three 20-minute sessions), the cancer cells appeared not only to be dislodged but also destroyed. Dr. John Kmetz reports these findings are significant, i.e. the possiblity they occurred by chance was less than one in a thousand. No data are presented to support these claims.

2. Influencing an unspecified instrument which measures electrostatic fields. Kraft was able to do this repeatedly, at will. This was done within a Faraday cage to exclude extraneous electromagnetic fields.

KRAFT made other interesting discoveries:
* EEGs recorded during healings demonstrated increased alpha waves. Simultaneous EEGs of the healees showed some activity which was synchronous with that of Kraft.
* Kraft was able to influence a magnetometer in an informal test.
* He has repeatedly demonstrated strong, focused PK ability, moving small objects such as pens at will. He has also assisted police with clairsentient clues which helped solve crimes and located missing persons. Kraft finds exercising his clairsentient and PK abilities much more exhausting than healing. He frequently faints with the exertion of PK demonstrations.
* He reports he could alleviate headaches, muscle and joint pains, paralyses following trauma, herpes zoster ('shingles'), colitis, ocular hemorrhage, congenital deafness, depression, and could cure a variety of cancers, including multiple myeloma.

Kraft describes his methods:

> As I did more and more healing I evolved a basic technique. Before I began I would concentrate on quieting my mind, blanking out all thoughts and tension, and relaxing my body by taking a number of slow, deep breaths. My intuition led me to these relaxation techniques.
>
> Having relaxed my mind and body, I usually spent five to ten minutes with each sick person, during which it seemed to me that I was giving him or her a 'dose' of my energy. I've never been entirely comfortable using the word energy in connection with what I do, since no one has ever established that there is a transfer of energy involved, but from the first time I did psychokinesis, it seemed to me that something like energy (in my mind I saw light) was coming out of me and connecting to the object, and a similar model seemed to apply to healing. Indeed, almost all the people I worked with claimed to feel a pulsating energy, like electricity, passing into their bodies, often accompanied by a sensation of warmth.
>
> Visualizing the person's problem area was very important. If a person had a cancerous tumor I would visualize the fleshy malignant mass. Then I would place my hands about half an inch above the skin over the affected area, at the same time imagining the diseased tumor beginning to disintegrate and dissolve. The more vividly I could visualize the troubled spot the more satisfied I was with my interaction with the ill person.

In curing a case of shingles, he reports:

> As I concentrated on radiating energy over the patient's afflicted area I visualized a stimulated blood flow in the woman's body to help speed the healing.
>
> [Kraft] ... feels that through deep mental concentration he is able to absorb energy from his environment, and that then, by the 'laying on of hands', he can channel that energy to an ill person ...
>
> I think that timing is crucial in healing. As a result of my reading and the findings of various tests in which I've participated, I have come to believe that numerous variables – among them, my mental state, the patient's mental state, the position of the moon and the sun, the electromagnetic and gravitational forces around the earth – contribute to a healing. These factors all have to line up, like multiple sights on a gun. If they are almost lined up I can get a temporary healing, perhaps, like a six-month remission in a disease. But if all the factors are lined up perfectly, that's when magic can happen.

Kraft once suffered symptoms similar to those of a patient.

> During that first session I had noticed a small, red rash on Yoko's face. By the time I reached home, a similar rash had broken out on my face in exactly the same location! I was startled, for I'd never considered the possibility of picking up a condition from a client. Then to my amazement, Yoko called that night to report that her rash had suddenly disappeared!
>
> After I hung up the phone, I studied my reflection in a mirror. Suddenly I felt a surge of anger, and I yelled aloud to the empty room, "I won't allow it! I won't be in a position to pick up someone else's symptoms!"
>
> The next morning the mysterious rash was

gone, but the incident made me realize that I had better protect myself. To me that meant that I must, through concentration, keep my 'energy charge' so high, so positive, during healings that I would be unable to receive any negativity from the ill person. Since then, no similar incidents have occurred.

Discussion Such descriptions by a healer of his observations, impressions, experiences and ideas are extremely helpful. KRAFT repeatedly states he is willing to participate in research. It is unfortunate that he has not undergone more rigorous study and that the research he mentions has not been properly published by the scientists involved. It is hard to see how highly significant statistical analyses could be derived from single-sample trials. The magnetometer and electrostatic field tests are insufficiently described by Kraft to permit comment.

Thus far we have focused primarily on descriptions of healing methods and the sources of healing energies. Healers also speculate on how healing works. One gets the impression from their varied reports that there may be a common denominator to their explanations but that these are filtered through the personalities and belief systems of each and thereby colored so differently as to appear distinct and even contradictory at times.

Harry Edwards – The Science of Spirit Healing

HARRY EDWARDS was one of the greatest healers in modern England. At the peak of his career he would receive thousands of letters weekly requesting distant healing. He felt he had assistance from spirits in healing.

He believed that healing can be divided into three types:

1. Magnetic healing ability is possessed by most people, especially if they are in good health. In fact, if the healer is not in good health, is tired, or otherwise not in top condition, he should not engage in magnetic healing because it can sap his own vitality. It is the simplest and easiest type of healing, recommended especially for painful conditions.

... the beginner should try lightly resting his hands over the region, and as he does so ... consciously direct with all the power of his mind that the pain will be smoothed away. The hand need only rest on the part for a short space of time while the mental effort is being made.

A visible sign of healing power experienced by many healers – as with the author – takes the form of subdued light streams of an irridescent pale blue colour flowing from the finger-tips. These streams are most easily seen in subdued lighting against a dark background.

If the tips of the fingers of both hands are held close together, the stream from one finger-tip will join up with that from the opposite finger. On increasing the distance between the fingers the stream or ray becomes attenuated. When the hands are moved alternately upwards and downwards, or in circular movement, the rays still link forefinger to forefinger and so on. When substances like two pieces of wood or card are placed in the centre of the light ray the latter penetrates both and is seen between the two separate pieces...

2. Spiritual healing was believed by Edwards to account for much of healing. (In Edwards' terminology, this is healing with the aid of spirits of persons who have died

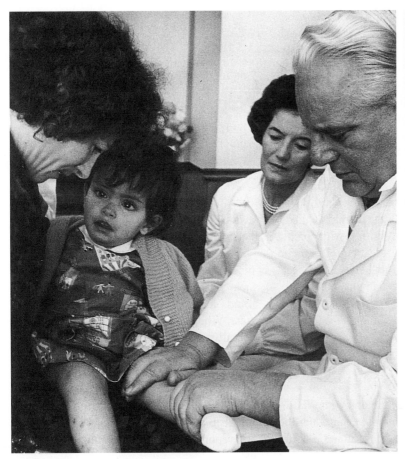

Fig. 1 - 3 Harry Edwards giving healing to Linda Martel, who was born with congenital spina bifida, hydrocephalus and heart problems but was a powerful healer from age 3–5, when she passed on (GRAVES).

Photo by courtesy of Psychic News

the total organisation of the healer: mental, physical, etheric, and spirit. Using the human instrument is the spirit-healing Guide or Guides. The two, the healing medium and the healing Guide become co-operators. The human mind interprets the condition of the patient – the spirit-healing minds are concerned with the diagnosis and correction of the disharmony.

Contrary to magnetic healing, the spiritual healer rarely feels tired or distressed after healing, no matter how many patients he treats or how tired he was previously.

but who still wish to help the living.)[7]

... There must be a healer to act as the human instrument or medium for the applied spirit-healing forces. Through him are the forces that can transcend and overcome the causes of the illness and restore the physical distortion of harmony. To enable the human instrument to be well used, there must be the willing co-operation of

... the patient also possesses the trinity of bodies. If that were not so, then the patient could not be receptive to the healing forces.

When a patient appears non-receptive, it may be that there is a disharmony between the physical and spirit bodies of the patient, so preventing any 'tuning-in' between the healer, his Guides and the patient.

EDWARDS mentioned that *manipulations* should also be included under spiritual healing. Here the healer allows his physical body to be "used by the Guide through direct control". Edwards reported numerous cases in which severe physical abnormalities such as arthritic, deformed spines were moved into normal alignment with return of physical functioning within seconds by such manipulations. Sometimes several sessions of treatment by manipulation would be necessary, realigning the bones in stages.

3. In *absent healing* only the intangible medium of thought exists, in contrast with contact healing where there is the tangible human link of the healing medium between the healing spirit guides and the patient.

> ... absent healing is directed by the healing medium on behalf of someone at a distance – generally a person whom the medium has never seen ... distance is immaterial.

Edwards often was called upon by intermediary persons to heal someone even when the healee was not present. This situation could occur when the healees were too debilitated to apply themselves for help; when they had no familiarity with spiritual healing; when they were mentally unbalanced or minors; or even when they and/or their families were opposed to spiritualism. He believed this made no difference to his ability to help.

He believed there was no set formula or procedure for absent (or any other type of) healing. Upon receiving the oral or written request the healer

> ... sends forth ... a thought force that help may be given to the patient.
>
> This thought emission is generally given at a set time of the day when the healer can

sit (either by himself or with friends) in seclusion and silence. He then divorces from his mind all considerations of a worldly nature and 'tunes-in' to his spirit Guides.

The healer must have full confidence in the knowledge that through the instrumentality of his mind-directing-consciousness the healing spirit Guides in association with him can receive the thought appeal on behalf of the patient.

Edwards noted that the healee need not be aware of when the healing is sent and that the healing seems to be more effective when the subject does not know that healing is taking place. He speculated that this may be because sick persons are unused to clearing their minds and entering a meditative, receptive state. When they anticipate healing, they may actually tense themselves and therefore make themselves unreceptive to the healing. Furthermore, the healer may not be aware that he is sending healing. In some instances Edwards forgot to write down a request for healing or to attend to it consciously yet patients still reported marked relief from their illnesses.

> The only logical explanation of these spirit healings is that, during the moments when the healer was being told of the patient and the illness, the healer mentally framed the desire to help. The essential thought emission was thus made and received by the healing Guide and acted upon. It may well be that the barest fraction of a second is all that is necessary for this to take place (the conditions for transmission and reception being favourable) to set the healing process into motion.

EDWARDS noted that he was often aware of the diagnostic condition of the healee during healings. This included incidents associated with the cause(s) of the illness, along with the time frame within which the ill health occurred. He also became aware on occasions of the healees' physical surroundings during the distant healing.

> What happens is this. The healer has 'tuned-in' to his spirit mentors, his eyes are closed, and his inner self is concerned only with asking for help for, say, 'Mr. Griffiths of Bradford, suffering from duodenal ulcers'. As the healer's inner self dwells on the situation, so there becomes pictured on his consciousness a vision of the room in which Mr. Griffiths is. This vision is as vivid and precise as if it were physically visible – as if the healer were actually in the room.
>
> The picture may last only a moment or it may appear to exist for a number of seconds. The vision, however, is so vividly and firmly impressed on the mind that every detail can be remembered with ease: The colour scheme of the room, the furniture and its characteristics, whether the patient is in a chair or in bed, the windows, curtains, etc., also the patient himself, whom, it will be remembered, the healer has never seen.
>
> ... normally to record such a picture mentally would require an appreciable number of minutes for a mind trained to observation, to absorb, individually, each item and register it in the memory. With spirit travelling, the picture is real and alive and so impressive that the picture lives on in the healer's mind and he can recall every detail without stress.

EDWARDS found that such perceptions could be verified later as having been entirely accurate in every detail, including the presence of other persons in the room with the healee. His explanation for this phenomenon is that

> ... man has three main bodies, of which the spirit body with the spirit or inner mind is the principal agent used in spirit healings. This spirit mind is not primarily concerned with recordings arising out of the automatic reactions of physical associations, such as everyday sounds, touch, etc. It receives these experiences, it is true, but they are inferior experiences. The principal function of the spirit mind is to act as the directive thought agent. This comes into play when the individual consciousness is at issue, i.e. when there is need for mental concentration or for the need of creative thought. It is the repository of human experience, the propelling power for action. It is the reflection of the individual's character, and, most important, applies the motive-power for the spirit body.
>
> When the healer 'tunes-in', he surrenders the thought superiority of physical matters to that of spirit healing, which becomes, for the time being, the dominant superior. So that, for spirit travelling the dominant spirit mind, freed from the inferior physical mind, is free to travel to the surroundings to which it is attracted, namely the patient's condition.

Edwards pointed out that, conversely, spirits are able to interact with the physical plane through this same process, using the human medium as their instrument for communication.

> ... If this is so, then when the spirit mind of the healer travels there should be some human instrument in the visited surroundings which can act as the medium for the recording of the vision.

A second hypothesis is that the spirit mind of the healer sees the spirit bodies of the patients, etc., as all are harmoniously 'tuned-in' in the same manner as in the case with normal vision, when a visitor calls. The vision of the appointments of the room, etc., being recorded by the spirit mind from their characterised etheric counterparts.

When a patient is ill, he is either very often in a state of slumber or his mind whilst awake is slumbrous – in other words, he is not very much concerned with normal physical matters. Thus his spirit self is in the condition to be in harmony with the visiting spirit mind or spirit-healing Guide.

EDWARDS emphasized that a specific request must be put forth for the healing to occur. It will not take place without this. Spirit guides are available to help but they do not usually interfere of their own volition.

He noted that the trance state in which he performs healings

... is the overshadowing of the normal consciousness by that of the Guide. The trance condition may vary from 5 to 99 per cent. Those healers able to work, and at the same time retain sufficient [sic] of their normality to be acutely aware of what is taking place, experience the greatest joy in healing – for there could be no pleasure which would excel the exquisite delight of the inward realisation of knowing when the disharmony has been removed.

The ability of the healer to attain to a condition of trance may be described in this way: He divorces from his mind every thought of ordinary things and allows his spirit mind to become superior. This art of surrender is the hardest part of psychic development, but with perseverance becomes a natural change. This change may be described (inadequately) as the healer feeling a sense or condition enshrouding him, as if a blind had been drawn over his normal alert mind. In its place he experiences the presence of a new personality – one with an entirely new character – which imbues him with a super-feeling of confidence and power.

An absorbing interest in the patient's condition occupies the entire mind and there is no room for any other thought. Should any outside interference occur, the healer feels it acutely. His whole energy and power is focused upon the patient with zeal and directiveness whilst endeavouring to investigate and remove the cause of the trouble.

The healer is conscious of intelligent movement with a directive purpose behind it. There is no automatic movement. If the hands are being used to dissolve a growth, it seems as if the mind occupies the fingertips they seem to become mentally sensitive. If the hand is used to remove pain, then the hand possesses the sense of 'wiping away' the pain. If the healer, aware that strength must be given to a weak part of the patient's body, rests his hand over the affected part, he feels the flow of vitalising power pass from himself, through his arm and hand to the patient. There is intelligent effort behind every act the healer performs under the direction of his Guide.

While this takes place, the healer may be only dimly aware of normal movement, speech, etc., taking place around him. If a question is addressed to him about the patient's condition, he will find himself able to respond with extraordinary ease and without mental effort – in other words, the more knowledgeable personality of the Guide provides the answer. Thus does the healer 'tune-in' – it is the subjection of his physical sense to the spirit part of himself, the latter becoming for the time being the superior self under the control of the director.

The great joy of healing in this way is experienced when the treatment is nearing completion. The healer becomes aware of a feeling of intense pleasure, as he knows inwardly that the healing has been successful. A feeling of ecstasy pervades his whole being.

No wonder is it that healers feel that the gift of healing is 'divine', is beyond price and cannot be commercialised!

EDWARDS speculated that some *healing rays* or *cosmic forces* may be involved in healing, but felt these are as yet not understood in conventional terms. He felt that spirits affect the body through the heart and/or bloodstream. Healing is possible, he noted, not only for physical and emotional problems, but also for relational ones. The interactions of people who had not related well to each other often improved with healing.

Discussion   Edwards was one of England's most acclaimed healers. He was also instrumental in forming the first (now the largest) professional group of healers, *The National Federation of Spiritual Healers*.

Edwards was painfully (to myself as a psychiatrist) unaware of the unconscious mind and its functions in monitoring the internal and external environment, in storing information and in programming responses according to previous experiences, especially traumatic ones. He may have attributed to spirits much that the unconscious mind could account for. On the other hand, some of what is currently accepted by conventional psychology as the work of the unconscious mind may at a future date be found to be related to higher consciousness or to spirits.

Edwards was able to alleviate symptoms and cure severe physical illnesses very rapidly. He sought to help healees connect with awareness of their spirituality. It appears that he may have removed symptoms in such a way that their symbolic purposes to the healee might have been missed. Much more can be said on this subject, but discussion will be deferred to Chapter IV-3.[8]

Edwards deliberately avoided learning medical diagnosis and terminology in order to leave his mind unfettered, to permit spiritual healing to occur. Though this may have left him free of conventional biases against unusual healings, it also prevented him from being able to describe in precise terminology the problems he was dealing with. This makes evaluation of his reports difficult. (For instance, when he reports a 'growth on the head', one does not know whether this was a traumatic lesion, a chronic infection, a benign or malignant tumor, or something else entirely.) Though much of his theorizing and speculations on spirit influences may appear unlikely within conventional western paradigms, anecdotal (M. LONG) and scientific evidence is gradually accumulating to support belief in such matters.[9]

The ethics of sending healing to people who are unaware or unwilling to have it are problematic. Most healers will agree to send healing to those who are not capable of deciding for themselves (e.g. infants or people in coma) if their relatives agree to it. Many will refuse to send it to a person who is of age and condition to be responsible for himself and has not requested it.

Ruth Montgomery – Born to Heal

RUTH MONTGOMERY describes the life and work of an extremely gifted healer whom Montgomery called 'MR. A.' to protect him from undesired publicity. A surgeon named DENA L. SMITH worked with him extensively and reports on numerous very difficult cases which he was able to help or cure. Montgomery describes the cosmology of the healer, a brief excerpt of which follows:

... I ... asked how he derived his information, and Mr. A. replied, "Why, from tuning in on The Ring." Pressed to explain in terms available to the layman, he said that a protective ring of energy encircles each planet and stores within it all knowledge since time began. All thoughts and inventions, he said, are 'taken off The Ring', and all such information is available to anyone who learns to listen. He says that the Ancient Wisdom implanted in his mind as a child is unchanging. The years have merely expanded it and brought to him increasing proof of all he learned as a boy.

"The theory of energy as the life-force and body activity is as old as the ages", he continues, "and there are many well versed in the Ancient Wisdom to whom most of this is known. This world we live in is composed of gases and energy. All substance – plant, animal, and human life – results from the unlimited combination of energy frequencies acting on these gases. Every plant, animal, and human has its own individual energy frequency to establish and maintain life, growth, and development. At birth, the first breath of life is our direct supply, our lifeline with the Universal Power... Life itself! At any time that this energy flow is cut off from the magnetic field, the energy which originally sets the field becomes a part of the Power it came from. So long as this energy is established and flows through without obstruction, we are in tune with the Universal supply of energy."

Mr. A. says that the master brain is in the lower abdomen, an intricate system forming the magnetic field, 'the grouping together of the main trunk nerves with their branches and relay systems extending throughout the entire body'. Normally, he explains, the magnetic field gives the lungs the strength to pull in all of the energies. But the field in turn draws its personal energy frequency from the lungs to itself, for distribution throughout the body. He says that some of the symptoms of insufficient energy distribution are shortness of breath, nervousness, confusion, restlessness, irritability, bloat, pain, and a feeling of heaviness. Their intensity depends on the degree of depletion of the magnetic field, which is caused by fear, anger, hatred, shock, or improper or deficient nerve fueling.

"A child is born with a strong or a weak nervous system", he says, "which is determined at conception and is the result of his parents' energies. If the mother and father are of mated frequencies and are well and strong at the time the child is conceived, that child ordinarily has an easy birth and a strong, healthy nervous system. If the child is the result of mismated energy currents, and the future parents are nervous, discontented, or unhealthy, the baby usually has a weak nervous system, and may also have a difficult delivery. Because of this, he is the victim of low energy and nerve depletion for most of his life. But even when a child inherits a weak magnetic field, that tension can be released shortly after birth by someone with the properly blended energy who is able to convey this energy to the infant's magnetic field so that the infant is freed from bondage and open to the universe, and is thereby able to draw his normal capacity of energy from the atmosphere."

Who can be a healer?

> Mr. A. says that the individual with a strong, healthy nervous system generates enough fuel or energy to maintain his own requirements and automatically to radiate a strong surplus. Such a person is best equipped to help others and can be taught, according to Mr. A., how to direct the energy, feed nerves, and release nerve spasms in a person with an energy pattern blending with his own. But apparently there are not many people like Mr. A., who on placing his ear to a patient's chest automatically recognizes his energy pattern and adjusts his own pattern to the ailing one's.

Discussion   This book is written in easy style but is uncritically enthusiastic. The 'ring' is a phenomenon reported by other very gifted healers such as TONY AGPAOA (STELTER) and EDGAR CAYCE (SUGRUE; STEARN). Mr. A.'s identification of the lower abdomen as the source of a magnetic field is of interest. This may correspond with reports of chakras (KAPTCHUK; MOTOYAMA) or the *hara,* energy centers described by eastern medicine and

those who see auras (e.g. BRENNAN). His views on genetic interactions with parental fields are unique. 'Mr. A.' seems to attribute the source of healing energies to the body of the healer. 'MR.A.' is revealed in a later Montgomery book to have been the late WILLIAM GRAY.

Victor Adamenko – Electrodynamics of Living Systems

VICTOR ADAMENKO of the former U.S.S.R. discusses various aspects of healing, including theoretical issues and the relationship of Kirlian photography to healing. He starts with a description of a healer.

> A. Krivorotov prepares himself for the treatment session by concentrating in thought on the patient. Thereupon by forcibly rubbing one of the palms against the other he makes his hands dry and in a slow motion over the patient's hair electrifies his hands. If the patient is healthy, he feels at 5–10 centimeter distance a 'subjective' heat from A. Krivorotov's hands pleasantly spreading throughout his body. The sensation of heat corresponds to a temperature of 45–50 degrees Celsius and cannot be measured objectively. Some people experience the feeling of light prickling, easiness, intoxication, or, on the contrary heaviness.
>
> As A. Krivorotov slowly passes his hands at some distance along the patient's body, there arises in the patient approximately at the site of the sick organ a strong subjective sense of heat, at times almost unbearable. A. Krivorotov also feels at this place an intensification of heat in his hand. Stopping his hand, he says: "You feel pain

here." A. Krivorotov's hand remains at the sick organ until the sensation of heat becomes annoying. It is a signal for the session to be terminated. As a rule, A. Krivorotov has no knowledge of diagnosis in advance. Perception of 'heat' in different people is different and is, apparently, related to whether the disease is more or less serious. In the case of a serious disease the treatment session takes less time, whilst as the patient makes progress the treatment increases in length. Sometimes the subjective sensation of heat at the site of the sick organ persists in the patient for two days. However, in the process of treatment there gradually sets in an adaptation to A. Krivorotov's field. In some patients the subjective sensation of heat is accompanied by the sensation of vibrations whose frequency differs from person to person. Remote 'heat' is not perceived by everybody and, until he met Academician Nikolai Zelinsky, A. Krivorotov used to place his hands on the patient's body. Nikolai Zelinsky experienced a very strong sensation of 'heat' and in order to allay the sensation he suggested that A. Krivorotov should keep his hands at some distance. When A. Krivorotov's hands were about 5 centimeters away, N. Zelinsky said: "The heat is just as strong as I need it."

Krivorotov deals primarily with nervous diseases. Particularly good progress is made in the treatment of nervous exhaustion, but there were cases of the curing of such diseases as lupus. Rather quickly cured is poliomyelitis, but hypertension, bronchial asthma, polyarthritis yield very slowly to treatment, the effect being at times completely absent.

Similarly to A. Krivorotov, the method of bioenergotherapy is possessed by his sons – Vladimir, a physician, and Victor, a mechanical engineer. However, the subjective sensations induced by them in the patients are different. A. Krivorotov produced in the patient, as a rule, the feeling of a strong avalanche as of 'heat' whereas his son, Victor, the sensation of slight pricking.

An analysis of A. Krivorotov's work has revealed that participating in the process is a strong electrostatic field. Occasionally slight discharges take place between A. Krivorotov's fingers and the patient's body. Subjective sensations of heat cannot be produced by a low-power source of electrostatic field as is A. Krivorotov and, moreover, it is absolutely inconceivable that this 'heat' can persist in the patient's body a few days.

Therefore, it is obviously a question of a reflectory [sic] effect of an electrostatic field from A. Krivorotov's hands on the patient's skin receptors, whilst a prolonged feeling of 'heat' persists in the patient's memory. Thus, A. Krivorotov's effect on the patient through electrostatic field takes place on the information level.

Semyon Kirlian, after examining A. Krivorotov's integument [skin], arrived at the conclusion that during preparation for the treatment process the dielectric properties of A. Krivorotov's hands are improving. This conclusion finds support in high-frequency photos of A. Krivorotov's hands in a high-frequency discharge field. S. Kirlian also cites experimental evidence in support of the electrostatic field being generated by A. Krivorotov. However, as already mentioned, a subjective sensation of heat due to A. Krivorotov's electrostatic field could not be produced with the aid of a technical electrostatic field. The sole conclusion to be drawn from this is that either A. Krivorotov's field is qualitatively different from a technical field, or it merely accompanies the effect of some other agent. In any case there exists a correlation between A. Krivorotov's electrostatic field and the subjective sensation of heat, produced in the patient.

Discussion Heat is the most common sensation reported by healers and healees during healings. It is often used as an indicator of seriousness of illness and as a measure of need for treatment. It is unusual for the sensation to persist for more than a few moments past the termination of the laying-on-of-hands. Objective measurements of heat during healing do not demonstrate a rise of temperature. This seems to suggest a synesthesia, or crossed-sensory perception. Nerve endings which perceive heat may be stimulated by healing energy of some sort which is different from heat but which overlaps with it in some manner to stimulate the nerves. An unusual feature in this report is that as the patient improves, Krivorotov's treatments take longer. The opposite is more often the case with other healers. The differences reported between the three Krivorotovs in sensations produced in healees implies that there may be differences between healers in healing energies or in other parameter of their treatments.

It is hard to know what to make of the Kirlian and electrostatic readings. Further studies of the correlations with these, with subjective sensations and results of healing appear warranted.

Victor K., Alexei E. and Vladimir K. Krivorotov – Bioenergotherapy and Healing

The KRIVOROTOV's assume that healing is biological PK, using energies originating in the healer. They report their experience and recommendations on a number of parameters of healing:

1. The healee should relax and focus his attention on the part(s) of the body in need of healing.

> … must be emphasized that the cooperation of the patient is of paramount importance if a cure is to be achieved through bioenergotherapy. If we examine the problem of human illness from the psychological aspect, it is conceivable that any illness, either directly or indirectly, is mentally initiated by the patient. Therefore, the patient himself must be induced to eliminate his own illness. When he begins to resolve the manifold psychological contradictions which can exist in the human mind, bioenergotherapy will have a greater effect.

2. The healer focuses his whole attention on the patient.

> The healer also imparts biological energy to the treated zone which supplements and reinforces the energy provided by the patient.
> We have all experienced the feeling of cheerfulness which is associated with the application of effort to the achievement of a goal. This is the very inner state which is needed for the healer to engage in bioenergotherapy. Specific sensations in the hands are linked with these feelings. These sensations can be distinguished once a person has developed sufficient ex-

perience. Thus a healer can learn how to voluntarily control his internal state to produce the feelings which allow biological energy to emerge.

3. Duration of treatment is from 1 to 20 minutes. Duration and depth of healer concentration depend on:

* the extent to which the healer is prepared for the activity by virtue of his training;
* the nature of the patient's illness; and,
* the degree of cooperation elicited from the patient.

4. Any illness in the healer may be intensified during healing. Certain patients may drain a healer's energy, requiring him to rest before he can treat someone else.

5. Sensations felt by the person being healed during treatments may include tingling; goose-pimples; generalized warmth; initial focal pain under the healer's hands in touch healings, often fading within one or two minutes. After treatment, some patients feel alert and cheerful while others are tired and may even sleep. Focal warmth may persist for hours after treatment.

6. The healer identifies areas on the subject's body in need of treatment by a sensation of vibration in his hands.

7. The Krivorotovs claim the bioheat emitted by healers is distinct from biological energy (i.e. measured with thermometers). The bioheat can produce sensations of asphyxiation, in which case the healer may have to continue with his hands off the body.

8. Methods of applying biological energy include the following:

* *static* – hands remaining stationary;
* *dynamic* – hands moving – for spinal treatments and widespread illness;

(i)   *linear* – on extremities of spine;
(ii) *rotary* – in region of heart or solar plexus;
* *local* – at sites of disease;
* *general* – energizes the local site plus the entire nervous system; used in cases of exhaustion and lethargy;

* *healer's hands held next to each other* – best for general method; hands feel tingly, painful, become warm;
* *one hand* may have different energy from the other; either hand may be used alone, depending on which is empirically found to be effective; and
* *directional energy application between hands* – hands placed on either side of problem area, with energy directed from one hand to the other; hands feel smooth and quiet, no temperature change, but definite sensation of 'current' flow.

Discussion   Why the Krivorotovs feel heat more than other healing sensations is not clear. Many western healers feel that if a healer feels tired after a healing he may be draining his own body energies. If the healer visualizes opening himself up to cosmic energies, he often does not tire during healings. Some healers even find that healing stimulates, strengthens, and refreshes them. The observation that healee illnesses are exacerbated during healings is not reported by other healers, though pain commonly is.

Victor K. Krivorotov – Some issues of bioenergy therapy (in: L.Vilenskaya (Ed.) – *Parapsychology in the U.S.S.R.*, 1981)

VICTOR KRIVOROTOV explains his understanding of Bioenergy Therapy (BT), based on many years of practice and research. He feels that BT is brought about by activation of energy in the healer's hands. He notes that electromagnetic phenomena are a part of the process, as demonstrated by photomultipliers (in the ultraviolet range), which picked up an increased emission during BT of 200% to 300%.

He adds that there appears to be a 'resonant nature' to BT

> ... because a healer using the method does not become tired. Tiredness appears in the periods of overcoming the inertia of the ordinary condition of the hand, in the process of maintaining the inertia of its active state, as well as in the process of overcoming passivity of the general condition of the organism. All these attempts require, at times, strong concentration of willed effort. One cannot exclude that a hand is only a means for the energy contact, and the information for the elimination of pathological processes is transmitted by additional channels, which at present are not known to us ...

He feels BT may act in concert with several other forms of therapy, such as psychotherapy and acupuncture, to bring about a healing. BT works in part via stimulation of acupuncture points.

> ... the higher stage of BT is not only the treatment of a disease but rather the entire interaction of two systems (two organisms) on all levels. Bioenergy exchange has its necessary place in this interaction, but not always the first place, because the bioenergy function does not take the highest position in the general hierarchy of all functions of a human being.

Krivorotov makes the following points:

1. Healing treatments require concentration by both healer and healee.
2. He recommends treatment be given for 10 – 30 minutes. A shorter time is insufficient for 'energy contact'. Longer times 'decrease the efficiency of therapy; the organism begins an adaptation to this stimulus, and in further sessions it can result in total ineffectiveness of therapy'.
3. Some healers, of less than maximal ability, are effective only at certain times of the day.

> Biotherapists of the medium level are able to perform healing only at the time of maximum psychophysiological activity of the organism; usually it occurs from 10 A.M. to 1 P.M. and from 5 to 7 P.M. Biotherapist-beginners are active in these intervals not every day, but only during days which are most favorable for their psychophysiological conditions; usually it is connected to climate factors and phases of the moon.

4. The healer 'has to be healthy and an energy active person. A practicing biotherapist has to observe a certain regime of nutrition, sleep and maintain contact with nature'.
5. Krivorotov divides the organismic (in contrast with cellular) functional systems, which he calls the 'macrobioenergetic systems', into the following categories:

I. Psychic functions
a. Thinking
b. Emotions
c. Control

II. Psychosomatic functions
a. Sexual function

III. Somatic functions
a. Digestion
b. Motor function
c. Respiratory function

The interaction of all macrobioenergetic systems has two regimes: an imbalanced regime at the conscious level and a balanced unconscious regime. Mainly the activity of a person occurs in the imbalanced regime: To perform some action one has to highly activate one of the systems, simultaneously suppressing activity of the others. This is a principle of existence of any organism. To solve a complicated mathematical task, one has to almost stop the activity of his muscles, stomach, etc. The degree of the imbalance has its limits; if the organism oversteps them, it often leads to pathology, because a subsequent balance regime cannot be achieved. This can result in long deformations for some systems of the organism. The balance regime is manifested considerably in the deep sleep (identified by delta-rhythms) and partly in the paradoxical stage of sleep as well as in the waking state in the periods of decreasing conscious activity (which is of a rhythmic character). The way of life of a contemporary person with a high level of conscious activity can cause an overloading of the organism by these imbalances. This leads to an increasing rate of diseases. Pathogenesis, as a result of imbalance, is a phenomenon characteristic of human beings in the civilized world. Animals cannot overeat or overexploit their sexual function. Human beings received this opportunity from nature but did not acquire enough knowledge to use it. Having lost unconscious ways of regulation, we must learn to use conscious ways.

What is the role of BT in normalizing the balance?

BT includes two essential energy procedures. The first is the attempt to achieve the equilibrium of all macroenergetic systems of a patient. Along with this 'tactical' procedure, the strategic approach is necessary: To convince the patient to change his way of life. 'Tactical' balance is achieved by the influence of the active hand of a healer, although sometimes it could occur due to the psychotherapeutic factor, i.e. by the patient's effort of will.

In some cases, the first session of BT can occur at the level of achieving the general energy balance until the patient learns how to preserve this state. The second energy procedure is activation of a pathogenic zone (this is the BT itself).

One of the main tasks of BT is to preserve, for a lengthy period of time, the level of activity of a pathogenic zone which was created by the energy-active hand of a healer, without damaging other functions of the organism. This task can be successfully solved if a healer is aware of macrobioenergetic laws … a person who has mastered the art of BT, clearly understands that without this inner transformation of a patient his recovery will be only of a temporary nature…

6. KRIVOROTOV postulates an internal organismic energy system which is correlated with the individual's value system. Behaviors contrary to the value system drain the individual's energy and leave him prey to biological and psychological malfunctions and diseases.

7. By contemplation a person may resolve conflicts affecting the macrobioenergetic and internal organismic energy systems mentioned in the fifth and sixth points above. Krivorotov proposes the following systemic subdivisions:

* *The System of Control:* "The healthy mind creates the healthy body."
* *The System of Thinking:* "Let our

thoughts clear the world from vanity and contradictions."

* *The System of Emotions:* "By negative emotions one kills himself and others, by positive emotions one constructs the world, and by microemotions one cognizes it. We came to this world for cognition and creation."

* *The Sexual System:* "It is not reasonable to dig a new well for each sip of water, moreover, if there are springs not far away; i.e., it is not expedient to exploit the system of reproduction for the sake of pleasure."

* *The Digestion System:* "Don't eat for pleasure, but rather eat with pleasure; if you've eaten more than you needed, you've violated the principle of the IVth precept and left somebody hungry, because one third of mankind is starving."

* *The Motor System:* "Your muscles are like a hound; when a hunter gives his hound an opportunity to regularly romp, the hunting is successful."

* *The Respiratory System:* "Breathing is like a Genie who awaits his moment; the moment will come when the healthy mind creates the healthy body."

8. KRIVOROTOV decries the views of modern conventional medical cosmology:

All methods of intervention ultimately decrease the resistive potential of a person. From the very beginning, these methods were intended to be used in cases of emergency when there was only one choice: death, or further life with decreased potential. In order to save a patient, physicians treated the disease but not the patient. Gradually 'the method of intervention' became the main method of medicine, which is applied for all, including non-dangerous, illnesses, without vital necessity. This unconscious orientation of contemporary medicine also decreases the potential of a human being as a biological system on the genetic level. In 'fighting for life' today, the 'medicine of intervention' unconsciously worsens the future of mankind. At present, the majority of people, beginning from infancy, apply one or another kind of medical treatment, and we encounter a sad paradox: In spite of the high development of medicine, the disease rate is ever increasing each year.

What is the reason for this strange situation? One of the main reasons is the spontaneous development of medicine, without a theoretical and philosophical consideration of global problems. The second reason, which is a consequence of the first one, is that while being spontaneous, it appeared to be under the influence of patients who demanded the usage of the 'methods of intervention'.

Observations show that the increasing number of patients who demand this method, results from an incorrect way of life and an egocentric being. However, the 'medicine of intervention' gradually changed human attitudes, and at present the majority of people cannot accept the idea that diseases result from violation of moral and ethical laws. Therefore, science looks for reasons for disease only on a physiological level, and non-scientists view appearance of a disease as an accident caused by fluctuations of external conditions. In this situation all mankind is forced to pay for delusions of mistaken people.

9. KRIVOROTOV points out possible broad social effects of psi healing:

> We see that patients who were subjected to BT increase their level of feedback concerning processes in the organism. They begin to feel a sense of responsibility for their health and actively participate in the process of recovery. Thus, the way to the world of self-regulation will lead people to the way of 'self health care' and will free the tremendous social forces which today are spent for health care.
>
> We also mentioned that on the basis of responsibility for their own health, people will become aware of their responsibilities for others. As we excluded religion from our life, we were unable to find a substitute for its function in the regulation of human ethical interrelations. We believe that after BT becomes a widely accepted method of therapy, a physician (who will be at the same time a healer) will take a mission of a spiritual teacher.

Discussion LARISSA VILENSKAYA has given us a beautiful gem of holistic medicine from Eastern Europe via her translation. KRIVOROTOV'S views are strikingly consonant with those of western holistic medicine. His observations on the effectiveness of some healers only at certain times of the day echo those of Shubentsov and of acupuncturists. This may explain some of the variability in results of psi healing.

KRIVOROTOV'S opinion that cognitive changes must occur in order for benefits of healing to be long-lasting is echoed by many but not all healers. His conceptualizations of the workings of the mind and body closely parallel western ones but are sufficiently different to be worth studying.[10]

I know of no other healer who claims that too long a healing treatment is deleterious.

Three books describe the late, well-known American healers, Olga and Ambrose Worrall.

Ambrose A. and Olga N. Worrall – The Gift of Healing: A Personal Story of Spiritual Therapy

This book presents a personal account of the Worralls' lives, recounting how each separately, and later both together, developed healing gifts.

Ambrose A. and Olga N. Worrall with Will Oursler – Explore Your Psychic World

This series of questions and answers explains the experiences and cosmologies of these very gifted healers.

Edwina Cerutti – Mystic with the Healing Hands: The Life Story of Olga Worrall

EDWINA CERUTTI reports on discussions with the Worralls, (especially Olga) regarding their experiences with and understandings of healing; letters and references documenting their work; brief descriptions of several studies in which Olga participated; and Biblical references on psychic phenomena, by categories (clairvoyance, spirit control, spirit voices, messages from departed spirits, spirit return, levitation, trances, and more).

OLGA WORRALL was one of the best known and best studied American healers. These books provide fascinating views of how a healing gift is discovered and developed.

Statements by Olga Worrall from Cerutti's book explore her understanding of healing.

Fig. I-4. *Olga and Ambrose A. Worrall were among America's best studied healers.* Photo by courtesy of Psychic News

According to Olga, spiritual healing is the channeling of energy into a recipient from the universal field of energy which is common to all creation and which stems from the universal source of all intelligence and power, called God. Emanations surround each individual, apparently caused by electrical currents flowing in the physical body. There are sound waves from the various physical organs and thought waves from the mind as well as vibrations from the spiritual body. Energy from the universal field of energy becomes available to the healer through the act of tuning his personal energy field to a harmonial relationship with the universal field of energy so that he acts in this way as a conductor between the universal field of energy and the patient.

"Now remember", Olga finished laughingly, "I'm no scientist and I don't really understand what everything I've just said is all about. But this is what the spirit world has told Ambrose and me. Of course, Ambrose, as a scientist, has always made sense of this explanation. He says that spiritual healing is a rearrangement of the microparticles of which all things are composed. The body is not what it seems to be with the naked eye. It is not a solid mass. It is actually a system of little particles or points of energy separated from each other by space and held in place through an electrically balanced field. When these particles are not in their proper place, then disease is manifested in that body. Spiritual healing is one way of bringing the particles back into a harmonious relationship – which means, into good health."

"My kind of healing, you see, has a psychic overlay. When I lay my hands on someone seeking healing, I often receive, psychically, background information or even a diagnosis that helps me know what to say, therapeutically, to a patient, or what to do."

"But how do you 'receive' this information?" I persisted. "Do you hear voices?"

"Not in the usual sense you're referring to", Olga said laughingly. "Mostly it's that specific thoughts are impressed on my consciousness so clearly and so definitely that I have the unequivocal feeling that someone has said something to me. Sometimes I actually hear a voice communicating. It's none that you would hear, though, because I sense it with my inner ear only. And still other times I actually see a spirit form near the person with the problem, and get messages from this spirit man or woman which are relevant to the problem and beneficial in its treatment."

Olga then went on to explain that the 'laying-on-of-hands' is an important part of a neophyte spiritual healer's development. As for her own approach, however, distant healing was equally effective because of her educated awareness of the universal field of energy which surrounds both her and the patients who ask for help. In absent treatments, for example, Olga declared that she not only could feel a cool kind of power flowing from her solar-plexus, but often was cognizant of specific instruction and assistance from the spirit world in general or, at times, from one or more of several discarnate physicians in particular.

Prayer on the part of a healer is a necessity: not the customary prayer of striving, petitioning, urging, or bargaining, but a request to be used as a healing channel and an expression of deep gratitude for the fulfillment of the request. Prayer on the part of the patient, however, is not an essential ingredient for successful spiritual healing.

HIROSHI MOTOYAMA, a Japanese biologist, tested OLGA WORRALL on his meridian-measuring device, which demonstrates findings apparently specific for healers.

Dr. Motoyama gave the results concerning Mrs. Worrall's psi ability as follows: One characteristic belonging to the psychic person is standard deviation of skin current of the 28 meridian (seiketsu) points which is very high compared with the ordinary person. For instance, in the average person the value is from 0.1 to 0.26, but Mrs. Worrall showed 1.0, a very much higher value, which means that Mrs. Worrall is a psychic person. Then after comparison between readings before and during faith healing through her hands and fingers, meridians of the left-hand fingers showed a (highly) significant difference between and before and during faith healing.

Consequently, we can infer that her psi ability is more easily projected from the left as compared to the right hand. The meridians which showed significant difference are of the genito-urinary system, the digestive system, and the heart circulatory system, which, according to the yoga chakra system, means in her case that the anahata, manipura and vishuda chakras are predominantly working.

Also helpful are segments from the WORRALLS'

book with WILL OURSLER. Ambrose Worrall states:

Individualized man expresses his individuality by his ability to select ideas of his own choosing and show them to others in observable form through the use of his will and the law of creation. This operation of the will of man upon the idea, or that which is desired, involves faith. The principle of creative law is without limitations. The demonstration of this principle is limited by the extent of man's belief in it. The passive selection of an idea, without the act of willing it into motion, will never produce an active demonstration. Man must believe in the creative law. He must learn to trust it, to know that it always works.

This combination of belief and trust is the foundation of faith, the kind of faith that Jesus spoke of when he said: "If ye had faith as a grain of mustard seed, ye might say unto this sycamine tree, Be thou plucked up by the root, and be thou planted in the sea; and it should obey you." That's from the 17th chapter of St. Luke, sixth verse. Since man cannot escape the results of the operation of creative law, he is selecting new ideas and motivating them. He can bring about such changes in his condition, environment, and activities that creative law will allow...

Reality is in the imperceptible. Man makes the error of seeing the effect as reality whereas the Cause is reality. Looking upon effect as reality brings confusion to man's mind. The enormous complexity of effect is so great that man's mind cannot encompass it. Yet man can think of Cause, the single source of all manifestation, God, without being overwhelmed with the multiplicity of formulas applicable to effect.

On using healing forces negatively, as in killing weeds:

I think it would work that way, too. But we are very, very careful never to tune in on destructive thinking. The problem with that would be that if we started to experiment in that direction, thousands of people tuned in to us might be affected. We don't know enough about the mechanism yet. It may work on plants, and it may work on a patient who is attuned to us at that time. So we are afraid to experiment.

On water held by AMBROSE WORRALL for Dr. Robert Miller:

I [Ambrose] asked him whether he had made any other tests on the water, and he said he had poured some of the water into a pie plate, that he had gotten some special photographic film from a photographer and put it over the pie plate and left it there all through the weekend. The photographer told him he couldn't possibly get any reaction on this film from distilled water in a pie plate. What he actually got was a photograph of the pie plate and water, which they have been unable to explain. This was special photographic film which was sensitive only in the high ultraviolet range...

On plants:

Ambrose, you say you prayed for the plant. What was your actual ideation? Was it an encouragement of growth, or what?

I think you might say that our attention probably creates a carrier wave and that this other force, whatever it is, modulates that carrier wave in some way and is carried through and does its work at the other end.

Discussion   The Worralls point to a complex interplay between healer and healee, involving beliefs, visualizations, energy transfers and probably other elements as well.

OLGA WORRALL stated that she did not believe healing could be taught (1981). She felt people either have the ability or they do not.

The following quotes from CERUTTI clarify the relationship between Olga Worrall's healing, psychic and spiritual experiences.

> You were explaining the 'psychic overlay' in your kind of spiritual healing...and frankly, it leaves me in a quandary. What I mean is: do I have to have some kind of psychic ability in order to do spiritual healing? Is that a prerequisite for setting up a healing service in a church, or for even attempting spiritual healing? Because I'm about as nonpsychic as you can get!
>
> "Definitely not", Olga reassured him. "The spiritual healing I do is enhanced by my psychic gift, but spiritual healing can be, and usually is, accomplished by people who are neither clairvoyant nor clairaudient, nor mediumistic in any way. The healing current flows through every clear channel available, whatever the healer's psychic abilities or, for that matter, religious beliefs. As a matter of fact, I don't profess to have psychic intervention available in every case. My clairvoyance is entirely spontaneous and can't be turned on and off at will. Many people call me and expect a prompt psychic diagnosis – as if their ten-cent pieces in the telephone

should start my motor up like coins in a washing machine. Sometimes it does, and sometimes it doesn't."

Discussion   Olga Worrall (1982) saw spirits from childhood and was in communication with Ambrose when he passed on before she did. Despite this, she was scathingly critical of anyone who believed in reincarnation, which she felt was a silly notion.

Harold Sherman – Your Power to Heal

This is a lovely book in which HAROLD SHERMAN considered many aspects of healing. In it, *AMBROSE WORRALL* explains his views:

> When I undertake to help a sick person, I sit with the patient and do what I call a 'tuning-in' operation. This is done by sitting in a relaxed state and fixing my attention on the patient, but not to any specific part of the body or the condition that may be existing. In this way I avoid being biased in the direction of a particular condition which the patient thinks he has and which may be an effect rather than a cause. After the 'tune-in' has been accomplished, the conditions are such that the 'force' can flow. It will flow providing the potential in the patient is lower than the potential of the healer. It will always flow from the high to the low potential. This is putting it somewhat in materialistic terms, but I do not know any other way to explain it. The power that flows is entirely impersonal. Although I am instrumental in creating the conditions which permit the force to flow, actually I have no control over it whatsoever.

I believe that it will only flow when the conditions are right and that the extent to which it will flow is governed by a condition which can be likened to two batteries, one that is highly charged and one that is not so highly charged. When they reach the same potential, there is no further flowing of power.

During a treatment, I do not feel a power flowing into me from an external source, but I feel that the power builds up within me. However, I do feel the power flowing from me. It seems to flow in the form of heat when I do the laying-on-of-hands. While using this method of treatment, the power flows from the portion of my hands that are in contact with the patient.

In the case of 'absent treatment', I do not feel power flowing from my hands but, instead, feel it flowing like a cool stream from my solar plexus. Usually I have the sensation that something in the form of a cylinder some twelve inches in diameter seems to extrude from my solar plexus to a distance of twelve to fourteen inches. A force then turns my body to focus this cylinder in the direction of the patient. After the cylinder is focused, I feel the power flowing for perhaps ten seconds, and that is the extent of the 'absent healing'. This force which I feel in 'absent healing' is a cool force, quite different from the warm force experienced during the laying-on-of-hands. I have no explanation for the apparent difference in temperature.

I feel that this discharge of power is probably accompanied by a lowering of my vitality during the treatments. Half an hour after I have finished the treatments, when I once again am in tune with my physical body, I become aware of a tired feeling. However, I think this is purely physical.

After I work all day and then work all evening, it is natural that the vitality of the physical body should reach a low ebb. This has nothing to do with the flow of spiritual power which, I feel, is something entirely independent of the physical body. The physical body is merely a channel through which it flows.

During a healing treatment I do not turn my attention to some far-off place up in the heavens, nor do I look for the source of power anywhere else or ask it to come to me. I just have a feeling that it will be available when the conditions are right and when I permit myself to become the channel for its use.

… Unfortunately, some people are not clean. When this situation exists, I do not feel at home and feel a discordant condition. I have a desire to get away from the person. To overcome this feeling requires effort and energy, and under such conditions, one can never attain the attunement which is necessary to get the best results.

Whether or not people believe they can be healed has no effect on me. If a person in active opposition said, 'I know you can't help me', it would probably build up a barrier and so prevent his receiving help, although I have no way of proving that this would be so. I have had cases where people have come not believing and received excellent results. I have had other cases where they came believing and received very little help.

When I put my hand on a patient during a healing treatment, I feel as if I am wearing gloves. When my hand touches the skin, something seems to be between the skin and my hand, and the feeling is not the normal sensation one gets in touching a person. There is a difference that is hard to explain. The feeling of some layer between the patient and my hands may be caused by my being out of tune with my physical body. Perhaps there is a dissociation of the spirit from the body to some slight degree which gives me this sense of separateness. I have never been able to explain this phenomenon to myself, although I have many theories.

When the power flows through my hands, I feel heat and sometimes I feel pins and needles. If I am treating a skin disease, I feel the pins and needles very strongly, and I feel it more strongly if I have some part of the body enclosed in my hand.

Discussion   AMBROSE WORRALL'S scientific background enhanced his observational powers. It may, as well, have shaped the expression of his healing gifts.

The divergence of experiences and opinions of healers is perplexing. While there appear to be common grounds between most of them, the differences often seem more striking. It will take much study to tease out their origins.

L et us turn now to other descriptions of how healers work.

David Eisenberg with Thomas Lee Wright – Encounters with Qi: Exploring Chinese Medicine

DAVID EISENBERG, is a physician in Boston who studied Chinese natural medicine techniques and now teaches complementary medicine methods at Harvard Medical School. In this book he explores theories and practices of *Qi Gong* (literal translation is *breathing skill*), part of which is the Chinese equivalent of psi healing.

Qi (also spelled *chi* and *ki*) is the Chinese name for energies believed to imbue the body with its life force. The Chinese feel that this energy flows through lines in the body which correspond to the acupuncture meridians.

Qi Gong is the study of harnessing and focusing these energies. A person may do this for himself through meditation and physical exercises, with special attention to breathing techniques and to visualizations of the energy being concentrated in the center of the body and then flowing where needed to other body parts. This is termed *internal Qi Gong*, contrasted with *external Qi Gong* where a person projects energies outside his body.

EISENBERG describes masters of these techniques who display extraordinary physical prowess, including great strength; resistance to harm when crushed by great weights or pierced by sharp objects; reduction of body weight, even to the point of levitation; psychokinesis; ability to light fluorescent bulbs (as long as they are not in a building higher than the fifth floor); and healing.

EISENBERG provides numerous anecdotal reports of healings. He echoes Chinese claims, based on unpublished studies, that *Qi Gong* can help with arthritis, asthma, bowel problems, cancers, coronary artery disease, diabetes, hypertension, chronic kidney disease, "neurasthenia", peripheral vascular disease and peptic ulcers. He briefly quotes a study of a case of myopia which improved and another in which bacterial growth was enhanced and decreased at will by a *Qi Gong* master. He also mentions that *Qi Gong* energies directed to acupuncture points can be used sometimes for anesthesia.

He cites Chinese claims that the emission of *Qi Gong* energies can be measured as heat and infrared radiations on various instruments. In addition, "nuclear magnetic resonance scanners, CAT scanners, and other sophisticated electromagnetic devices have been employed to document and quantify *external Qi Gong* activity. Our hosts made available no details of this research."

EISENBERG describes sensations he and other westerners experienced when *Qi* was directed to their bodies by various masters. These included "pins and needles", "electrical impulses", pressure, numbness and dulling of consciousness or confusion. The latter was noted during an experiment in which the master apparently caused a subject to move in various directions by merely directing *Qi* energy at him from several feet away.

After extensive studies, including many visits and a year's fellowship at various Chinese medical facilities, Eisenberg notes that a comparison of Chinese and western methods of treatment is very difficult. He gives the instance of a patient with pneumonia. In the West, this infection is presumed to be caused by specific bacteria or viruses. The treatments are aimed at the elimination of the infecting organisms.

> ... You have a high fever, chills and cough. When you arrive at the office of a Western doctor, a detailed medical history is taken and a physical examination and laboratory tests are performed. Evidence from your physical examination and abnormalities in your chest X-ray lead the doctor to decide that you have pneumonia. A sample of your sputum, stained for bacteria, confirms the diagnosis. You are treated with appropriate antibiotics and sent home to rest in bed.
>
> Now imagine going to the office of a traditional Chinese doctor with the same symptoms. The physician listens to your

story and then asks a number of questions about the 'type' of chills you've had and the manner of your sweating. He takes your pulse and examines your tongue. The doctor is aware that your lungs are troubling you, but his diagnosis, according to traditional medicine, refers to the underlying imbalances in your body. The pneumonia with its associated fever, cough, and sputum production is the *manifestation* of the underlying imbalance. It is the 'uppermost branch', not the 'root', of the illness. By studying your tongue and pulse and by listening to your story, the physician identifies the precise excess or deficiency affecting your body. This may involve an imbalance of an organ distant from the lung. The doctor treats your imbalance rather than a condition known as pneumonia.

Discussion   This is a valuable book on Chinese folk medicine. It illustrates the caution with which western scientists must examine therapeutic systems from other cultures in order to learn what might be meaningfully applied to their own. The authors take no cognizance of western studies of healing and their reports and assessments in this book appear understated. Type II errors (rejecting a useful treatment) are quite likely.

Joseph Zezulka – Biotronic Healing

JOSEPH ZEZULKA had been a healer in Czechoslovakia for about 30 years when he shared his experience and advice in these articles. He calls himself a biotronic healer.

> Every individual is characterized by a balance of ... material, psychic and vital com-

ponents that are essential to survival, health, and growth. Ordinarily, these ... are in a steady state with only slight fluctuations. A disturbance of equilibrium leads to a disease caused by vital insufficiency. These vital powers are essentially the pulsations and rhythms of the life force itself. The physical and psychic spheres of our organism are vitalized and given life by this third sphere – the vital powers.

The vital powers flow in through the breath, solid food, liquid food, and sleep. In these ways one's basic supply is replenished.

Malfunctioning is characterized by feebleness or by chaotic activity of the vital sphere. Disease is caused by a disturbance of the bodily centres of the vital powers, and by deformation of the lines of force through which organs influence each other.

The biotronic healer is a person whose special talent is the ability to transfer vital powers from the environment to diseased individuals without losing any of his or her own vital powers in the process. This second or additional stream of powers has importance only for the patient, and is always separate from and in addition to the healer's own reserve of vital powers.

ZEZULKA differentiates between the types of healers:

1. *Magnetizers* can passively transfer vital powers but they do not know exactly what they are or how to regulate them. They use touch healing. "I would presume that the magnetizer's healing is accomplished by strengthening the centers of power in the sick person's body with the translated powers, so that the lines of force regain their balance."

Unconscious coloring of the transmitting power by each magnetizer's own qualities may produce greater success in healing certain kinds of diseases than others.

2. *Sanators* can actively and purposefully regulate and control the vital powers as they transfer them from the environment to the sick person.

The sanator cannot administer an overdose of the vital power. No matter how much is given, the body will only take in what it needs. The excess will flow away. The sanitor's operation can restore health, but it cannot do any harm.

A sanator rectifies the energic net of power centers on the levels of a cell, an organ and even centers of the whole bodily organism.

For instance, the whole bodily centers contain a morphological center. Its insufficiency may cause a defect in the developing body form. This center takes part also in healing of trauma. Benign tumors may grow if it weakens. It may also contribute to growth of malignant tumors, often transformed from a benign tumor. To influence the cause of the disorder we influence this morphological center.

Zezulka feels some people can only relieve pain and that this can be harmful because it may mask disease processes which would then go untreated.

He makes recommendations for healing cancer. He stresses that diet is a crucial factor, giving the following food lists:

* *Forbidden:*
– All smoked victuals / smoked meat, sausages, ham, smoked cheese, etc.;
– roasted food / including all decoctions from roasted materials, e.g. coffee, cocoa, chocolate, etc;

– all fried and baked victuals; if baking cannot be avoided the food must be eaten without crust, e.g. bread; other types of pastry must be taken only in a mildly baked form and to a limited extent only, e.g. mildly baked rolls;
– food prepared in tins containing benzoic acid; and
– tar in any form, e.g. in ointments.
* *Recommended:*
– Food should be taken mainly in the fresh form, e.g. fruits, vegetables, esp. roots, nuts, milk, butter, etc. If food is cooked then only boiling or stewing is allowed. Every pot with food going on a fire must contain water. This diet must be observed consistently because patients to whom this diet is prescribed are oversensitive to various elements contained in the forbidden food. Any slightest deviation from the diet may hinder the healing process or make it completely impossible.
– Diet is a factor contributing to healing but it does not heal or remove the disease itself.

These suggestions are based on the observation that plants lose their *vital capacity* with time after being harvested. This he apparently deduces from Kirlian photography, which shows an aura around plants that gradually diminishes after they have been plucked.

ZEZULKA then describes his psi healing ability.

Besides the classical 'taking off' the plasma [*aura*] spoilt by disease and an overall filling of the patient with vital energy, I influence locally the liver. I try to increase its detoxicating function and to strengthen it generally. It is especially the part to the right of the sternum.

In the next phase I influence the morphological centre (my view and term) which I presume to exist in the cerebrum. It is a centre which commands the bodily form of the body as a whole, then the individual organs and cells.

I exercise an effort to disturb the pathological neoplasm and to achieve balance in the morphological signals whose chaos may be caused both on the afferent and efferent tracks.

Only in the last phase I exercise local influence on the cancer. I concentrate on its cells and modulate the stream of energy towards tranquillity. I try to pervade the organism of the cells and to disturb their excessive and excitative activity. In this the tranquillity power may be given in greater amounts. This is why I often use water and work with wet hands. In this way the overall vital energy is modified and its tranquillizing part is increased. The same manner is used later to dissolve the tumor. The process of dissolving may not be equally easy in different types of cancer. This is why it is good to ask the surgeon to remove the tumor after the healing process is over. The afflicted spot is the 'locus minoris resistentiae', where new cancerogenous process might start after some time. The surgeon should operate only after the healing process is over because in some cases the operation may not be necessary. If the surgeon agrees to remove the remainder of the tumor, then the preceding healing process diminishes the possiblity of metastasis. This depends upon the ability of the healer and the period of healing before the operation – with an able healer 10–15 'sittings' are necessary. It is good to repeat the healing process after the operation as soon as possible.

During the postoperational healing the healer will concentrate on centripetal healing besides the tranquilizing effect on the tissues. If possible he will again use water as a complement. Further for at least five years it is advisable to repeat the protective healing twice a year–again 10–15 'sittings.' It is necessary to follow the diet during this period and if possible also hereafter.

Discussion   ZEZULKA's two distinct types of healers complement LAWRENCE LESHAN's observations.[11] Zezulka's warning on healers who might endanger a sick person by masking a warning pain signal from the body, echoing several other healers, is logical but has never proved a problem in my explorations of healing. His comments on confirmation of his dietary theory by increased relapse rates if patients stop the diet are questionable. Rather than attribute relapses to dietary indiscretions, why not ask why a person would go off the diet? Not sticking with a very strongly recommended diet seems to me far more likely an indication of psychological self-destructive motives, which could themselves lead to relapse. Of course no theory can be established without proper controlled experiments.

Therapeutic Touch (TT) is the most widely used method of healing in the United States. It was initiated by DOLORES KRIEGER, R.N., Ph.D., at the New York University School of Nursing, with DORA KUNZ, a gifted natural healer and psychic. TT is being increasingly accepted in professional and academic circles as a result of Krieger's work. She has personally taught many thousands of nurses these simple methods of

diagnosis and healing. A growing number of hospitals have nurses utilizing these techniques, though TT is often given quietly and unobtrusively. These methods clearly provide an exciting adjunct to conventional therapies.

Carefully controlled studies have validated the efficacy of TT[12] and more are planned and in progress. The full range of efficacy of these techniques is just beginning to be uncovered.

Dolores Krieger – The Therapeutic Touch: How to Use Your Hands to Help or to Heal

KRIEGER explains that TT involves these steps:
1. Centering – The healer clears his mind and relaxes his body, finding within himself 'an inner reference of stability'.
2. Scanning – The healer passes his hands around the body of the healee, sensing for any asymmetries or irregularities in the energy field which might indicate a portion of the body in need of healing. Often a second healer will simultaneously scan the opposite side of the body, after which the two switch places and scan the opposite sides of the body, comparing impressions at the end. The consensual validation obtained through working in pairs is helpful in learning to trust one's diagnostic and healing abilities.
3. Unblocking the healee's field – The healer may sense areas which do not have a normal 'energy flow'. He will direct his healing energy to these areas to smooth them out.
4. Transferring energies to the healee – The healer consciously sends energies, often with visualizations of light of particular colors for healing.

Krieger feels that to become a healer a person must have clear intentionality, motivation to help and an ability to understand his own motivation for wanting to heal. She observes that people practicing TT also improve their intuitive and psi abilities.

Krieger shares her vast experience in healing and in teaching healing. She recommends TT for relaxation; alleviation and/or elimination of pain (e.g. arthritic, traumatic); acceleration of natural healing processes; nausea; shortness of breath; rapid pulse; pallor from peripheral vascular contraction; poor circulation in the extremities; physiological development of premature infants; assistance in pacifying irritable babies; and more. She does not know of any illness in which she feels TT is totally or always ineffective. She has found (per Estebany) that cotton can both store and facilitate healing.

Krieger finds that belief in the effectiveness of healing does not affect the success of healing. She feels skeptics can be helped. "However, two personality variables – denial of illness and hostility – do have a negative effect on TT, perhaps because they both may translate themselves graphically to the healer and inhibit the healer's efforts."

Krieger teaches healing to relatives of healees so that they may give treatments at home.

Krieger's approach has been the most effective of all the methods in opening professionals and lay persons to healing, as well as in generating research. There are tens of thousands of nurses and others in the U.S. and around the world doing TT.

Discussion   This is an extremely helpful introductory book to anyone interested in learning about TT. It also contains excellent 'how-to' exercises. KRIEGER has lovely de-

scriptions, occasionally waxing poetic, of the inner changes accompanying the learning/development of healing skills. This book has some of the best descriptions of how healers learn to heal.[13]

It is more clinically than research oriented, however, and open to Type I errors.

Jane Tinworth – Dynamic Healing

JANE TINWORTH is a healer who finds that her healees often move about in unpredictable ways during the course of healing treatments. They may arch their backs, enter complex yoga positions, shake portions of their body vigorously, and more. Jane does not suggest these motions to them. Both she and the healees are often very surprised at the complex contortions produced. Healees experience these as strong urges which they simply comply with because they feel they will be beneficial. They may resist, with an effort of conscious willpower, if they wish.

Jane Tinworth writes:

> However skilled a description of dynamic healing may be, it has to be experienced to be accepted. Even witnessing the phenomena is only part of the picture. A familiar remark from clients at the end of a session is "I wouldn't have believed it if I hadn't experienced it myself."
>
> The term *dynamic healing* is given to a particular manifestation of spiritual healing in in which clients respond to the healer's energy by performing spontaneous movements with no conscious direction or control. For example, a person with a structural or arthritic problem may 'observe' their trunk, limbs or head mov-

Fig. 1-5. In dynamic healing patients may arch their backs, wave their hands and make many other self-corrective movements. Photographs by John Stubbs

ing around in certain patterns or vibrating, rippling or stretching. Movements may be slow and gentle or rapid and strong. The body may be in a prone position or it may execute a variety of seemingly impossible movements over a lengthy period. It is not unusual for even elderly clients to have an hour of really vigorous movement and yet feel relaxed both during and after the session. The experience is of the movements 'doing themselves' and of a sense of 'rightness'.

Dynamic healing is a 'density' of the healing force and I have no doubt that it demonstrate our innate ability to heal ourselves. Results are always positive, even when the movements seem to bear little or no relation to the presenting problem. Injury through making movements which were previously difficult is unknown. Pain is only occasionally experienced in the process but seldom to the point of the client wishing to stop.

Dynamic healing does not always involve physical movement as this obviously is not appropriate for all conditions. During healing many clients access underlying causes of problems – physical, mental, emotional and spiritual – together with their own intuitive guidance for resolving them. Others may enter altered states of consciousness akin to deep meditation.

It is important to be aware that these responses during healing are quite spontaneous and not the result of therapy or suggestion.

Clients are often startled by their own unusual movements, which are often very funny to observe. Their resulting laughter and light-heartedness can also be a part of the healing process.

Once they have experienced dynamic healing, clients can be shown how to put themselves into the healing 'mode' and continue the process alone by attuning directly to the energy source.

The only side effect is improved well being.

For myself, I had been healing for about 15 years without such visible effect before the dynamic aspect began to occasionally and gently manifest. The first 'strong' session came in 1987 when a man, severely disabled and in pain for fourteen years through a spinal injury, arrived for healing, hardly able to get himself onto the treatment couch. I was taken by surprise as his body contorted violently from head to foot and I actually thought he was having an epileptic fit. However, when I asked him if he was alright, he answered very calmly, "I am in your hands. I am content." An hour later he walked upright and pain-free from the room. After that the self-healing manipulations grew to become everyday occurrences.

Spontaneous self correction has been known to happen for some time but until a few years ago researchers in England were aware of only three healers consistently producing dynamic effects. Now I am delighted to report that a significant number of colleagues and other healers who have passed through our development courses are having similar effects on their clients. This reinforces my belief that by dealing with our own problems and constantly seeking to raise our levels of love and awareness, many of us have this potential.

Margaret *(assumed name to protect anonymity)* – Personal communication

MARGARET found at the age of 17 that she could calm a woman diagnosed as 'mental breakdown, homicidal' by rubbing the bottom of her spine and talking with her. She did not immediately pursue her healing career after that.

I was put off by a family friend who offered to train me to develop my skills. The little purple light and the nasty smell (probably joss sticks) were totally alien to my experience. They thoroughly put me off healing at that time.

At age 24, skiing in an international event, Margaret severely injured her leg, sustaining a compound fracture of the right tibia and multiple fractures of the fibula.

I was left on the dump heap, told I'd never ski again. After five months in casts and another 18 months of physiotherapy, I was back on the slopes and racing again. The fibula had a cartilagenous union which left the leg unstable. Healing from a doctor who was also a healer helped that. He showed me how to put my hands over a trouble spot and thus to develop my own healing abilities.

Initially I worked on animals. My first

patient was my Laborador retriever, who was cured of an infected claw and later of scabies. I worked on a cat with viral pneumonia with good results. Hearing this, a woman with viral pneumonia requested my help, and she was cured too.

MARGARET studied physiotherapy for 18 months and radionics in order to understand and focus her efforts in a more professional manner. Later she abandoned the radionics, relying on her intuition to guide her work.

Soon after taking up healing she found that her healees moved their bodies in unusual manners during healings.

The first person who did that was a 21-year-old woman with severe cervical disc problems and headaches as well as bad asthma. She had been warned not to turn her head when it was inclined forward. The first thing she did when I started my laying-on-of-hands was to go down on all fours and turn her head rapidly and vigorously from side to side! Then she went into complex yoga postures which I had never seen before, though I'd done a little yoga myself. Then she did ballet steps and belly dancing. This is all the more remarkable because she was totally unathletic.

A remarkable series of healings followed over the course of several decades. Margaret will typically have a healee lie on her couch and will place a hand on or near his head. Within a few seconds to a few minutes he develops an altered state of consciousness. His eyes will often be glazed and unfocused and he will blink only a very few times per minute. He may lie still for many minutes or for a whole treatment. She may move her hands to the spine, chest, abdomen, to points of pain or dysfunction, or to other portions of

the healee's body as instinct directs her. At times he will move his body in a wide variety of ways. Limbs may be stretched or exercised vigorously; his back may be twisted or arched backward; he may rise from his recumbent position to enter yoga asanas, to perform classical dance exercises, to stand on his head or to do other exercises and contortions. Movements may be in twitches, rhythmic motions or coordinated sequences.

Often the motions the healee goes through are new and unfamiliar to him and beyond his capabilities when he is in his ordinary state of consciousness. Margaret reports she cannot predict and is often surprised by the particular motions displayed. "I have several times had to go to books to find out what they were up to!" She finds that they may repeat particular patterns within sessions and from one session to another, but she in no way directs or leads them through particular sequences of her choosing.

It all seems to come from within them. They do what they need to do to release their old patterns and to correct their problems. Though their contortions may seem strange to an observer, the healees themselves often sense which particular muscles or joints are being exercised for self-correction. They are not directing this consciously, however. It is purely an instinctual process.

These varied exercises appear to be self-corrective for neural and musculoskeletal disorders. A person with a bad back might produce loud 'cracks' in his back during such exercises, much as are heard under chiropractic or osteopathic manipulations. Animals (including a horse) treated by Margaret also went through such self-corrective contortions. This is further support for the claims that these movements are not consciously directed by Margaret or her healees.

During healings, a healee may be totally unconscious; conscious of his inner and outer surroundings but unresponsive to the environment around him; or totally conscious and interactive with the environment. If conscious, he will report he moves as he does in response to a very strong inner urge or compulsion to do so. It is not a voice or 'spirit guidance' directing him. Following a healing a person may experience further inner urges to resume his unusual exercises after leaving Margaret's presence. One healee reported, "I need only to lie down to reinvoke this process. It is usually more a matter of resisting a frequent urge than of setting up a mental state to commence these exercises." In relaxed social situations, some have succumbed to such urges in public, much to the amusement of their friends. Healees feel their self-healings are more intense when Margaret is providing healing than when they are on their own.

Margaret seeks to work as closely as possible with physicians, osteopaths, physiotherapists, and other health professionals. Although she addresses her work in a very serious and responsible fashion, the atmosphere in her treatment room is light and often jocular. Margaret is able to engage in healing without the need to be in a special meditative state. She is able to converse freely while ministering to as many as four healees at a time – limited only by the number of limbs she has to extend a touch or healing presence to each. The light atmosphere, particularly the laughter, is reported by some healees to intensify the effects of her healing.

Margaret's healings generally last from one to two hours but may go even longer. Though they may continue their self-corrective exercises without her touching them constantly, she feels she needs to be available to each

person to provide extra healing touches, emotional and physical support and protection from danger of banging and injuring themselves while moving about her living room (though no one ever has been hurt).

Discussion   How and why healees perform their self-corrective 'dances' during and after TINWORTH's dynamic healings is unclear. A few other healers, including the late JOHN CAIN (see following review), produce similar movements in healees. HANS ENGEL, a physician-healer in California, reported uncoordinated gross muscle contractions in two people with *tic doloreux* and one with osteoarthritis of the hip during healings.

I have reviewed videotapes of the healings of Tinworth, as well as those of two other dynamic healers, RON STALEY and MARGARET. Dramatic improvements have occurred with many musculoskeletal and neurological problems, including chronic fatigue syndrome and multiple sclerosis.

These healings seem to hold clues to what healing may be about. I must admit the answers elude me. Several sensitives who see auras report that the healings of Margret affect people through very refined levels of their being.

The spontaneous appearance of *yoga asanas* may indicate innate human physiological patterns in the origins of yoga. F. SMITH explains some yogic healings through involuntary movements (*kriyas*) which occur as body energy blocks are apparently released.

Ron Staley gives healing in the name of Christ. He does a laying-on-of-hands, turning the proceedings over to the care of Jesus. He finds that a small percent of his healees lie very still, experiencing an intensely blessful state. He calls this "resting in the spirit".

All three of these dynamic healers find that

intense emotions may be released during healings. These appear to be the stresses (long buried in healees' unconsciousness) which precipitated their illnesses.

Pat Sykes – You don't Know John Cain?

Valerie Wooding – John Cain Healing Guide

Peter Green – Heal My Son

PAT SYKES, a reporter, interviewed a number of healees who had been treated by the late *JOHN CAIN*. Cain could induce altered states of consciousness in healees through individual and group treatments. He sometimes worked in a hall with about 70 healees to whom he simultaneously 'beamed' his energy. They usually went into a trance-like state during which they were partially aware or totally unaware of their surroundings. It was a calming, restful state for most, during which anxieties and depressions were markedly diminished. Many physical symptoms abated during such treatments, either instantaneously or gradually and with repeated healings over a period of several weeks or months.

In about 5% of the cases further very unusual processes developed during healings. Healees experienced sensations of warmth or tingling rising through their backs from the base of the spine. There was initially a sexual arousal, then an intense feeling of love with a desire to share the love. Shortness of breath and intense feelings of peacefulness were common. These states lasted about one to two hours. Such sensations have been re-

ported by meditators, usually occurring only after many years' practice. The feelings are known as the raising of *kundalini* energy in the spine. Cain referred to his healees' sensations using these same terms.

During some healings healees might involuntarily assume various yoga asanas, dance intricate patterns, move portions of their bodies rhythmically and vigorously, tumble about and even grab Cain in various judo holds. Such motions were usually totally unknown to the subjects in their waking states and often were clearly beyond their normal capabilities. The actions seemed to facilitate recovery from various musculoskeletal problems but may also have been related to internal organ systems according to yogic traditions.

VALERIE WOODING suffers from multiple sclerosis, which improved greatly under Cain's treatments. She reports:

> ... it is an amazing sight to watch Cain's patients whilst healing [is] taking place. Some lie unnaturally still, not moving a muscle throughout the session. Others move un-self-consciously as the needs of their body dictate. Stomachs dilate, spines bend, arthritic joints crack as they move with full mobility. Yoga exercises, Eastern dancing, physiotherapeutic exercises could all be seen side by side with patients banging the floor or practising judo on Cain.
> ... [I] frequently exercised in ways which I *never* considered within my capabilities – yoga, ballet, judo, even head-stands... I am fully conscious of what my body is doing – almost as if I am observing it – but I am also aware of the reasons for it.

While not receiving healing she could not stand up straight, sit up from a prone position or bend her spine. Her muscles did not atrophy because of the exercises she performed while in an altered state of consciousness during healing treatments. She felt that her awareness of the exertions her body could tolerate during healing also increased her optimism.

WOODING cites a 'patient-helper' who was of the opinion that healees being treated by CAIN had access to some source of universal knowledge. This helped them to know what to do for their own benefit.

> When I cannonball (backward/forward rolls at great speed) across the hall at Bromborough my head could be heard cracking loudly against the parquet floor. I am aware of this, I, too, could hear it – and feel the contact. But *it does not hurt,* nor have I ever pulled a muscle or received a bruise. I have exercised in the most athletic manner in the midst of a crowded hall without ever hurting myself or anyone else present, occasionally negotiating a patient's outstretched arm or coming to a sudden stop inches away from a chair. There is an inbuilt safety device – and it seems to include radar!

Many people asked Wooding how she was able to do these things. She had no answer other than that she could not do them in her normal state of consciousness.

Cain had no idea how or why all these phenomena occurred. He never saw anyone hurt himself, even in the most violent of physical manipulations. He himself was familiar with judo, yoga and dance, though not particularly adept in these activities.

Cain also differed from most healers in his distant healing. He asked healees to gaze at a photograph of himself in order to make contact with him for healings.[14] This could be successful with or without his awareness that a healing was being sought at a particular

moment. On occasion he also asked healees to focus the healing on a particular part of the body by placing the photograph there. Another method he used in distant healing was a link-up between Cain and the healee via a surrogate person who did a laying-on-of-hands under Cain's instructions (usually over the telephone). This was even more effective if the surrogate had been conditioned by a healing treatment from Cain.

Cain reported he had several spirit guides who directed his treatments. He occasionally produced dramatic, instantaneous cures of physical disabilities with a direct request to a spirit entity to intervene, without resorting himself to a laying-on-of-hands.

Cain was a somewhat controversial figure in healing circles because he was extremely blunt in his manners and outspoken in his opinions. He smoked almost constantly, even during healings. He openly derided healers of lesser abilities. He sometimes gave telepathic commands to healees to perform certain actions which appeared to be more for exhibition of his own powers than for the good of the healee.

He was able to help especially in cases of arthritis, emotional problems, multiple sclerosis, circulatory and neuromuscular difficulties. Dramatic improvements were also noted on some occasions in cancers and hormonal difficulties. He estimated that 95% of his healees showed some improvement.

Cain was undoubtedly a powerful and unusual healer. Other healers have demonstrated some of the same effects, including the kundalini phenomenon.

Discussion   I observed Cain treating a group of seven select healees who experienced kundalini phenomena.[15] My reaction was very mixed. Though obviously seeking his healees' improvement, Cain also appeared to be seeking his own aggrandizement. This was especially evident when he gave telepathic commands for various actions even when one of the healees seemed to be clearly opposed to these. Subsequent discussion with these healees, however, revealed nothing but positive regard for Cain and his treatments. The kundalini phenomena seemed to be limited to blissful sensations, not extending to transcendent experiences.

Cain perhaps produced some of his effects of apparent healing by hypnotic suggestion, possibly on an unconscious (to himself) basis. Reports in the books, cases related by Cain himself and discussion with the seven healees all strongly suggest that some of his results represent genuine healings.

Ethel Lombardi – Personal communications

ETHEL LOMBARDI, a peppery, Scottish-Irish, middle-aged woman with red hair and sparkling green eyes, is trained as a *Reiki* master. *Reiki* is the Japanese word for the life force or energy, a variant of *Qi*.

The *Reiki* system of healing originated in Japan toward the end of the eighteenth century (ARNOLD/NEVIUS). Lombardi learned this system from the late HAWAYO TAKATA, who at that time was the sole remaining *Reiki* master. Lombardi came to appreciate *Reiki* healing through being healed herself of severe arthritis and other illnesses. When giving her a healing, GORDON TURNER correctly predicted she would one day be a great healer.

Healers learn the *Reiki* method through practice under a master's tutelage. This is enhanced via an induction procedure in which the master attunes the student's vibrations to healings.

The basic *Reiki* methods involve a standardized set of laying-on-of-hands treatments which are given to the entire body. A *Reiki* healer allows universal energies to flow through him to the healee. The healer does not visualize anything other than the healee receiving as much energy as he needs to heal whatever problems are present. The healer does not presume to know what the true problems are, inasmuch as symptoms apparent to the healee and his examiner may only be manifestations of more severe or causal factors at a deeper level than can be seen from physical examination. These could also be on psychological or spiritual levels, which can be reached only through the deep, unconscious mind of the healee.

There is a strong psychological component to *Reiki* healing. Feelings may often be activated during a healing, with the healer encouraging their abreaction and release. This may clear up physical symptoms which were connected to the feelings.[16] The *Reiki* tradition suggests healing is effective through energy fields that permeate the body, involving chakra and other energy centers.

Lombardi was long frustrated by the fact that far more people applied for healings than she had time to help. She appealed to the cosmic intelligences who guide her (she hesitates to call them spirits, inasmuch as she feels they are not the spirits of departed humans) to instruct her in faster methods.[17] In answer to her request she reports she was given a new and extremely potent method of healing which she calls *MariEl* (a name coined by herself from the combination of *Mary*, Mother of Christ, and the Biblical *El* meaning God). This method requires only about a minute to achieve results, while a *Reiki* healing would take 20 minutes or longer.

Lombardi is a very powerful and innovative healer and teacher. She is constantly honing and refining her methods to achieve ever better results. At times she will project energy from her eyes, use gemstones, or gather a whole group of student healers around the healee to enhance the potency and effectiveness of a healing. She feels that a very important part of her work is the healing of the earth itself and of all living things, as part of a preparation for a new age of consciousness which many psychics and healers report we are on the threshold of entering.

Ronald S. Miller – The Healing Magic of Crystals: An Interview with Marcel Vogel

MARCEL VOGEL, who worked for IBM for many years, studied crystallography. He then developed and taught methods of healing. He believed that when a crystal is properly cut, a person's mind can induce it to emit vibrations which are, in effect, amplifications of the user's mind. He felt that because a crystal has a very regular molecular organization in its structure, the healing energy emitted by crystals is similar to that emitted by lasers, i.e. coherent and concentrated.

Vogel believed that emotional distress weakens the energy field around the body, which may then permit disease to enter the physical body. A healer can use a crystal to release the negative patterns of the energy body, which then permits the physical body to become whole again.

At the start of a healing, Vogel said a brief prayer and took a deep breath. He projected his consciousness lovingly into the crystal, seeking a resonation with it. After holding his breath briefly, he exhaled quickly and forcefully. This produces the sensation of a vibration in the crystal. Vogel scanned the subtle body of the healee with the charged crystal, seeking areas that appear out of balance and in need of healing.

He believed the focal point for healing should be in the chest at a point he calls the *witness bone,* located at the sternum over the thymus gland. He felt that this is where thought forms and inner feelings are manifested.

> During treatment the patient draws in a deep breath and mentally scans this area, to discover the root cause of his disturbance. The patient, not the healer, makes this appraisal. Then, by amplifying the field through the use of the crystal, I help the patient visualize and bring to awareness the root cause of the physical disturbance in his system. Then I suddenly say the word 'Release!' As I snap the crystal like a whip cracking, the sudden movement of subtle energy – directed to the root cause of his disturbance through visualization – evokes a complete relaxation in the patient's system. Stress leaves the body, and he quickly is restored to wholeness.

The reporter observed:

> The release, then, is caused not only by the flow of energy from the crystal, but also by the person's willingness to face the truth of his own being. Often when a person has a problem, he doesn't have enough energy to face it, but through the crystal, the healer amplifies the available energy, and the higher energy can become the solution to the problem.

Vogel responded:

> Exactly right. I call this process *transformational medicine,* because it gives the

soul the opportunity to reconnect with the body, and the resulting wholeness is equivalent to good health. One of the main tenets of transformational medicine is that all forms of disease are the result of inhibited soul life. So, the art of the healer involves assisting each person to align himself with the soul and to release those patterns which inhibit the soul's activity.

VOGEL briefly mentioned cases of blindness, herpes simplex, surgery for an ovarian cyst and an abscessed tooth which responded to his methods. He taught his techniques and had an active following throughout the United States. He felt the students' main work is to relinquish their rational thinking, utilizing their more intuitive sides. He believed that healing may occur without love, but that such healings will be only superficial and temporary. He theorized that interactions of mind and crystal are possible because both of them process information holographically.

Discussion Crystals may provide an important tool for understanding how the human mind functions and interacts with energies and matter. Much work must be done before Vogel's speculations can be accepted at face value. The crystal may be no more than a placebo, suggesting to healer and healee that healing can occur. It is also essential to have more detailed reports of the treated cases. Blindness, for instance, may be caused by hysteria and its cure due to suggestion rather than to healing.[18]

Other reports (e.g. BAER / BAER; SILBEY) describe the use of crystals as adjuncts to healing but none mentions careful research. My personal impression, based on workshops with healers who use crystals, and ob-

servations of sensitives who see aura changes enhanced in healing with crystals, is that they do potentiate healings and may create energy fields and/or provide ancillary healing powers which are beneficial.

Native healers can be found in every country. These are people who either spontaneously exhibited innate healing abilities or studied with other healers. They often assume complex roles within their cultures. Their ritual practices have been well described in literature on *shamanism* but their healing abilities have been given insufficient attention.[19]

Max Freedom Long – Recovering the Ancient Magic

MAX FREEDOM LONG lived for many years in Hawaii and delved into the secrets of the local *kahunas* (medicine men). He presents observations of his own and of others on a broad gamut of native practices involving the full range of psi phenomena[20] (anticipating in an anecdotal way this review on healing).

Long explains *kahuna* healers' understanding of psychology and mind-body connections, tracing these back to India, the presumed origin of the people of the Pacific Islands.

... in India there has been an ancient teaching that there exists a *'Body, Mind, and Soul'* – a body (subconscious), a mind (conscious) and a soul (superconscious). The kahuna names for these are *unihipili, uhane and aumakua*. To be certain that we are right we have but to go to the ancient scriptures which Sri Ramakrishna studied and accepted in part, to find there the division of the human consciousness into the 'Lower Self, the Self and the Higher Self'.[21]

The *unihipili* (subconscious) is believed to consist primarily of memory and morals without reason, stored in computer-like fashion. It also maintains vital life functions. The memory includes behavioral complexes associated with belief systems. For instance, if the person is taught "Thou shalt not steal!", the command is ingrained in the *unihipili*. Should the person steal, his *unihipili* suffers from guilt and expects expiation or punishment.

The *uhane* (consciousness) has reasoning but no memory. It may partially separate from the body in sleep or other states of awareness. The *kahuna* may use his *uhane* to influence the *unihipili* of a healee in order to heal. LONG notes that for these interventions to be effective the *kahuna* generally had to touch the person being healed.

An illustrative case is helpful:

As one of my friends was involved in this case – a Chinese-Hawaiian gentleman – I was able to observe from the side lines, from the inception of the trouble to the cure, and to see that the trouble never returned once in the six years that followed.

'Henry' was a healthy young man who worked in a salt factory several miles from Honolulu. One morning, while driving along the open road to his work, he fainted. His car was wrecked and he was badly bruised. For over a period of two months these fainting spells recurred. In one of them he fell into an open fire. In another he fell on his bed and his cigarette set the bedding on fire, resulting in a narrow escape.

After three doctors had been consulted and had failed to discover the cause of the trouble, the young man's Hawaiian mother insisted that he should go to a kahuna for help. Henry did not believe in kahunas, being a modern young man and well educated, but in desperation he did as his mother advised.

The kahuna listened to the story with half-closed eyes, and when it ended closed his eyes entirely. He sat there quietly for several minutes, then addressed Henry sharply:

"I think you hurt some Hawaiian girl, no? You hurt bad and she grumble to spirit friends. They find you got shame feeling eating you inside, so they find easy for punish you. Come! Confess up!"

Henry was amazed, but he confessed. He had intended to marry the girl some day, but his Chinese father had another young lady in mind for his son. In the end Henry had allowed his father to have his way and had stopped calling on the Hawaiian girl. He did not know how she had taken his action.

"It is bad kind of hurt," said the kahuna. "Your shamed feeling is eating you inside, and when something is eating inside, then spirits can do bad things to you. Now, you got to go to the girl and make present and aloha until she forgive you. You do that and then come to me some more."

Henry did as he was directed and found the girl not unreasonable when she heard of the father's part in the matter. In due time she forgave him and accepted his present.

Upon his return to the kahuna, the old man again closed his eyes and made an examination of the case. He reported that the attacking spirits of 'grandma and old auntie' had gone away content.

"But", said the old man. "Funny kind thing is inside of everyone. That spirit live inside you got no sense. It's not very smart. Long time it take to throw away your shame feeling. Even when other spirit in you know you make all right with girl, that spirit what make body grow thinks you still got to be punished. Even when grandmama and auntie spirit go home, it going keep on make for same kind push uhane outside body so you fall down and hurt you. You not understand this kind. All you got to do is like I tell to you to do. You think you can believe I know what everything about?"

Henry nodded. He had been convinced that the old kahuna knew his business.

"Good! That fine! All you need is be good in faith in me. Now I tell you something. In me is power from gods to forgive you for hurt girl and for everything bad you ever do. I going forgive you in kahuna way what lots more better than church way. Kahuna way forgive both spirit in you. Now I take this raw egg. I hold it over cup. When I do that, both of us hold breath. I put cleaning *mana* into egg. I break in cup. I give to you, you swallow quick and all at once. Then we breathe again. You understand?"

Henry understood. He obeyed orders. The egg was poised over the cup. Henry held his breath. He was nearly bursting when the egg was finally broken and handed to him. The moment he had gulped it down, the kahuna seized him and rubbed his stomach violently, at the same time panting out compelling words:

"Egg and mana is inside! It clean away all your sin! You clean like baby now! You not need shame for anything! You all clean now! No one can punish! You no can punish yourself! You never go black and fall down some more! You all new and clean and happy and well!"

The kahuna smilingly declared the cure complete and permanent. He collected his modest fee, and Henry went back to his work. Never did the fainting spells return.

The *kahuna* treated illnesses of infectious origins as well as apparent psychosomatic illnesses (as in the above case). They were successful with western people as well as with natives:

A young white woman, once an ardent Christian, and married, developed a deep sore on the ankle. The doctors found it to be caused by a tubercular bone. They proposed an operation which would stiffen the joint for life.

The kahuna examined the case and was none too anxious to take it. The girl was almost hopelessly complexed by the dogmas of 'sin' absorbed in early life.

The kahuna set to work to kala the guilt complexes after preparing the patient by having her fast and do penance that she might be consciously convinced that she no longer deserved punishment at the hands of God. He left the *unihipili* to overcome the infection and heal the sore. This it did in a few weeks.

In the meantime, to keep the complex from being reformed, the kahuna had used a method which is a last resort, but which will have to be used on this generation, perhaps in the West. The method is this: Where complexes are so deep-seated and spring into action at once because the convictions of the *uhane* cannot be changed, the commission of 'sins' under the complex must be avoided. In this case the patient had considered many harmless things either sins of commission or omission. Cards, drink and normal sex life were sins to her way of thinking. The kahuna could not convert her to his saner 'test of hurt' philosophy, so he ordered her to give up all things she considered sins.

She obeyed orders. He *kala-ed* her in the name of Jesus Christ – a wise thing to do considering the source of her faith – and so freed her guilt in *uhane* and *unihipili.* At once the *unihipili* responded and healed the sore, as I have said. But soon after the sore was completely healed, she disobeyed the injunction to cease to do things she considered sinful. Thinking her cure permanent, she again went back to her gay parties and to the few healthy activities which were sins against her dogma-complex which the kahuna could not remove because he could not change the beliefs of her *uhane* or mind by his most reasonable arguments.

Suddenly the sore broke out again as if the unihipili had resumed the old punishment for sins or had ceased its protective work. The kahuna refused to renew his treatment. The operation was performed successfully by the doctors, but the ankle left stiff.

The *kahuna* may also enslave the *unihipili* of a deceased person by a process akin to hypnosis. He can then direct that entity to be his agent for influencing people at a distance. He may even hex a person to death using such methods if he feels a social or moral wrong has been committed. If the target of the hex is innocent he will not be harmed. If

the accuser of the hexed person acted maliciously he may be hit by the rebounding hex. The goal of the *kahunas* was not vengeance but redressing wrongs and maintenance of social order. If the victim sought out the hexing parties he could be given ways in which to make restitution for his transgressions and then the hex would be lifted.

These methods were learned by some of the non-native Hawaiians through processes of discussion and deduction. The kahunas always remained secretive and would not deliberately teach their magic techniques.

The *aumakua* (super-conscious) is presumed by LONG to be the agency for more far-reaching changes in healing, including instantaneous, miraculous cures. He arrives at this conclusion by inference and analogy, as no kahuna would reveal their secrets.

Long writes of an old Hawaiian woman, known to be a most powerful kahuna and generally considered more or less a saint, who lived in a house built on a sand beach.

One afternoon a car drove up and visitors began to get down. The car stood high on solid ground beside a hollow filled with soft sand. One of the visitors, a kindly Hawaiian man, missed his footing and fell, breaking a bone in his leg just above the ankle. He was slightly intoxicated at the time – a thing not too unusual on a holiday.

The kahuna was standing by to receive her guests. The man fell and the sound of the breaking bone was plainly heard. Immediately she knelt beside him and took his leg in her strong old hands. The skin was pushed out over the ragged end of the protruding bone and the swelling had commenced.

Forcing the bone back into place, she commanded the man to remain quiet. She closed her eyes for a moment, then opened them and spoke the words of power, 'Be healed,' in Hawaiian.

The healing was instant. The man rose to his feet and walked with the other guests to the house. No one was more amazed and intrigued than was my friend. He had seen and heard everything and had been convinced that the bone had been broken.

Discussion   In healings the *kahuna* makes a clairsentient or telepathic diagnosis. He directs the healee to mend the wrong underlying the problem and then helps him to relinquish his guilt complex from his subconscious. The treatment seems to involve psychotherapeutic techniques that are little different from western ones. The *kahuna* utilizes the full range of suggestion, from exhortation to hypnosis. This parallels the methods of hypnotherapy; Neurolinguistic Programming; western psychoanalytic theory[22] and conceptualizations of Victor Krivorotov.

Long shares many of his own experiences in searching his mind via dream and meditative states for processes that might explain the *kahuna* healings. He hypothesizes that 'realization', a 'being-one-with' the healee nature and the powers of the universe are involved in the miraculous cures.

His methods of linguistic analysis for teasing out kahuna healing secrets (LONG 1976) are also worth reading.

*V*oodoo or *hexing* has been associated in many cultures with healing. A shaman is said to use healing energies either to heal or to harm. Some researchers point out that these negative effects are utilized to maintain social order within the community, as described by Long, above. The next discussion expands upon these issues.

Daniel A. Slomoff – Traditional African Medicine: Voodoo Healing

DANIEL SLOMOFF studied healing in Togo. In taking their professional vows, healers in this society agree to harm as well as to heal people in order to maintain the social order. For instance, a theft within this culture affects the entire community, putting it out of balance. The healer's task is to restore communal order as rapidly as possible.

… The victim believes he knows who stole the property. He approaches the healer and requests that a spell be cast on the perpetrator… The healer then casts the spell and the accused thief becomes ill. The person suffering now approaches the same healer or another healer… The diagnosis is quickly made that a spell has been cast and a substantial sum must be paid for a healing ceremony… and the community gathers for the ceremony. It may last six hours or six days, depending on the nature of the illness. During the ceremony, members of the community go into trance and… the voice of the spirit comes through one of them and reveals that harm has been done, the truth shall be known and the guilty punished. Everyone suspiciously looks around the group, knowing that the gods have spoken. Anxiety builds because this is a close society and people know each other's business. It is difficult to hide and often someone in trance will blurt out the name of the culprit…it may be the person who is ill if he is guilty or another. In either case, the illness will lift when the guilty party has paid his debt and the harmony in the society is restored…

The guilty man gives the victim twelve

goats and this man must slaughter two goats and make an elaborate feast in honor of the person who has done him harm and who has paid just retribution. In this way, the community returns to a state of comradeship and balance very quickly and efficiently.

Without the healer's agreement to utilize his healing powers to harm, social justice could not be carried out unless police, courts and jails were established. *Voodoo* traditions provide for confessions of crimes without leaving animosities. When the gods resolve the problem, no grudges are held.

Discussion   In western society the use of healing for negative purposes is strictly avoided and eschewed by healers. I have talked with hundreds of healers and scores of teachers of healing. All, without exception, are totally committed to using healing solely for positive purposes. The use of hexing as a social regulator would seem limited to more homogeneous and less mobile cultures than those of western society.

The potential to harm via these processes remains, however. Fear of misuse of healing may be one of the reasons that western society has consciously and/or unconsciously avoided involvement with this modality of treatment. That distrust and anxiety regarding the potential misuse of healing might exist is not surprising – in a society where nuclear weapons are stockpiled and the killing of entire populations is contemplated as a potential strategy. (BENOR 1990; EISENBUD 1983).

David St. Clair – Psychic Healers

DAVID ST. CLAIR describes a number of healers[23], including the following:

1. BROTHER WILLARD FULLER and his wife, *SISTER AMELIA FULLER*, are Pentecostalist healers specializing in dentistry. Brother Willard is reportedly able to materialize gold- and silver-colored fillings by praying to God. The material is said to be "a metal unlike anything known by science today." Sometimes cavities simply disappear under his ministrations and the teeth are restored without fillings.[24]
2. BOB HOFFMAN is a 'psychic-psychiatrist' – a healer of the mind. He has a spirit guide named *DR. SIEGFRIED FISCHER*, who was a psychiatrist friend of Hoffman prior to his death. He is able to zero in psychically on core psychiatric conflicts with Dr. Fischer's aid and he cures psychiatric problems "with only a three-hour weekly visit over a little more than a month's time".

St. Clair excerpts a number of letter testimonials to Hoffman's methods.

Discussion   The reports in this book provide a spectrum of healer phenomena in a descriptive, non-critical manner.

At a lecture/demonstration by Fuller I attended in Philadelphia, no visible results were obtained. I have spoken with several people who did witness fillings appearing at other healing sessions given by Fuller.

Mary Ellen Carter and William A. McGarey – Edgar Cayce on Healing

EDGAR CAYCE was a gifted clairsentient who was able to make accurate diagnoses at a distance, given only the name and location of a healee. Under hypnotic trance Cayce gave many details of ailments and then recommended treatments. Some of these treatments were for conventional medications. A large number were for unconventional approaches, including chiropractic and osteopathic manipulations, special diets, electrical stimulation, unusual chemotherapies and more. For instance, Cayce would recommend application of castor-oil packs to the chest for pneumonia, with resultant dramatic relief of the illness (in days prior to antibiotics). He reported he got his information from *Akashic* (universal) records in another dimension. The treatments were successful even in most difficult cases.

Discussion   Cayce's recommended treatments and remedies seem very strange in terms of western medical *Weltanschauung.* This is healing in a different way from that of most other healers described above.[25]

Sadly, no scientific assessments of his abilities were made during his life. Retrospective review of 150 randomly chosen case reports (CAYCE/CAYCE) showed 43% with documented, confirmed diagnosis and positive results of treatments; negative results in 7%; and no information on the rest.

The *Association for Research and Enlightenment (A.R.E.)* in Virginia Beach, Virginia, was founded in 1932 for exploration of modern applications of these cures. Records of thousands of cases are preserved at the *A.R.E.* Drs. William and Gladys McGarey, American physicians, have been studying these remedies on their patients for many years (W. MCGAREY).

Clairsentient diagnosis is yet another area where healing may make a major contribution to modern medicine.

Alfred Stelter – Psi Healing

Psi-Healing is an excellent review of healing literature. It focuses on German material but also includes some of the more prominent studies in English. The author, a chemistry professor, has broad experience with healers (especially the Philippinos) and a scientific approach to the subject.

1. A biomagnetic effect was described by a German engineer, FRITZ GRUNEWALD, when he studied *JOHANNSEN*, a medium, around 1920.

> Johannsen could do simple feats of psychokinesis such as depressing one side of an evenly balanced scale. Grunewald found that each time, just before the scale descended, the magnetic field strength in the medium's hands – which he held out toward the object to be moved – grew markedly weaker, only to increase after the psychokinetic act. It looked as if something which had produced the strong magnetism in Johannsen's body...displaced itself outward and released psychokinetic effects.
>
> A few times Grunewald, by means of iron filings strewn on glass plates, was able to obtain pictures of the magnetic field within Johannsen's hands. In this way, he found several magnetic centers in the hand's magnetic field which Grunewald believed were evoked by electrical eddies in the medium's hands... But strangely, the magnetic centers seemed at times to lie outside the medium's hand. We must recall the hypothesis that the biofield can move outside the body.

2. Citing a report by ALAN VAUGHAN (1972), STELTER notes that if healers 'treat' unrefrigerated food, it keeps much better than control samples. Stelter speculates this is due to the killing of bacteria by the healing energies.He then postulates that this effect could explain how healers can help cure infected wounds – presumably by killing infecting micro-organisms.

3. STELTER briefly reviews the life and work of *TONY AGPAOA*, a Philippino healer. When Tony was asked how a healer learned to heal and to do psychic surgery, he replied:

From earliest childhood, Phil A. (another healer) received a steady stream of instructions and explanations from 'higher powers' about life and the production of human energies. He could not describe this more fully to others, but it seemed so natural that he assumed everyone must be receiving similar knowledge. He believed these instructions and information were available to everyone who understood how to 'listen'. (Tony Agpaoa said more or less the same thing when he explained that all human knowledge is somehow stored up – perhaps in some sort of cosmic memory – and that meditation could impart all kinds of instruction drawn from it.)

4. Agpaoa seemed able to project intense energy from his eyes. He reportedly used his gaze to start fires; prepare blossoms for herbal medicines; and heal skin disorders. He claimed he lost this ability at the age of fourteen because he was not mature enough in using it.

5. Stelter quotes *EDWARD NAUMOV*, a Russian scientist who studied the gifted healer *NINA KULAGINA* (no reference cited):

It is difficult to explain to some scientists that emotions have a profound influence on the medium's achievements. These scientists believe people can be turned on and off like machines. They do not seem to understand that their own force fields can also affect the medium. Some of them, who have no understanding of psychology and bioinformation, radiate hostility and mistrust, emanations caught by the medium.

Generally, we can give demonstrations of psychokinesis at any time, but if the observers include people with a negative attitude, the medium often requires up to four, even seven hours before phenomena take place. On the other hand, if the medium is surrounded by people with a friendly attitude, it only takes five minutes.

6. The phenomena of Lourdes are generally attributed to some *healing powers of the place.*[26] Stelter suggests otherwise:

Decades ago the French physician and parapsychologist Dr. E. Osty, reported on a well-to-do lady of his acquaintance who spent much time in Lourdes as a voluntary helper at the spring in the grotto of Massabielle. Her chief activity consisted in helping the patients into the pool and immersing them briefly. In the course of her long activity, more than once she witnessed extraordinary spontaneous cures of severely disabled persons bathing in the spring. During the patients' submersion in the cold spring water, at the moment in which the cures presumably set in, she always felt as if all her strength were withdrawn from her. She required several days to recuperate from these attacks of weakness.

Discussion   In discursive, easily readable style, STELTER presents evidence and expounds his theories in critical though not comprehensive manner. It is sometimes difficult to distinguish where presentation of evidence ends and discussion and speculation begin.

This is one of the better surveys on healing in theoretical discussions and richness in details. It is especially good on psychic surgery. It contains 326 references.

(Several reviews of healing deserve special mention. Materials from these books are reviewed in later chapters of other volumes.)

George W. Meek *(Editor and Contributor)* – Healers and the Healing Process

This is the best overall discussion on psi healing I have found. It briefly describes healers from Brazil, U.K., U.S., the (former) Soviet Union and the Philippines. It reviews many aspects of healing.

Especially noteworthy are the discussions on
1. the acceptance healing has attained in the British hospital system. Healers are permitted to assist either at the request of the patient or of the physician;
2. theories of healing[27];
3. paranormal healing in the Philippines;
4. information from trance mediums (who claim to act as channels of communication for discarnate spirits) concerning healing.

Discussion Though the various authors provide stimulating material, they have uneven style, depth and breadth of expertise and writing clarity. The editor, an American engineer, shares a wealth of knowledge from his broad experience with healers and healing.

Spirit communications need careful and cautious scrutiny. Experts in the field have repeatedly observed that information from spirits does not necessarily represent the last word from 'on-high.' Such communications seem only to warrant credibility as the intellect and accumulated knowledge of that particular individual spirit might warrant. Furthermore, the information is subject to severe distortions in transmissions and translations through the medium.

Stanley Krippner and Alberto Villoldo – The Realms of Healing

STANLEY KRIPPNER, a parapsychologist with vast field and laboratory experience in research, and ALBERTO VILLOLDO, a psychologist with considerable field experience with healers in various cultures, review the practices of many fascinating healers[28] and discuss various theories of healing.[27]

The following points are of particular interest:
1. There are difficulties in assessing the validity of psychic surgery, as practised in the Philippines,[29] with the yardsticks and cultural assumptions of western science.
2. South American spiritual healers have an uninterrupted tradition of healing over many centuries from which much can be learned.[7]
3. Evidence from Kirlian photography[30] suggests that healing may involve a transfer of energy from healer to healee.

Discussion This book is a must for anyone seeking to comprehend the intricacies of healing phenomena.

Anthea Courtenay – Healing Now

This is the best review of British healers, written by a journalist who was a greatful recipient of healing. It provides an excellent survey of a spectrum of healers and sensible discussions on aspects of healing.

This concludes the sampler of anecdotal material on healing. It has been hard to omit many other relevant descriptions of healing experiences,[31] but publishing limitations dictate I must do so.

The cameos of the various healers presented in this chapter may appear confusing in their range and varieties of practices and beliefs. This is the challenge to anyone wishing to understand healing to a depth greater than the teachings of any one healer.

Also confusing is the fact that healers evolve in their personal practices and understandings of healing. F. W. KNOWLES (1954, 1956), for example, was initially taught healing rituals but later discarded these as unnecessary. Most of the better healers find that their healing develops different characteristics with experience over periods of time.

We have much to sort out to unravel these mysteries.[32]

Let us examine next some studies of physical effects healing.

CHAPTER I-2

Measurements of Healers' Effects on the Physical World

Unfortunately, Nature imposes her own conditions for the manifestation of her phenomena and is tactless enough to ignore man's criteria or convenience.

Edward W. Russell

This chapter reviews technical studies showing that healing can bring about physical changes in various substances. Some of the studies point to biochemical effects and mechanisms whereby healing may act within the body. These effects might also be used as screening tests for healers.

Healing Effects on Water

ROBERT N. MILLER (1977), an industrial research scientist, measured some physical effects produced by a gifted healer, the late OLGA WORRALL.

Miller instructed Worrall to treat several containers of copper salt solutions as she would if she were healing someone. When the copper salts were crystallized out of solution they were noticeably a different color from those of control samples which had been treated identically except for a simulation of healing. The crystals from the treated solution were coarser.

Miller hypothesized that the treatment had altered the water in the copper solution. Samples of treated water were then examined for viscosity, electrical conductivity, capacitance, refractive index, infrared (IR) absorption and surface tension. Consistent differences were noted in surface tension, which was measurably reduced in the Worrall samples. Infrared spectrophotometry indicated changes consistent with an alteration in hydrogen bonding. Changes in the other measures were not consistent.

Miller also found that Worrall could create a pattern in a cloud chamber by holding her hands around the unit. In a later experiment, Worrall produced similar patterns in the cloud chamber from a distance of many miles.

Miller then investigated the effects of magnetic fields on similar systems. He found that a very strong field of 4,500 gauss applied for 15 minutes to water produced changes in the crystallization of copper salts that were similar to those of the Worrall experiment. Surface tension was also reduced when six magnets were inserted in 500 milliliters of water for more than four-and-a-half hours. The surface tension of the water treated with magnets gradually returned to normal over a period of 30 hours. If the water was swirled in a stainless-steel beaker the surface tension returned to normal within minutes.

Further tests revealed that when rye seeds were sprinkled with water held by a healer and water treated with magnets, sprouting increased 28 percent and 60 percent, respectively, over that of control seeds (for which untreated water was used). Further clarification of these comparisons is required because Worrall had held the water in her experiment 30 days prior to the running of the experiment.

Miller proposes that the reduction in surface tension be used as a measure of a healer's ability to produce healing energy. He would call the energy *paraelectricity* according to the designation of the late AMBROSE WORRALL, Olga's husband. Ambrose, who was also a healer, said, "It is recommended that the unit of quantity for paraelectricity be named a 'Worrall' and be defined as the energy required to reduce the surface tension of 100 ml of distilled water from its normal state (72.75 dynes/cm at 20° C) by 10 dynes/cm." Miller gives specific details of the procedures he follows to measure the healers' production of paraelectricity. He used wires held at one end by the healer while the other ends were immersed in water.

DOUGLAS DEAN and EDWARD G. BRAME (1975) also studied healer-held water with IR spectrophotometry. They demonstrated changes in the water which persisted for three years after the treatment. Calorimetric measurements were consistent with altered hydrogen bonding.

DEAN reported further on measurements of healer-treated water (1982; 1986). Heat of dilution of this water is exothermic. When a healer treated a fluorinated polymer film, the same IR effects were observed. Ultraviolet (UV) spectrophotometry demonstrated a peak peculiar to the treated water in the vicinity of 188.8 millimicrons. Both IR and UV measurements must be made on special equipment, including a multiple internal reflection (MIR) chamber, which is sensitive to wavelengths outside the normal laboratory range (FENWICK/HOPKINS). Dean found that healers who produced strong effects in the UV range might generate weak results in the IR range and vice versa. More intense effects were noted when the healers treated water in partly filled bottles than when they treated water in full containers. Distillation of treated water sometimes did and sometimes did not eliminate the effect. Treatment of steam in a distillation apparatus produced the same alterations in the distillate. The half-life for the spectrophotometric effects in water varies with different healers. About three days is most common, but it may be up to two-and-one-half years in a partly empty bottle. Another discovery that Dean reported was that just prior to remelting, a new crystal structure could be observed in the water (1982). This is a bi-refringent (a doubly refractive crystal) stage, which has not been previously reported and which, subsequently, Dean himself could not reproduce (DEAN 1987).

GLEN REIN (1992) reports that non-Hertzian fields may impart a patterning in water which conveys healing properties.[1]

STEPHAN SCHWARTZ ET AL. published a detailed study of healing IR effects on water. Some of the healers were actively engaged in healing outside the experimental situation and some were volunteers with no healing experience. They placed water in vials which were held against the palms of healers' hands during healings. New vials were placed thus for five-minute intervals from the start of healing, covering the first 15 minutes of treatment. Samples were taken as controls for calibration of the spectrophotometer and for the treatment situation. The treatment room control samples were taken to the room where the healers were studied but were not placed in the healers' hands. Measurements performed by two independent researchers under double-blind conditions were consistent with each other. When all treated samples were compared with all controls, a significant difference was noted (p < 00.02). When treated samples were compared only with calibration controls (which had not been taken to the treatment room), the difference was even more pronounced (p < 00.002). The difference between the treated versus the session-control samples was not significant. The variation was not meaningful for intensity of effects at the various time periods sampled. The results suggest that water in the vicinity of healers can be affected even when healing is not focused directly or even intentionally on it.

V. PATROVSKY, a Czechoslovakian scientist, studied the effects of electromagnetic (EM) fields and of healing on water.[2] He reports that two distinct types of effects can be produced in water. *Polarised water* is produced by electrostatic or static magnetic fields. Traces of hydrogen peroxide and free radicals are formed via a magnetohydrodynamic effect but the physical properties of the water are unchanged. Polarised water is effective for stimulating plant growth but will not prevent calcareous precipitations.[3]

Resonant water is produced when EM or magnetic fields break hydrogen bonds in water molecule clusters. A peak for this effect is found around 16 Hz.

According to PATROVSKY (1978):

In this water, $(H_2O)_5$ and $(H_2O)_6$ clusters predominate as detected from the IR spectrum (3.9 microns) and from reduced surface tension. This type has little effect upon plant growth, but can prevent sedimentation of calcareous deposits...

There appears no difference in the actions of suitable magnetic, electrostatic or biologic (healer's) fields, showing that: The biological field is the only physical field generated by living matter.

Table I-1 compares and contrasts resonant and polarised water.

Patrovsky says that the biological field consists of at least two components: (1) a direct current (DC) aspect (e.g. electrostatic charges) which may emanate from eyes or fingers; and (2) an alternating current (AC) aspect which may emanate from the brain and muscles. In healer-activated water, therefore, one may detect free radicals and a diminution of surface tension. Patrovsky demonstrated this with 10 samples treated by a Czech healer, *J. ZEZULKA,* in which surface tension was measured by capillary elevation. Zezulka's samples averaged 8.7 centimeters; 30 control samples measured between 9.3 and 9.6 centi-

Table I - 1. Comparison of resonant and polarised water

	Resonant	Polarised
Origin	Alternating magnetic or electric fields of optimal frequency 5-25 hz & HF (Ghz)	Static magnetic/electric fields; ultraviolet light and ultrasound
Physical changes	Infrared absorption increased at 3.9 microns; surface tension reduced	None, or small change in ion polarisation
Chemical	Little or not observable	Traces of hydrogen peroxide and free radicals
Technological and biological action	Sedimentation and crystallization retarded; little effect on plants	No influence on dissolved salts; stimulation of plant growth and seed germination
Detection	Infrared spectrum and surface tension change	Detection of hydrogen peroxide with luminol; seed germination
Probable	Resonant molecular absorption; reduced H-bonds; paramagnetic nuclear resonance UHF	Magnetohydrodynamic effect; increased negative charges on ions
Stability*	20-25 hrs. stoppered; 3-5 hrs. exposed to air decomposes with heating	14-30 days; decomposes with heating

* Inserted from PATROVSKY 1983 b

meters. This is a 9.4% decrease, close to the 10.3% decline produced by *Olga Worrall* (MILLER, 1977).

PATROVSKY speculates that natural water may become activated by passing through magnetic gradients in the earth or through action of solar flares.

JERZY REJMER of Warsaw mentions in a very brief translated note that when deuterium plus normal water 'with a solution strength under one percent plus DSS indicator' was subjected to bioenergetic influence for five minutes the entire spectrum was displaced 0.3 parts per million under Nuclear Magnetic Resonance (NMR) spectrometry (1985).

Patrovsky's last observation is extended by yet another study, which is unfortunately also sketchily reported (by the editor of *Spiritual Frontiers*, 1980). J. SCHONEBERG SETZER placed water in three church sanctuaries (Catholic, Episcopal and Methodist) before Sunday services and collected them an hour after the services. Plants treated with the church water grew faster than the control samples but only during the second and fourth lunar quarters.

In 1974 BRAME repeated the experiment, examining the church water with IR spectrophotometry. His results confirmed an effect on Sundays close to full and new moons.[4] He reports, ". . . neither the number of worshipers in the sanctuary nor the religious importance of the date had any significance on the results." (No measurements or statistics are given for either study.)

ALOK SAKLANI studied the effects of an Indian healer's treatment of water for enhancing plant growth. He found no spectrophotometric effects in healer-treated methanol but did not use an MIR chamber. PETER FENWICK/ ROY HOPKINS (1986) found no effect of healing on water but reported that their

equipment was not as sensitive as Dean's.

Two researchers report that healer-treated water tastes distinctly different from untreated water (DINGWALL 1968, VII, p. 60; LEICHTMAN 1986). Leichtman observes that wine treated by healers tastes smoother and less acidic. Dingwall adds that he found one patient who was sensitive to whether the water was *magnetized* by her own magnetizer or by another; that she could say how many *passes* (movements of his hand) he had made over it; and that if she drank water magnetized by another magnetizer she experienced cramp. In several casual trials I have not found that healed water has a different taste from other water. This study seems worth repeating.

Confirming Miller's findings, JAN A. SZYMANSKI, a Polish scientist, reports on an experiment in which five *bioenergy therapeutists* held their hands one to three centimeters from a laboratory plate containing copper chloride solution and concentrated intensely (1986a). After 24 hours, visible differences were noted in samples on which three of the healers were focusing. "The samples had smaller but more densely distributed crystal grains and because of this the optical density of the pictures was greater." Their color was darker than the control samples. Five people who were not healers were unable to produce crystal changes in such a procedure.

Photon Emission

S. GRABIEC ET AL. report that photon emission can be used as an indicator of 'degree of activation by the biofield'. They state:

Freshly prepared 0.1% pyrogallol solution in a 0.15 M phosphate buffer medium with pH 7.2 + 0.1% hydrogen peroxide was exposed for about 30 seconds to a 'bio-field' at a distance of 2-3 cm from the 'bio-field' source. The same freshly prepared solution without exposure to a 'biofield' served as the control sample. Temperature and pressure were kept constant during the tests and efforts were made to eliminate the possible effects of the infrared radiation. Photon emission of the control samples fluctuated from 370 to 425 pulse/min; of the experimental samples from 464 to 950 pulse/min.

It is unfortunate that more details are not provided. Further study of chemical systems are warranted.[5]

Photographic and Electromagnetic Effects of Healers

Several researchers have reported on photographic effects of healing. GRAHAM WATKINS performed a series of experiments on PK-accelerated awakening of anesthetized mice.[6] He reports that when photographic film was placed in light-proof envelopes under target animals the film was exposed. The degree of exposure decreased with distance from the animal. Watkins notes that several plates underwent exposures resembling pictures obtained with electrical discharges. He also observes that one of the PK subjects demonstrated a high static charge which tended to recur rapidly after grounding and that another successful PK subject in his own laboratory was found to have similarly high electrostatic charge. He hypothesizes that healing may, therefore, involve electrostatic or EM fields. An alternative, he points out, is that the electrostatic phenomena may merely

be concomitants of the PK process that are not essential to its occurrence. If this is so, they could still be theoretically useful indicators of healing. In Watkins' experience, however, they did not prove to be so. A third possibility, Watkins suggests, is that healing involves a form of energy, the properties of which overlap with electrical energy.

GORDON TURNER reports that when photographic film is interposed between the hands of a healer and parts of a living organism in need of healing, images can be produced. He points out that these effects do not occur when the film is placed between the healer's hand and a part of an organism that does not require healing.[7] Similar effects are reported by the *Chinese Academy of Science* and by ZHAO YONG-JIE ET AL. Researchers found that nuclear emulsion film and thermoluminescent film shielded from light were exposed in the vicinity of the target during studies of clairvoyance.

Support for Watkins' observations on EM effects is suggested by MICHAEL SHALLIS (1988). In a survey of people who experienced 'unusual electrical phenomena' he found many who produced unusually strong electrical discharges from their bodies. About 70 percent of these people were gifted with psi abilities, including healing.[8]

CYRIL SMITH/SIMON BEST review further evidence for overlaps of EM fields with biological processes. They describe experiments in which EM fields reproduced allergic symptoms in sensitive patients and where appropriately tuned fields could also neutralize such symptoms. Water could be *patterned* by EM fields and used as a vehicle for these therapeutic effects. Details of controlled trials are not provided to permit statistical analyses of results.

GLEN REIN (1992) studied the magnetic

field emissions from the hands of a healer, DR. LEONARD LASKOW.

The magnetic fields were measured using a flux-gate magnetometer sensitive from D.C. to 500 Hz. Laskow cupped his hand over the probe but did not touch it... Non-healers were unable to influence magnetometer readings. Touching or moving the probe gave characteristic, sharp patterns which were readily distinguishable form energetic patterns.

An initial and critical part of the holo-energetic healing process is opening the crown chakra.[9] The magnetic field pattern generated when Laskow opened his crown chakra was recorded. It appeared distinctly different from other patterns obtained in that it had a very sharp onset, an equally sharp dissipation and only lasted eight seconds. This result implies that the event was short-lived and caused a shift in the magnetic field pattern only during its duration. The return to normal baseline was characteristic of patterns produced by other states of consciousness when Laskow consciously chose to shift into another state or end the particular experiment.

...in some tracings the energetic pattern shifts down, implying a decrease in the magnetic field strength in the environment around Laskow's hand...

Since we had observed that only certain contents of consciousness resulted in magnetic field patterns which were different from an ordinary state of mind, it was of interest to compare the patterns from two states which gave different biological responses measured as an inhibition of tumour cell growth. We therefore compared the magnetic pattern obtained when Laskow was in an *unconditional loving state* and in

the *return to natural order state.* The results indicate that indeed these magnetic patterns were different from each other. Compared to the robust effect with the natural order state, the unconditional loving state produced a weak, non-specific pattern...

In general these patterns were obtained most consistently when Laskow was allowed to generate the different states and contents of consciousness spontaneously, rather than being told a given sequence. One of the most interesting spontaneous magnetic field patterns was obtained when Laskow inwardly asked that Spirit flow through him. He asked Spirit to demonstrate its presence to science with a characteristic signature pattern. The tracing obtained gave a uniquely different pattern form the other patterns obtained and was characterized by sharp, frequent peaks in the negative direction.

REIN speculates that the effects of healing may be mediated by non-Hertzian waves.[10] Non-Hertzian waves cannot as yet be measured directly on scientific instruments. Rein placed a device which is believed to shield out non-Hertzian waves in Laskow's energy field in the course of one of his studies.

The tracing obtained indicates that prior to addition of the device, the magnetic pattern was repetitive, containing numerous sharp, small positive peaks. Upon addition of the shielding device, the magnetic field pattern was substantially altered. The new pattern was qualitatively similar in shape but gradually increased in overall magnitude. These results suggest that non-Hertzian quantum fields enhanced the magnetic field emitted from Laskow's hands during hologenergetic healing.

R. MACDONALD ET AL. (1977) studied three well-known healers: Rev. John Scudder, Dean Kraft and Olga Worrall. The researchers attempted to replicate the experiments with cloud-chambers, magnetic-fields, high-voltage and passive photographic film exposures, object-weight measurements, spectroscopic analyses of water, animal blood pressure and EEG measurements. The authors report, "Most of the attempted replication did not confirm the reports of the previous experimenters." They did note that small changes in electrical-field strength near the subjects were detected by means of a 10-ohm input high-impedance voltmeter (HIVM).

In a brief, controlled experiment, the healers were asked to hold saline which was then used to water rye grass seeds. Kraft's water produced significantly less growth in the experimental versus the control plants (various measurements gave a confidence range of $p < 0.05–0.001$); Worrall's water produced growth which was significantly greater ($p < 0.05$ on all measures).

Discussion   Experiments by MILLER, DEAN/BRAME, and SCHWARTZ ET AL. showed changes suggesting a decrease in hydrogen bonding in healer-treated water. It is unclear what effect a decrease in hydrogen bonding and reduced surface tension of the water might have on chemical reactions in animals and plants. Because water constitutes about 65 percent of the human body, the changes in water alone might account for some of the effects of healing, either directly or through enhancements of biochemical reactions secondary to the presence of altered water. Many of the consequences of healing are manifested as an acceleration of natural recuperative processes. This might, for example, account for more rapid wound healing after treatment with psi healing.

DEAN observes that the water effects may represent something other than altered hydrogen bonding because the effects are sometimes carried over to a distillate, which would not be expected if they were due to hydrogen bonding alone (1985).

Since the effects of the hydrogen-bonding and treated-water experiments (together with the crystallization results that MILLER noted) are similar to those produced by a strong EM field, this may mean that some healings are produced by an energy similar to magnetism. (We must differentiate between magnetism as it is used here to refer to EM fields surrounding an actual magnet and its use in the last century to describe hypnotic effects.)The impact of healing on the crystallization of copper salts may result from interactions with the salts or may be due to alterations in the water in which they are dissolved.

WATKINS' and TURNER's studies on photographic effects of healing provide another indication of some sort of transfer of energy between healer and healee, or of EM/photographic effects secondary to a healing influence. These observations are supported by findings in Kirlian photography. The Kirlian aura of the healer may decrease in size and intensity after healings; conversely, the aura of the healee may increase in both respects, a phenomenon that also suggests a transfer of energy from the healer to the healee.[11]

REIN's work on quantum energy fields may be a breakthrough in linking quantum physics with healing. One must be cautious, however, in jumping to conclusions before these results are replicated by Rein and others. For instance, it is possible that the enhancing study with LASKOW was due to suggestions which created expectations in Laskow and led to his producing different effects for psychological rather than energetic reasons.

The physical effects reviewed here could be used to screen or test for healing ability: spectrophotometry and surface tension of water; crystallization of copper salts; and exposure of photographic film. Further research is required, however, to establish whether any or all of these results are produced by all healers, only by some or only under certain circumstances.

We must likewise clarify if any of these physical effects correlate regularly with the degree of healing ability. Miller's suggestion that surface-tension results be used as a measure of healing energy seems premature. If the expression of healing ability follows the patterns of distribution of PK gifts this may mean that while each healer may be gifted in healing, not all will be able to produce water effects.

OLGA WORRALL's ability to create a pattern in a cloud chamber may give us further clues about healing. The experiment obviously needs repetition and clarification before any serious conclusions can be reached.

Some healing effects reported in Chapter 1 were produced as readily over great distances as they were locally. This contradicts conventional theories of energies known to classical physics. Ordinary energies act more powerfully upon objects which are closer to their source than at greater distances. For instance, a radio receiver picks up the signal from the transmitting station more weakly the farther it is from the station. The diminution of effect with distance is readily measurable and mathematically predictable. Healing and other psi effects seem to act at great distances with no apparent diminution of their power – even over thousands of miles. Simple studies would be to see whether healers are able to alter water or crystallization of copper salts from a distance.

Many of the above reports overlap with psi research. The following section examines psi effects in greater detail in order to put healing in a more clear perspective.

CHAPTER 1-3

Psi Phenomena

On trying to formulate a theory of psi phenomena, one has first to proceed like the hero of a medieval mystery play: he must slay, or come to grips with, the dragons guarding the entrance to the sanctuary of science. The first dragon is the challenge of scientific fact-finding. The data of parapsychology have to be assembled and validated by the consensus of qualified workers in the field, while doubtful or spurious evidence must be discarded. On the other hand, all the evidence that has stood the test of scientific scrutiny has to be included – regardless of the consequences. The second dragon is the paradox that although we feel duty-bound to apply the principles of the scientific method to our findings, they run counter to some of the basic propositions of science itself. The third, fourth, and fifth dragons stand for the classical Kantian categories of Time, Space, and Causality which are clearly incompatible with direct action and thought at a distance implied by telepathy, clairvoyance, and psychokinesis, while precognition seems to arrest time's arrow in its flight and to reverse the purportedly irreversible chain of causal events. The sixth dragon guards our conventional doctrine of cerebral localization, confining consciousness and other specific functions to more or less circum-scribed areas of the brain cortex, or perhaps to lower echelons of the central nervous system. The seventh dragon is the picture of personality structure, suspended in splendid isolation in classical Euclidian space, functioning in Newtonian, prerelativistic time, and subject to strictly foreordained laws of cause and effect.

Jan Ehrenwald

Summary

The psi (ψ) phenomena include telepathy, clairsentience, psychokinesis (PK), precognition and retrocognition. These have been so closely and carefully examined that their existence is in my opinion no longer to be seriously questioned. These are clearly related to healing.

Psychokinesis resembles healing, as both entail the mind influencing matter. In fact, healing may simply be PK on living things. Similarly, clairsentience appears to be the basis for psychic medical diagnosis and is probably the means by which healers know how to help healees. Telepathy, which can span vast distances, may prove to be an aspect of distant diagnosis and healing.

A brief explanation of the various aspects of psi will provide an introduction to this subject (See also Table I -2).

Telepathy: Extensive experiments carried out by JOSEPH B. RHINE at Duke University in the U.S., by LEONID L. VASILIEV in Russia, and by uncountable others around the world have demonstrated that some people are able to obtain information directly from the minds of others. People can also transmit information or even give orders via mind-to-mind communication. Distances do not appear to weaken telepathic effects, even when thousands of miles separate sender and receiver.

Clairsentience: Experiments have shown that some people obtain information about a person or object through extrasensory perception (ESP) that does not involve telepathy. This knowledge seems to come to the mind of the perceiver directly from the object. For instance, J. B. RHINE showed that there are people who can identify the order in which cards lie in a deck after the experimenter has shuffled them face-down but before he has

turned them over.[1] It has been demonstrated that people can know clairsentiently what is happening at a distant location without sensory cues or other contact (e.g. telephone) with that place.[2] Some clairsentient people

Table 1-2. Definitions of psi phenomena

Telepathy: The transfer of thoughts, images or commands from one living being to another, without use of sensory cues.

Clairsentience: Knowledge about an animate or inanimate object, without the use of sensory cues (sometimes called psychometry). This may appear in the mind of the perceiver as visual imagery (clairvoyance), auditory messages (clairaudience), or other *internal* sensory awareness.

Precognition: Knowledge of a future event prior to its occurrence.

Retrocognition: Knowledge of a past event, without use of sensory cues.

Extrasensory perception (ESP): The above four modes of acquiring knowledge without cues from any of the external senses: sight, sound, smell, taste, touch, or kinesthesia (position-of-body sense from muscles or tendons).

Psychokinesis (PK): The ability to move or transform an object without use of physical means; commonly referred to as 'mind over matter'.

Psi *(from the Greek letter ψ):* ESP and PK.

Sheep/goat effect: Believers ('sheep') score significantly better than chance, while disbelievers ('goats') score significantly poorer than chance expectancy on psi tasks.

have been known to identify the location of a dead body (POLLACK). In such cases telepathy could not have been involved. Clairsentient impressions may be perceived as sensory information (visual images, voices, smells, etc.) or intuitively apprehended gestalts. They may be experienced as inner impressions or as images in the world outside the perceiver.

Pre- and retrocognition: Gifted subjects are able to 'read the future' for themselves or for other persons. To initiate the perception they may hold an object belonging to a person, just be in his presence or may be given only a name. Likewise, such individuals can often give information about that person's or that object's past. Laboratory subjects have been able to guess correctly series of cards before they were shuffled and to describe places visited by experimenters before these places were selected (JAHN/DUNNE).

Extrasensory perception (ESP) refers to the above abilities.

Psi refers to ESP plus psychokinetic abilities.

Psychokinesis (also called *PK* or *telekinesis):* RHINE (1970), HELMUT SCHMIDT (1974), and others have shown in repeated, highly significant experiments that matter can be manipulated by the mind. Rhine used dice, asking his subjects to roll the desired faces (chosen by a random number table). Helmut Schmidt developed very sophisticated electronic devices which subjects were able to influence at will.

Much has been published on the PK effects produced by *URI GELLER* and many others who are able to bend metal without the use of normal physical force. The successful bending of metal objects sealed in transparent containers and observations of objects disappearing from sealed containers is even more impressive (HASTED).

In East European countries, reports and films have been made of gifted subjects who are able to move small objects by PK. Western observers whom I consider sufficiently critical and reliable have also observed such feats directly.

Sheep/goat effect: When groups of subjects are tested for psi powers the data taken as a whole are often totally random. It appears as though subjects are merely guessing answers and obtaining purely chance results. GERTRUDE SCHMEIDLER suggested that such data be divided according to whether the subjects believed or disbelieved in the existence of ESP. The results of this exercise showed that believers tended to score as a group significantly better than chance on ESP tests and disbelievers scored significantly poorer than chance on the same tests. Schmeidler applied the term 'sheep' to the believers and 'goats' to the disbelievers. Analyses have been made of data from experiments both before and after Schmeidler made her proposal. The preponderance of evidence supports the sheep-goat hypothesis (PALMER 1971). The Biblical *Matthew 25:31-33* appears to have been the source for these terms.

Psi phenomena have been investigated with sufficient rigor to convince the *American Academy for the Advancement of Science* that Parapsychology is worthy of inclusion among its ranks.

I believe that the existence of psi has been established beyond reasonable doubt. For this reason I present this summary of psi phenomena prior to presenting research specifically related to healing.

Let us look first at descriptions of a few people who have strong psi abilities. These examples are not all-inclusive but are representative of some of the unusual capabilities demonstrated by people gifted with psi.

Demonstrations of Psi Abilities

SAI BABA, a holy man in India, claims to be in his second of three reincarnations devoted to the progress of mankind. He teaches that there are many paths of spiritual advancement. He may punctuate his teachings with amazing displays of psi powers. He materializes objects such as jewelry with intricate designs which are deeply meaningful to the specific persons for whom he does this. He also materializes *vibhuti,* a so-called holy ash with alleged medicinal powers. He is gifted to the point of appearing almost omniscient. He is able to provide his devotees with the most intimate details of their lives – past, present, and future. He has reportedly healed many illnesses, including fractures, arthritis, blindness and cancers. Skeptics have observed him carefully during materializations for sleight-of-hand tricks and have even searched his garments for pockets which might conceal objects but no one has been able to find any hint of trickery.[3]

Sai Baba uses his gifts to enthrall his devotees, convincing them of his deep understanding of themselves, of the meaning of their lives and, above all, of the wisdom he teaches. It is difficult to imagine him submitting to scientific scrutiny for purposes of linear, materialistic analyses of his talents. Indeed he has declined all invitations to submit to laboratory investigations.

PAOLA GIOVETTI, an Italian reporter who has been interested in psi for years, is one of a privileged few who have been well received by *GUSTAVO ADOLFO ROLL*, an Italian with a wide range of psi talents (W. ROLL ET AL. 1982). The 78-year-old Roll is able to materialize and psychometrize objects, to read minds and to perform other unusual feats. He refuses to submit to formal laboratory test-

ing, maintaining an independent attitude towards his gifts. For the select few to whom he demonstrates his abilities, he has produced drawings and oil paintings through PK without touching the paints, even designing these to the composite specifications of a group of observers. Each of the observers suggests an element which he then includes in the piece of art. He destroys most of his work, wishing to avoid creating a commercial product. Giovetti, however, has preserved some of Roll's productions in photographic slides.

Roll is an extremely intelligent person. His complex demonstrations of his talents are original. For example, he had an investigator pick cards from a deck to determine the volume, page and line in an encyclopedia where a certain quotation he cites could be found. Asked why he refuses to be studied formally by parapsychologists, he answers, "I am but as a rain gutter for the rain. You should analyze the rain, not the gutter!"

THOMAS G. M. COUTINHO, or '*THOMAS*', as he is known in Brazil, has PK and healing gifts. He has been seen to materialize coins; transform coins of his country into those of other nations; bend metallic objects; reunite pieces of torn paper; produce flashing lights around vehicles in which he and others are driving; dematerialize his body and disappear; and perform unusual feats of near and distant healing, involving apparent removal of diseased portions from the subject's body. Western scientists have studied Thomas, including WILLIAM ROLL, an American parapsychologist (no relation to the above-mentioned Roll), ELSON MONTAGNO, a South American physician, and LEE PULOS, a Canadian psychologist.

Pulos describes Thomas as being totally in the present, in the *now.* He shows little concern for past or future. He derives great amusement from the spontaneous, un-planned appearances of his PK abilities, such as when a metal chair on which he was sitting in a restaurant collapsed because the legs bent. He is warmhearted and emotionally responsive. When exercising his gifts, he often consumes large quantities of alcohol and may also ingest copious amounts of table salt and lime juice with no ill effects. He charges very high fees for healings and spends money lavishly. PULOS makes the interesting observation that THOMAS (as well as another 19 out of 23 children gifted with metal-bending abilities) received severe electric shocks at some time in his life prior to being able to demonstrate PK abilities.[4]

The above are individuals with exceptional development of psi abilities. I find even more convincing the reports of children who are found to have telepathic, clairsentient, precognitive, psychokinetic and other psi abilities (PETERSON). The children are often confused both by their psi interactions with the world and by the fact that most adults do not understand, much less possess, these.

Skeptics will naturally suspect that the above are no more than reports by gullible observers of clever prestidigitation and/or mentalist-type deception (RANDI). Let us proceed, therefore, to more rigorous reports.

The Nature of Psi Effects

The above observations of subjects who are highly gifted with psi powers were made by people familiar with such phenomena. Their comments contribute to our appreciation of psi, yet leave us with questions and doubts. Could the subjects have been clever magicians, deceiving their investigators? Could accomplices have participated in some of the

demonstrations without the knowledge of the observers?

For this reason parapsychologists have worked diligently in the laboratory to isolate and identify the nature of psi effects more precisely. For example, MONTAGUE ULLMAN, a noted parapsychologist, describes (1974) two very gifted Soviet psychics. NINA KULAGINA, a 47-year-old housewife, could move objects such as matches lying on a flat surface without touching them, under conditions that preclude physical means of interacting with the objects. She could also levitate objects and deviate magnetic needles. Kulagina experienced severe physiological stress when performing many of her PK feats, with racing pulse, pain in her spine and weight loss of up to two kilograms in an hour. Kulagina also demonstrated strong healing abilities.

ALLA VINOGRADOVA, a child psychologist in her late 30s, can also move objects by PK and perform healings. She demonstrates far fewer and less severe physiological effects from her psi activities. During some of her PK demonstrations electrostatic charges appear on and/or around target objects.

Soviet researchers have concentrated more on the telepathic sender than their western counterparts have. LEONID VASILIEV describes experiments in which telepathic inductions of hypnotic trances were achieved from a distance in controlled, statistically significant studies. Though similar experiments were successfully performed in the West in the nineteenth century, they were abandoned for no apparent reason (EISENBUD 1983).

Vasiliev also reports on hypnotized subjects who could be made to contract specific muscles merely by the approach of an experimenter's finger near (but not touching) the involved muscles or near the nerves innervating those muscles. Vasiliev reviews further research on insect muscles that contracted when the experimenter approached the recently killed but still-responsive insect bodies. The insect muscle contractions sometimes were synchronous with the rate of breathing of the experimenter. It is unclear whether these represent PK or interactions of biological fields of the participants.

JULIUS KRMESSKY reports on tests in which delicately balanced objects were moved by PK. The power appeared to be projected from the eyes of subjects.

GRAHAM AND ANITA WATKINS (1974) studied a gifted psychic, FELICIA PARISE. She was able to use PK to deflect the needle of a compass so that it would not respond to an iron knife or small magnet so long as the compass remained where it was when she had focused on it. When the compass was moved a few feet away it reacted normally. Returned to its original position, the deviation and unresponsiveness to iron objects were again present. This effect lasted about 25 minutes. Photographic film lying under the compass was exposed, the intensity of exposure decreasing with distance from the compass in all directions.

HAROLD PUTHOFF AND RUSSELL TARG comment on the ability of URI GELLER and INGO SWANN to produce apparent magnetic effects which registered on sensitive instruments. Geller also affected a laboratory balance by PK, raising and lowering the balance pan with a force of up to 1.5 grams.

WALTER AND MARY JO UPHOFF (1980) provide many scientific and personal details about two Japanese PK subjects. Particularly noteworthy was the detection of ultrasound waves in the vicinity of 30 mega-Hz which emanated from the left frontal regions of their brains during PK activity. Another

report (LARISSA VILENSKAYA) notes that NINA KULAGINA was able to produce a burning sensation on the skin of a subject through quartz glass.

The Metal Benders

JOHN HASTED, Professor of Experimental Physics at Birkbek College, University of London, published an outstanding work on metal bending, both in scientific rigor and in appreciation of motivational factors in the subjects.[5] Clear parallels exist between these gifts and those of healing. The metal benders are able to demonstrate their abilities only some of the time; they are able to transfer these powers to others; they sometimes report associated aura effects; and they may conduct experiments that involve instantaneous transportation of metal from inside sealed containers to places outside. No dangerous side-effects with such abilities have been noted, though laboratory instruments and other metal objects are occasionally damaged unintentionally.

MARK SHAFER points out that the relaxed social atmosphere of a small group can facilitate metal bending. This was the start of a new research technique which accommodates to the nature of the psi phenomena. An extension of Shafer's theory is the metal-bending party,[6] at which several metal benders are interspersed among a group of people. The group is encouraged to bend metal and many with no prior experience are often able to do so.

One such party in which I participated occurred during meetings of the Combined Society for Psychical Research/Parapsychological Association at Cambridge, England, in August 1982. The organizers selected about

50 participants for their openess to experiencing psi phenomena and for their social compatability. They explained that metal bending is a common latent psi ability which can be brought out in such a group setting. Three experienced benders were in separate parts of the room to facilitate and potentiate the group process. Silverware, metal bars and other similar items, which had been bent in other groups, were displayed. This was the preparation phase.

The leaders then laid out a collection of normal silverware, urging participants to choose a piece that appealed to them by intuition or with the aid of a pendulum. Within minutes the experienced benders were demonstrating their successes in twisted, rolled and curled forms. The inexperienced participants were soon exclaiming excitedly as they found their silverware suddenly 'gave' and became malleable to slight pressure. Most impressive among the more exotic bends and twists were the pig-tail curls and tight spirals (in spaces of 1/4 to 1/2 inch) in stems of heavy cutlery – twists that would have been difficult even with the use of heavy tools. By the end of the evening 75 percent of the participants had succeeded in bending metal.

My own experience? I worked on a spoon of fairly rigid construction. Applying moderate force, as permitted, I found the threshold of muscular effort required to bend the spoon with normal pressure. I suddenly found the spoon 'gave' and bent easily to the point where the bowl lay folded back against the stem. I wondered, however, if in the charged, excited atmosphere I had exerted more pressure than I consciously realized.

This questioning is termed *retrocognitive dissonance* in psychological lingo (INGLIS 1986). It is what we commonly experienced when we witness psi events which so clearly

and grossly contradict everyday expectations of the way things ought to be. The mind simply balks at digesting such a bolus of strange

> It is much easier to rationalize experience than to re-examine and alter the commonly held axioms of our existence.

experience and seeks every possible maneuver to expel, reject and explain it away.

Such internal quarrels between unusual observations and conventional expectations occur also with psi healings.

Table Tilting and Rapping

Another form of PK includes *table tilting* and *table rapping.* This has been familiar in the seance room for at least a century. Typically, a group of people gathers around a table in a darkened room. They may pray, sing hymns or other songs and invoke the intervention of spirits with whom they wish to communicate. After a time the table may start to emit raps, rumbles or other sounds and to tilt or even to levitate. A code is often suggested by the participants where one rap or tilting to one side may signal *yes* and two raps or tilting to the opposite side *no.* Questions are asked aloud and the table proceeds to answer them in code. Often there is one member of the group who is felt to be the medium facilitating such phenomena.

In the past few decades table tilting and rapping have been researched by several people. KENNETH BATCHELDOR was the first to conclude that such occurrences were manifestations of the participants' PK abilities rather than interventions of spirits from outside the group. He studied such seance phenomena extensively but published very sparingly.[7]

Research into seance phenomenon resembles in many respects the metal bending parties. An atmosphere of levity facilitates the occurrence of the phenomena.

One of the most impressive bits of evidence for a paranormal effect comes from oscilloscope analyses of the raps produced in these settings. A normal physical rap shows a gradual decrescendo pattern, as the energy of the initial impact dissipates. PK raps show a distinctive crescendo and/or very rapid fall-off pattern (OWEN).

Random Spontaneous Psychokinesis (RSPK)

Outbreaks occur in which household objects move around without apparent cause (BAYLESS 1967). Such events are often violent, with objects falling off shelves or flying across a room. These occurrences were once thought to be caused only by ghosts or spirits and were labeled *poltergeist* phenomena.

Many such cases have been investigated to rule out fraud and appear genuinely attributable to PK.[8] A force/distance relationship to the presumed subjects was noted in one report (ROLL 1972).

In recent years parapsychologists have often linked such occurrences to the presence of a particular individual. One hypothesis is that unexpressed, unconscious emotions may be the motivating forces behind these PK events. Further evidence is adduced from the observation that psychotherapy with presumed PK agents and their families may bring about cessation of poltergeist activity.

Numerous popular films have featured such poltergeist activity.

Spirit entities are reported to produce poltergeist effects as well. A classic, familiar example is the stopping of clocks in the homes of relatives and friends of the deceased when a person dies. (There is even a popular American song with this theme.) Some will argue that such effects are due to the living, who use psi unconsciously, both to identify that a relative has died and to bring about the physical effects.[9]

I am personally familiar with a related instance:

Over a period of several months I met regularly with '*NADYA*', a psychic reader. I asked her many questions, being at the time especially interested in the range of psi abilities she possessed. The one area in which she was definitely lacking was 'green-thumb' ability. She said, "I have a black thumb! Any plant I touch quickly withers." When I moved to another town I gave her as a parting gift a glass vase with a plastic flower. Although pretty, the vase was obviously inexpensively made. (A seam showed where two halves of molded glass had been bonded together.)

Several years later I visited Nadya. She related to me that her elderly mother, who had lived in a distant city, used to visit her home several times a year. For some reason she liked the vase and requested that it be placed close to the bed whenever she stayed with Nadya. A few months prior to my visit Nadya awakened during the night to the sound of a loud bang. She found the vase split in half along its seam. She immediately felt that her mother, who was at her own home, had died. Indeed, a few hours later a telegram arrived confirming her mother's death.

To the uninitiated, such claims for PK must sound far-fetched. Even veteran investigators in this field admit to being uncomfortable with these effects. They question their own eyes and ears, searching for a misperception or alternative ways to explain phenomena which so grossly contradict everyday experience that major shifts in views and under-standings of reality are demanded.

It is impossible to prove definitively whether such events represent PK activated by the deceased person just prior to death; PK by the spirit of the departed; or PK by a member in the household where the PK occurred.

Statistical Studies of Psi Powers

The above examples come from highly gifted psi subjects or from settings in which psi is en-couraged consciously or unconsciously to oc-cur. Though many people possess psi abilities, they are expressed so subtly or infrequently that they often go unnoticed or are dismissed as chance occurrences. However, if an average subject is tested many times for such abilities it is often possible to demonstrate statistically that he does possess them. These tests can be rather tedious and boring. It is often easier to gather the necessary numbers of trials for sta-tistical analysis by using groups of subjects. Such studies clearly show that most of us have some psi powers but that we are unable to ex-press them on demand. Oddly, we may experi-ence them either in times of need or on appar-ently random occasions.

For instance, HELMUT SCHMIDT devised boxes on which a series of lights were lit at ir-regular intervals through a link with a ran-dom number generator (RNG). It did not matter whether the RNG functioned on elec-tronic scramblers or even on the emission of radioactive particles. Subjects were able to influence these devices in the direction the experimenter demanded, producing highly significant results over long series of trials. PK effects were also demonstrated by ROBERT JAHN, emeritus professor at the

Princeton School of Engineering, and BREN-DA DUNNE, his assistant, with computer RNGs and with a mechanical cascade of sty-rofoam balls. 'Goats' as well as 'sheep' sometimes produced results opposite to those which were requested.

Remote Viewing and Enhanced Psi

A psi viewer sits in a laboratory with an ex-perimenter while another experimenter goes to a remote place which is randomly chosen from a pool of such locations and revealed to the outward bound experimenter after he lea-ves the laboratory. The subject then uses his psi abilities to describe as many aspects of this location as he can. This experimental format has repeatedly pro-duced significant-ly positive results in a num-ber of different laboratories (JAHN/DUNNE; PUTHOFF/TARG). The successful research on remote viewing supports the possibility that healers can diag-nose illnesses from a distant location.

CHARLES HONORTON and others have de-veloped the *ganzfeld technique* for enhancing psi expression. They have the subject in a quiet room, viewing diffuse white light through plastic eyepieces and hearing a non-descript hiss *(white noise)* through ear-phones. Under these conditions, psi occurs more often. Statistical meta-analyses of se-ries of ganzfeld-studies show astronomically significant results (UTTS).

Psi Displacement in Time and Space

JAHN/DUNNE showed that subjects could de-scribe the remote places accurately prior to the arrival of the outward-bound experimenter at the target location.

HELMUT SCHMIDT explored backwards-in-time PK effects (1976). He prerecorded a series of outputs from a RNG. At a later time he played these back through the RNG output display for subjects who were asked to alter the output of an RNG. The subjects did not know that the RNG output was pre-recorded. Subjects produced highly significant deviations of the RNG from random output. No such deviations occurred in the RNG when subjects were not set to alter the later output display of the recordings.

This may compare with healing effects that appear to be displaced in time.

General Observations on Psi

STEPHEN BRAUDE summarizes (1979):

> ... there is a growing (if not always coercive body of evidence that success in PK experiments does not depend, or depends very little, on subjects' knowing (at least by normal means) such apparently relevant facts as the nature, mechanics, or existence of the PK target system, or even whether they are being tested for PK.
>
> There is evidence, also ... that subjects tend to perform best when they do not actively try to affect the experimental outcome ... we begin to get a rather surprising picture of PK. In fact, to some, it begins to look as though success in PK tasks might be accomplished without any form of computation or information-processing by subjects.

This conclusion is consistent with observations of LAWRENCE LESHAN on common de-nominators of healing, which are discussed in Chapter IV-2.

REX STANFORD developed the *conformance theory of psi events*.[10] This predicts that psi will function best when an organizing force or intention is influencing a random system. Several studies seem to confirm this theory, including a few on animal systems.[11]

Discussion The *conformance theory* may be directly relevant to healing. The factor of heal-ee need may be a potent organizing force which activates psi powers latent in most people.

Many of the body's biochemical and neu-rological processes include a random aspect in their functioning. For instance, chemical reactions occur randomly between molecules. Theoretically, this places healing in a strong position to succeed under experimental conditions, assuming the validity of the conformance theory. Meta-analysis of numerous psi experiments lends support to these speculations. When results of research with living targets are compared with those of other psi experiments there is a much higher success rate with the healing studies (BRAUD 1989).[12]

The idea that psi powers operate in our lives is disconcerting and disorienting. Such abilities appear to contradict our everyday experience. They show that our usual perception of the world is a limited-range experience. Acceptance of psi may require a paradigm shift in our thinking.

This is similar to what happened when classical (Newtonian) physics was found to be a limited-range explanatory system relative to modern physics. The observations and rules of classical physics describe properties and relationships of objects which we experience through our senses. These rules *make sense* to us.

The observations and rules of modern physics relate to particles and waves which are deduced to exist through various experiments designed around complex instruments. For instance, we are told that an electron may be either a particle or a wave, depending on how we examine it. We are told that objects such as billiard balls, which appear solid to our senses, actually consist more of space between atomic particles than of matter. Though these observations are counter to our intuitive grasp of nature, we have come to accept them.[13]

The same may prove true of psi and healing. We may find that there are rules for interactions of body, emotions, mind and spirit which are counter-intuitive and will be explained by new theories, which Newtonian medicine has been slow to grasp.

Observations from psi research are confusing when we apply everyday linear reasoning to them. Most experiments can be explained by more than one psi power. Receptive telepathy may be a special case of clairsentience. That is, a person might read information from the brain of a sender rather than from his mind or thoughts. Broadcasting telepathy may be an instance of PK, or direct effects of a sender's mind on the brain or mind of a receiver. Clairsentience may in some cases involve reading the mind of the experimenter who placed a given object in the experimental room. Ostensible clairsentience or telepathy may actually be precognition. The subject may see the results of the experiment or obtain his information from the future rather than from the telepathic sender or object he is supposed to be viewing clairsentiently.

Moreover, psi phenomena exhibit a lawfulness of their own:

1. They occur more often in early and late trials in a series of tests.

2. They are frequently demonstrated in the first of a series of experiments but not in attempted replications of the same experiment.

3. Psi perceptions are often cloaked in images and metaphors in a similar manner to dreams and other unconscious material.

4. Even gifted psychics have only a partial success rate over large series of trials.

Everyone seems to have some measure of psi ability. In most of us it only occasionally becomes conscious. It is unclear whether this is because it occurs only rarely or because it is a function of the unconscious mind and occurs frequently but goes unnoticed most of the time. Much evidence supports the hypothesis that psi acts via the unconscious mind. If this is the case, in most instances psi ability would be as inaccessible as most of the other unconscious materials we hide from conscious awareness for various defensive reasons.

Ask several people what they would think of a situation in which everyone had telepathic powers. You will find that most people are very uneasy about such a proposition. Ask psychics how people responded to their psi abilities when, as children, they revealed telepathic or clairsentient glimpses uninhibitedly. Most will say that the reaction was discouraging, sometimes including fright and occasionally even (PETERSON) anger. Western society generally inhibits the expression of psi abilities so that gifted subjects tend to withhold them, unexpressed. With sufficient discouragements psi powers may then be repressed by the unconscious mind. This would spare the person the discomfort of confrontation with an unaccepting environment.

SCHMEIDLER's 'sheep/goat' dichotomy seems to indicate that everybody has psi ability but that it is used in directions consistent with the beliefs of the subject. We may speculate that believers use psi to obtain positive results. Conversely, disbelievers filter these through their belief system and produce negative results in order to avoid the cognitive discomfort a positive outcome might produce, were it consciously perceived in unaltered form. This also comforts them that no such thing could happen.

Psi effects occur irregulary and infrequently. Many people therefore question whether psi phenomena are more than random fluctuations in observations.

There is a marked tendency for *hits* (successful attempts) to occur at the beginning and end of a series of trials. This effect is like that observed in the testing of memory for nonsense syllables and similar psychological tasks. It may be related at least partially to attention, which is greater at the beginning and end of a series of trials.

The problem of unrepeatability of experiments is much more vexing and serious. Subjects may do well in one series of trials and poorly in another for no apparent reason. Attempts to increase successful performance by rewards, feedback and other methods have been largely ineffective. Many skeptics cite this as reason to question whether psi actually exists. They claim that a person should be expected to demonstrate psi powers repeatedly if he possesses them. There is no a-priori reason, however, that psi phenomena should conform with expectations of repeatability, just as procrustean measures taken

> We do not insist that viruses are not alive because they do not breathe.

from any given scientific field need not apply to any fields outside their own.[14]

HASTED and SHAFER, referred to earlier in this chapter, and IRIS OWEN/MARGARET SPARROW, among others, have noted that *will-*

ing PK effects to occur is counterproductive. Being in a frame of mind that *allows* them to happen without conscious direction works much better. REX STANFORD has found support for this approach in the psi lab (1974). He gives the example of a young woman who was very successful in a psi experiment. Upon questioning, it became apparent that she did not even understand the instructions properly. Her technique was simply to hope that everything would turn out well.

Perhaps this unfocused state of mind is also produced by the ganzfeld-method.

Healers' reports of healing-conducive states of mind parallel laboratory studies of psi-conducive states. As LAWRENCE LESHAN and JOYCE GOODRICH summarized, the healing state of mind is not one in which the healer actively pursues changes in the person being healed. The healer seeks a oneness with the healee and allows whatever healing can take place to occur. This suggests that investigators of psi and healing ought to alter their laboratory techniques to accommodate the practices of those who do not usually produce psi phenomena and healings on demand. Pressuring them to do so may be counterproductive.

How are we to understand this need for a nondirected state of mind if psi and healing are to occur? LeShan suggests that the healer enters alternate realities in order to heal. In these mental states matter and mind and time may have different relationships from those in our everyday, sensory reality. Healers may be able to bring about unusual changes because of different laws of nature in those realities. The nondirected, meditative state may be a way to gain access to the other realities. A second possibility is that the psi-healing functions reside in the right part of the brain.[15] Meditative states may help either to activate the right brain hemisphere, to de-activate the left one or to synchronize both (CADE/COXHEAD). Another hypothesis is that by quieting the mind, one relinquishes counter-productive beliefs and habits for bodily tensions and other malfunctions, allowing healthy, normal functions to re-assert themselves.

The irregular occurrence of psi and healing in a laboratory environment may relate in part to their being *need-determined*. A strongly felt need in someone associated with the situation may facilitate espression of psi abilities. In natural settings one would expect the greatest need to reside in the healee, fol-lowed by the healer with altruistic and/or ego-involved needs (e.g. reputation, finan-cial gain).

In the laboratory, the needs of the healee are often subordinated to those of the experi-menter. With respect to healers, the laborato-ry situation where the experimenters' needs are clearly paramount is often little better. Most people tested for psi or healing say that the laboratory is not only boring but also irrelevant to their work. Healers often dedi-cate much or all of their lives to helping large numbers of people in serious need of healing or counselling. Working on bacteria or mice is not something on which they want to waste valuable time. Some even say that such frivolous use of their healing gifts might lead to a diminution of their powers.

The intrusion of others into the healer-healee relationship has to be distracting at the least. The monitoring of physiological pa-rameters by means of various instruments with their wires can cause the healing rela-tionship to lose much of its healing quality. Neither healer nor healee is likely to feel the experimenters' needs are as strong as their own and they will probably not experience their own needs as important as when they are outside the experimenters' frame of ref-erence. The challenge is for the experiment-er to take his studies to the field or to create an encouraging atmosphere in the laboratory. It is almost surprising that despite such ob-stacles healing and psi experiments have pro-duced convincing evidence.

Healing involves clairsentience and/or tele-pathy. Many healers are able to detect and identify specific bodily dysfunctions without being told by the healee or by anyone else what the health problems are. In some cases the healer may be obtaining information from the minds of the healee, those who accompa-ny him or those who know his diagnosis (such as his physician). In other instances the heal-er clearly transcends the information availa-ble via such telepathic sources. Healers have been known to make detailed diagnoses which were previously unknown to anyone but were later verified on medical examina-tion. Very talented clairsentient diagnosti-cians have been able to name the patient's ill-nesses, using medical terms that they never learned and do not comprehend. Precognition may also explain some of these diagnoses.

PK seems to be involved in some healings, according to the definition that the mind of one person acts on an object outside itself. This seems more likely in instantaneous, 'miraculous' healings and psychic surgery, where the interventions of the healer are quite dramatic. Tissues may be demated-ized and materialized. We cannot be certain, however, that this is healer PK. He may be activating processes within the healee rather than acting upon him. In this case it seems as though telepathy may be invoked because healers can work at a distance and without the knowledge of the healees, while still obtaining significant effects.

The studies reviewed in this section point to a variety of interesting possibilities in unraveling the mystery of healing.

MONTAGUE ULLMAN's descriptions of the different styles of psi and healing of Kulagina and Vinogradova suggest that several very different channels or modes may exist whereby psi and healing are expressed. This is supported by the observations of effects of healers on water which may show up either on IR or UV studies. Alternatively, healer methods may be identical but may be colored and distorted by personalities and belief systems of the healers and healees.

LEONID VASILIEV's observations on apparent PK-induced muscle contractions seem open to several interpretations. Simple PK may be involved. This appears more likely in the case of the insect muscles because here the experimenter knew the desired result. Supporting the PK proposition is harder in the case of the hypnotized subjects because the experimenters were naive with respect to the anatomical structures involved. They could, of course, have obtained the required information telepathically from experimenters or others who did have the knowledge. This would be what is commonly called *super-ESP* which has been demonstrated in other instances (e.g. STANFORD ET AL. 1975; SOLFVIN 1982).[16] Another possible explanation of the muscle contractions is some sort of a biological-field interaction between experimenter and subject, per the synchronization of insect-muscle contractions with the experimenter's breathing. In any case, these experimental situations suggest overlap with aspects of healing.[17]

The metal-bending and the less rigorous observations of *SAI BABA* and *THOMAS* suggest that a subject may be able to cause matter to alter or even disappear instantaneously from one place and/or appear in another location. This suggests that either the healer or healee may be able to materialize or dematerialize body tissues to bring about a healing. Reports of mediumistic materializations may also be relevant here.[18]

Psychic subjects have been able to induce PK and healing abilities similar to their own in other subjects who did not previously display such abilities. *URI GELLER* is especially noted for transferring his ability to soften/bend metal and possibly also to restart broken timepieces. Filippino healers reportedly bring out healing and psychic-surgery abilities in others (STELTER). Any study of PK or healing force/distance effects should, therefore, exclude investigators from the vicinity of the target objects. Otherwise the experimenter close to the object could be a secondary, induced agent for PK, thereby complicating the study.

The induced-healers often report that their healing was effective only when they were in contact with their mentors. The precise distance relationship is impossible to ascertain from the limited information given in the reports. In one case Stelter stated that a student healer was able to reproduce psychic surgery while in the Philippines but not when he returned to Germany. Confidence/skepticism feelings in the healer and/or belief/doubt/negative 'vibrations' effects of other participants and observers may confuse or obscure distance effects.

Some healers report they regularly induce healing abilities in relatives of healees, initiating absent healing over great distances.

Another parallel between metal bending and healing is the report of observers that they may sense a tingling when they place their hand between that of the bender and the target object.

HASTED and SHAFER both comment on the need for a proper atmosphere for the metal bending to occur. Again this parallels reports in healing. Hasted mentions that a significant percent of metal benders in time develop healing abilities (1982). They complain the metal bending gets boring after a while.

The UPHOFFS' report on ultrasonic waves with PK is a novel observation which is worthy of further investigation. I do not know of any studies on healers involving these frequencies. LARISSA VILENSKAYA's report on Kulagina's ability to produce a burning sensation through quartz glass suggests ultraviolet radiation may be related to this effect.

STANFORD's theory that PK may occur most readily when an organizing need acts upon a random system seems a reasonable description of many of the physiological processes that may respond to healing. The body's immune system, for example, requires that antibodies and white blood cells, which circulate randomly throughout the body, attack invading organisms. The healer may aid the *targeting* of these elements. This may also be the case on a chemical level. Many body processes entail complex biochemical reactions of molecules distributed randomly throughout the body. They often require specific enzymes to facilitate reactions with each other. The healer's psi might facilitate the completion of these random chemical processes.

HELMUT SCHMIDT's RNG study, demonstrating backwards-in-time causation, closely parallels healings that are reportedly displaced in time.

As with all psi phenomena, differentiating who is producing the effects in a given case is impossible. For example, the experimenter could conceivably be the true agent for Schmidt's effects, using clairsentience and

PK. The subjects could also be precognizing the future experimental situation and affecting the RNG prior to reaching the laboratory. The same is true of healing. We can never know whether healer or healee produce given results.

Several aspects of RSPK investigations have bearings on our understanding of healing. All of the propelling force in moving the object in RSPK can be reasonably presumed to originate in the human agent. This may then impose force/distance limitations on the abilities of the subject to affect the object. In the case of RSPK it is usually inanimate objects that are affected. If people are influenced it is only to move them in gross, bodily fashion from one place to another. In healing, energies and awareness/ intelligence are available in the healees to help in effecting changes. This adds a possible dimension of participation of the healee in the effects of healing, which would generally not occur in instances of RSPK. The range for healer effects may be far greater, therefore, than for RSPK effects.

The mechanisms for healing may or may not be different for distant versus present touch-healings. Healers are of the opinion that there is little difference in effectiveness between distant and present healings. Careful investigation is required to substantiate the clinical impressions.

The unrepeatability of many psi experiments is cited as a basis for discounting the existence of psi. This is a problem that also

> Many centuries ago Heraclitus observed that it is impossible to step twice into the same river.

concerns psi believers. It is not exclusive to this field. H. M. COLLINS points out that similar repeatability problems exist in the harder sciences, such as in studies of laser design and gravitational fields. It may be that too many unnoticed and uncontrolled variables enter into psi effects and produce unrepeatable experiments.

We could conclude from the unrepeatability of psi effects that psi has natural laws which are different from those of other phenomena. The 'sheep-goat' effect has been helpful in clarifying one source of discrepancies, hinting that there may be others which are explainable in linear terms. There is evidence that geomagnetic activity may contribute to variability of telepathic transmission.[19] Anecdotal evidence has also been produced for variability of healing with thunderstorms (TURNER 1969) and with lunar phases (SETZER). Psi effects may be more sensitive to these influences than are other phenomena. This may ultimately provide clues to the nature of psi energies and processes. Moreover, the experimenter(s) themselves may be a part of tests to a far greater degree than has been appreciated, which could account for variability that precludes repeatability.[20]

The lack of clarity in this discussion is partly due to our limited understanding of the involved processes. Sufficient experiments have been performed to demonstrate beyond any reasonable doubt that psi exists. We know enough to realize that psi effects occur with less intentional control than other types of interactions with the environment. Perhaps we shall never produce these effects entirely at will. My own belief is that the lessons from psi research require restructuring of our conventional scientific paradigms.

For those interested in skeptics' views on psi, I recommend the comments of reviewers along with the original works.[21] This is to provide a balance to the skeptics' views, which are often laced with selective presentations of poorer evidence for psi, while ignoring the better evidence; application of Procrustean standards and measurements using yardsticks which are not properly applicable to psi; demands for stringent scientific methodology which far exceed those applied in other fields of research; and even misrepresentations of materials.

In summary, major components of psi phenomena are relevant to healing:

1. Telepathy, clairsentience and PK may be components of the healing process. They have been demonstrated conclusively in the laboratory.

2. Telepathy and clairsentience have been shown to occur at vast distances, which may be a basis for, or parallel with, distant diagnosis and healing.

3. The undirected state of mind which is psi-conducive may be identical with or similar to states of mind that are healing-conducive.

CHAPTER I-4

Controlled Studies

There is really no scientific or other method by which man can steer safely between the opposite dangers of believing too little or believing too much. To face such dangers is apparently our duty and to hit the right channel between them is the measure of our wisdom.

William James

There are more controlled studies on healing than there are on all of the other complementary therapies combined (excepting hypnosis and psychoneuroimmunology).

Controlled studies answer with precision questions posed in a scientific manner. Paradoxically, the more precise the question the more limited the information obtained by this narrow, exact focus. This is the way of science.

In walking the fine line between possible research errors, Type I (accepting as true that which is not), and Type II (rejecting as false that which is not), this chapter is strongly biased towards refuting everything that is not demonstrated beyond a reasonable doubt.

The following minimal information must be included in a research report for such purposes:

1. Description of selection of healees must be clear in order to allow generalization of the results from one study to another. For instance, we must know whether a study of healing was conducted with chronic patients who reached the end of the conventional medical road of treatment or with people who came for help for the first time. We also want to know whether healees volunteered or were selected by the researchers, as their motivations may differ greatly.

2. Randomization of subjects between experimental ('E') and control (comparison, 'C') groups hopefully distributes evenly among the groups all extraneous differences in subject characteristics which might bias any of the groups to respond differently to the treatment under study. Observed differences between experimental outcomes can then be attributed with greater confidence to differences in the treatments of the various groups. Furthermore, to preclude experimenter bias (conscious or unconscious) from influencing

the distribution of subjects, assignment of patients should be via random numbers generated by carefully automated procedures, preferably outside the researcher's own laboratory.

3. Blinds (measures to keep subjects and experimenters unaware of which person is receiving which treatment) prevent experimenters and subjects from responding differently to E and C conditions by preconceived anticipations of outcomes. Experimenters might otherwise bring about results through suggestion or placebo effects.[1] Experimenters evaluating outcomes will thus also be impartial in their assessments.

4. Procedures employed in the experiment and measurements used to evaluate results should be described in sufficient detail to enable replication of the study by others. It is impossible to duplicate precisely any biological experiment because of the indescribable complexity of subjects and healers and hosts of relevant yet unknown variables, but we must make every effort to come as close as possible to doing so.[2]

5. Data must be presented in sufficient detail to permit independent evaluation of the results.

6. Statistical analysis of differences between E and C groups assures that the differences found did not occur by chance. Statistics are reported as probabilities. A scientific minimum for acceptable *probability ('p')* representing a true difference between E and C groups is that the observed results would have occurred only five times in one hundred (abbreviated as *p less than 0.05* or $p < 0.05$). Naturally it is more convincing to find results that are even less likely to have occurred by chance (e.g. less than once in a hundred – $p < 0.01$ – or less than once in a thousand – $p < 0.001$, etc.).

The before mentioned are required for assurance that an experiment was performed to accepted scientific standards. Several more are required in order to allow assessments of the relevance of the study to any other setting:

7. Healers must be described. Different levels of competence and experience could account for variability between studies.
8. *Type and duration of healing and ritual practices* may vary widely between healers. At a minimum one would like to know whether touch, near or distant healing was employed and how long healers worked with subjects.

The studies in this chapter have been scrutinized for adequate attention to the above criteria. Where lacking, this has been mentioned in the comments following the review. With WILLIAM JAMES' caveat in mind, comments have been made both from vantages of possible Type I and Type II errors.

For those who enjoy solving mysteries this chapter offers the most reliable clues to the question, "What is healing?"

For those with little patience for the minutiae of such scrutiny I recommend the studies of healing for anesthetized mice. This series nicely illustrates the process of refining the questions posed in experiments so that the answers are ever more certain and precise.

L et us begin with a look at studies of healing effects on enzymes. We will then progress to studies of increasingly complex systems and organisms.

Healing Action on Enzymes

Justa M. Smith – Paranormal effects on enzyme activity (Human Dimensions Institute; Professional paper 1972)

Researchers studied the effects of the laying-on-of-hands by a healer, OSCAR ESTEBANY, on the enzymatic activity of trypsin under carefully controlled conditions.

Solutions of trypsin (500 mg per ml in 0.001 NHCl, pH 3) were divided into four aliquots; one was retained in the native state and will be referred to as the control; the second was treated by Mr. Estebany in the same fashion as he treats patients, this is, by the laying-on-of-hands (simply putting his hands around the stoppered glass flask containing the enzyme solution for a maximum of 75 minutes from which 3 ml portions were pipetted out after 15, 30, 45, and 60 minutes); the third was exposed to ultraviolet light at 2537 A, the most damaging wavelength for protein, for sufficient time to reduce the activity to 68–80 percent, and then treated by Mr. Estebany as above; the fourth was exposed to a high magnetic field (3,000–13,000 gauss) for hourly increments to three hours. Three to five activity measurements were made on each of the above samples for each time interval. The mean and standard deviation of the mean for each were calculated daily. Finally, a mean of the means and standard deviation over all the days were calculated for each sample and compared.

Enzyme activity was increased 10% over 75 minutes when Estebany carried out his laying-on-of-hands treatment.

Mr. Estebany's effect on the native and on the partially ultraviolet denatured enzyme is practically the same.

It is interesting to note that the qualitative effect of a high magnetic field and a paranormal 'healer' are the same, and quantitatively similar up to one hour exposure.

SMITH speculates on possible chemical mechanisms whereby the enzymatic activity is enhanced. She concludes:

Perhaps it is unrealistic to attempt to parallel too closely the magnetic field effects with the apparently similar effects of treatment by a paranormal 'healer'. While it has not been possible to explain the enhanced enzymic activity due to a magnetic field to everyone's satisfaction, this explanation must be sought in physical-chemical mechanisms. However, the result of treatment by a 'healer' is not of the same nature. The healing activity might be more comparable to a 'life force', or to a 'psi field'.

SMITH repeated the experiment with three people who did not claim to have any healing power, and three who did. None had a positive effect on enzymes.

Mr. Estebany returned in the late fall of 1967 for a two-week period at Rosary Hill College campus in order to repeat the experiments. It should be noted that during his summer visit there was little college activity and a very tranquil atmosphere, with Mr. Estebany completely composed. However, in the fall it was not possible for him to live in a residential hall, and because of circumstances personal in nature, he was not at ease. As a result, in the same type of tests, he had no influence upon the enzymes. Therefore, it may be deduced that the ability of a healer depends upon his personal state of mind.

These results, together with those obtained with Mr. Estebany, would indicate that a person blessed with healing power can affect the enzyme trypsin by increasing its activity. Metabolically this increase in activity reflects a more rapid digestion of protein. It is possible that this effect could contribute to overall good health and to general therapy, since it helps provide the blood with amino acids necessary for growth and repair. But the question can now be asked whether a true healer can increase the activity of all enzymes and would this be desirable or useful in therapy?

It was in searching for an answer to this question that it was decided to introduce other enzyme systems into this research. Accordingly, enzymes with totally different types of reactions were chosen. NAD (nicotinamide-adenine dinucleotide) is necessary for the electron transport system to function in its internal anaerobic reaction to assist the metabolic production of ATP (adenosine tri phosphate), an energy releasing compound. However, the body tissues also contain NAD-ase, the enzyme which frees nicotinamide, adenosine phosphate, and protein, i.e., breaks up the necessary NAD into its components.

When the three psychics were asked to 'treat' this enzyme, the results were a decrease in activity. This would appear to play a positive part in the art of healing, for it leaves more of the NAD intact to perform in ATP formation.

The third enzyme used in this study was amylase–amylose, which involves carbohydrate metabolism. Amylose is a polysaccharide released from starch in plants when the protein coat is removed by heat. This polysaccharide is made up of glucose units which can be entirely broken down by the enzyme amylase. If the activity of this enzyme were increased by a healer, it would mean that the amylose was being broken down into glucose more rapidly than normal, which would trigger an increase in insulin secretion. This is the route to diabetes.

The source of the amylose was the psychics' own blood serum. It was thought that this source might be more 'alive' than the other highly purified and processed enzymes used in this study.

The results of the psychics' ability to change the activity rate of this amylase was that none of them was able to affect anyone's amylose level, including his own. There is the possibility that the crude, unrefined amylase from the blood serum contained too many other factors that could have been affected and which were not being measured. There is the other possibility that the amylase–amylose system is balanced and a change in this balance in either direction is not involved nor conducive to healing.

Discussion

A. SMITH demonstrated a healing effect on enzymes in the laboratory. Enzymes are catalysts for chemical reactions in the body. Perhaps healers can influence the action of these agents for physiological change in the body of a living organism. This could bring about healing by either hastening their activity (as in wound healing, blood clotting, fighting invading infective agents) or slowing detrimental processes (as in growth of cancers, hormonal imbalances, etc.).

Smith's speculations on reasons for her different results with various enzymes are premature. Healers feel that a *native intelligence* inheres in aspects of the healing process, so that the healer does not have to know such disciplines as biochemistry or anatomy in order to bring about physiological changes. Smith's results are in line with this assumption.

It would appear that Smith is skeptical regarding healing, as she places 'healer' in quotation marks. This, too, might be a factor in the negative results in the second series with Estebany.

The similarity between effects of a healer and of very strong magnetic fields suggests that there may be overlaps in the involved mechanisms. However, electromagnetic measurements of healers during healing have not revealed magnetic field alterations except with the most sensitive magnetometers, and these were set to register unconventional (non-Hertzian) magnetic fields (REIN 1991).

B. Though these studies were well run, SMITH does not present statistical analyses. The trends as graphed in the report appear to be significant in the directions indicated, but a clearer statement of outcome significance is needed. Though this report does not mention temperature controls, Smith reassured me in personal correspondence that these were strictly maintained.

Smith presumes that Estebany's state of mind in the second study negatively influenced the results. This is clearly an educated guess rather than a demonstrated fact.

A number of replications would be necessary before one could begin to accept the validity of her report and conclusions. Her results may represent effects due to very different causes such as chance variations; differences between healers; expectations of healers concerning the 'proper' direction for results; similar expectations on the part of the experimenter; and many other causes as well.

Hoyt L. Edge – The effect of laying-on of hands on an enzyme: An attempted replication (*Research in Parapsychology 1979*)

HOYT L. EDGE attempted a replication of Smith's study. Edge used Anne Graham, a well-known Florida medium and healer. In five experiments using undamaged trypsin, only one produced significant results (p <0.05). If data from the series are combined, significance reaches p < 0.01. In experiments with trypsin damaged by ultraviolet light no significant results were found.

Trypsin held in magnetic fields of 1,300 gauss for 75 minutes was likewise not affected to a significant level.

Discussion

A. This study begins to confirm that healing can significantly influence enzymes.

EDGE mentions that conditions seemed unfavorable for the healer although details are not provided. Smith obtained positive results when more powerful magnetic fields were applied for twice the length of time used in this study. **B.** Although this study supports Smith's findings of a healing effect on trypsin, it is too scantily reported, omitting details which would allow the reader to make an independent evaluation of the results.

Glen Rein – An exosomatic effect on neurotransmitter metabolism in mice: A pilot study *(Paper presented at 2nd International Conference of the Society for Psychical Research, Cambridge, England, 1978)*

GLEN REIN studied the effects of noncontact (hands near mice) healing on the neurotransmitters dopamine (DA) and noradrenaline (NA) in the peripheral nervous systems of mice. Two healers "... were asked to alter the impulse flow of the peripheral nerve which innervates the adrenal gland". Ten pairs of inbred mice were studied under double-blind conditions.

NA increased up to 130% in half of the animals (p < 0.05).

> In the remaining animals, NA levels either remained the same or were slightly decreased (approximately 10%) relative to the controls... DA levels also increased in the same five animals showing increased NA, reaching a similar maximum of 130% relative to controls. In the remaining animals the decreased DA levels observed (approximately 25%) paralleled the smaller decrease in NA (p < 0.04).
>
> For the combined effects there is a p < 0.01.

Rein suggests that individual animal variability in response to healing (of unspecified type) may account for the differences noted between responders and nonresponders. Such individual variability in response to many types of treatments is common in animals and even in yeasts. Healer performance variability may also be a factor. For instance, one of the healers was menstruating during a particular study in which three-quarters of the animals demonstrated decreased neurotransmitter levels, an observation that has also been reported in some other psi studies (SCHMITT/STANFORD; KEANE/WELLS).

Discussion
A. Here we see that healing can significantly influence enzymes in a living organism.

It is surprising that others have not studied hormone responsiveness to healing. This neurohormone would appear to be a fertile area for further work.
B. This is a well-controlled study with clearly significant results.

Glen Rein – A psychokinetic effect on neurotransmitter metabolism: Alterations in the degradative enzyme monoamine oxidase *(Research in Parapsychology 1985)*

REIN'S Summary:

> Blood platelets isolated from healthy human volunteers were treated by Matthew Manning (a well-known British healer). These blood cells contain monoamine oxidase (MAO), an enzyme involved with metabolising certain functionally critical chemicals in the brain called neurotransmitters.

Enzyme activity was measured before and after PK exposure in intact cells and in those which had been disrupted. For both preparations, activity of the enzyme either increased [9 trials], decreased [7 trials], or did not change [2 trials] relative to untreated blood cells – $p < 0.001$. These results are the first to successfully demonstrate a PK effect on an enzyme in its natural environment using a physiological substrate at both the cellular and sub-cellular level. The results are discussed in reference to their physiological significance in regulating the amount of neurotransmitters in the nervous system, also known to respond to PK.

Only five minutes' treatment was required.

Discussion

A. This is an important pioneering study, well performed. MAO is an enzyme associated with neural transmission. Its function in the brain is to aid the degrading of certain chemicals which are active in the junctions between nerve cells. Activity of this enzyme has also been roughly correlated with depressive mood states.

This may be yet another mechanism whereby a healing occurs. An alteration in MAO activity could produce changes in nerve functions and/or in emotional moods conducive to recovery from illness. This might also be a mechanism for improving mood alone and might explain why some healees report they feel better even when no objective improvements are noted by medical examiners.

B. Why PK should sometimes increase and at other times decrease MAO activity in the laboratory is unclear. Further research is needed to clarify whether this is a consistent finding. The possibility of laboratory error (highly unlikely to be of this magnitude) or extraneous factors influencing the system would have to be ruled out in replications of this study.

Herman K. Kief – A method for measuring PK ability with enzymes *(Research in Parapsychology 1972)*

HERMAN KIEF very briefly describes a manometric method for measuring healing effects on an enzyme, carbondioxydeanhydratase.

I chose this enzyme for two reasons: it can be obtained in a highly purified state and it gives a very standardized reaction velocity...

If we record a curve of the carbon dioxide absorption by the enzyme over time (which is very easily and very exactly measured by reading the manometers every five or ten minutes), we get an S-shaped curve which starts out flat, then rises sharply, and finally flattens out again. In the first part of the curve the enzyme is adapting and taking up molecules of its substrates. At the point where the curve begins to rise the reaction is started efficiently and the carbon dioxide is rapidly absorbed. At the point where the curve flattens out all the carbon dioxide in the closed system has been used and the reaction ends due to lack of substrate. The inclining portion of the curve is usually a straight line and makes a sharp angle with the time axis. This angle can be measured very exactly and is a good parameter of the reaction velocity.

I did a PK experiment using this apparatus, in which a number of flask-manometer systems were randomly divided into two equal groups. All the flasks got exactly the same quantities of enzyme, substrate, activator, buffer, etc. Then one group was 'treated' by a subject, while the other group was not. The 'treatment' consisted of making 'magnetic passes' over the flasks for about two minutes. In this pilot study there was no significant difference between the reaction velocities of treated and untreated enzymes.

Discussion

A. KIEF's attitude towards healing is skeptical, judging by his use of quotation marks for 'treatment'.

B. The design of this experiment seems sound, but Kief does not provide sufficient information to permit independent assessment of his results. How many samples were run? Who was the subject?

Andrzej F. Frydrychowski, Bozens Przyjemska, and Tadeusz Orlowski – An attempt to apply photon emission measurement in the selection of the most effective healer (Psychotronika 1985)

The authors describe their experiments:

A photomultiplier was used during oxidation–reduction reaction (patient's serum = 1% solution of pyrogallol buffered with phosphate buffer to pH 7.2 = 1% hydrogen peroxide solution). Photon emission range of the sera of 10 endogenous depression patients varied from 100 to 300 puls/min. (Normal rate is 8–10,000 puls/min.) Sera were later treated by two healers whose large biopoles were previously confirmed by laboratory in-

vestigations and clinical effects.

Results of the treatment: Healer A – in 4 out of 5 cases photon emission increases reaching in one case 8,600 puls/min; Healer B – in 3 out of 5 cases photon emission increases reaching in two cases 7,600 and 8,100 puls/min. When healers A and B acted jointly on sera of two patients: In the case of one patient the puls/min score was higher than that obtained by healers A and B acting separately and in the second patient considerably lower than that obtained by healers A and B acting separately.

After these in vitro tests, healers A and B treated the patients themselves. Improvement of the clinical condition was achieved in these cases in which an increase in photon emission in vitro was observed. The health of 3 out of 10 patients was improved considerably and they were released from the hospital. For reasons of medical ethics it was decided not to check whether health deterioration would occur with those patients whose sera photon emission scores were reduced in vitro tests.

Discussion

A. Photon emission from serum is not sufficiently understood to say what it represents. It may be related to the serum's biochemical properties, possibly to states of health and/or illness. On an empirical basis alone, these methods seem to warrant further exploration. Much time would be saved if a screening test could be devised to predict which patients might benefit from healing.

B. This report is typical of studies from Eastern Europe. Small numbers of patients are studied, procedural details are omitted, and no statistical analyses are possible. Any conclusions based on this study are highly speculative. For example, though the authors tentatively conclude that simultaneous treat-

Table I -3. Healing effects on enzymes

Subject of healing	Researchers	T/N/D*	Duration	Healers	Results	Significance
Trypsin	J. Smith	T/N	Up to 2 mins	Estebany	Activity increased 10% over 75 mins.	Significant (?)
Nicotinamide adenine dinucleotice (NAD)		T/N			Activity decreased	
Amylase-Amylose		T/N			No effect	
			to 3 hrs	magnet	3,000-13,000 gauss	
Trypsin	Edge	T/N	?	Graham	1. Undamaged trypsin activity increased in one of five studies Combining results of 5 runs	p< .05 p< .01
					2. Trypsin damaged by UV light	NS**
				magnet	3. Trypsin + magnetic field 1,300 gauss	3/6 runs Significant
Dopamine	Rein	N	15 mins	2 healers	Increased up to 130% in five mice, decreased down to 25% in five mice	p< .01
Noradre-naline					Increased up to 130% in 5 / 10 mice	p< .05
Human platelet monoamine oxidase (MAO)		T/N	4-5 mins	Manning	Increased in 9 trials; decreased in 7; no response in 2	p< .001
Carbon-dioxydean-hydratase	Kief	N	2 mins	?		NS
Human serum	Frydrychowski, et al.	N?	?	2 healers	Photon emission increased in individual treatments	NS

* T/N/D: Touch/Near/Distant   **NS: Non-Significant

ment of one patient by several healers may not be beneficial, it is impossible to say this with any certainty based on only two cases.

The experiments on enzymes are sum-ma rized in Table I – 3.

L et us turn now to studies of the effects of healing on cells. Some of the studies deal with human cells, others with fungus, yeast and bacteria. These provide insights into possible mechanisms of healing.

Healing Action on Cells in the Laboratory

William Braud, Gary Davis, and Robert Wood – Experiments with Matthew Manning
(Journal of the Society for Psychical Research 1979)

MATTHEW MANNING is gifted with a variety of PK abilities but focuses now primarily on healing.

The authors report on the experiments:

> Five experiments are described in which Matthew Manning attempted to influence living target systems mentally and at a distance, i.e., psychokinetically. Experiment 1 involved attempts to influence the locomotor activity of a gerbil in an activity wheel. Experiment 2 involved attempts to influence the spatial orientation of an electric fish. In Experiment 3, the physiological activity (GSR reactions) of another person served as the PK target. GSR activity was also the target in Experiment 4, but in this case, the activity had been pre-recorded; thus, the experiment involved 'time-displaced' PK. In Experiment 5, Matthew Manning attempted to decrease the rate of hemolysis of human erythrocytes which were being stressed osmotically. In all experiments, with the exception of Experiment 4, the living target systems were successfully influenced.

The fifth experiment is reviewed here in detail because of its relevance to healing effects with cells. (The first two are of interest in terms of telepathic controls over animal mobility but not relevant to healing.)

Erythrocytes (red blood cells) can be stored for long periods of time if kept in solutions of similar concentration to normal body fluids. If placed in more dilute (hypotonic) solutions, osmotic pressures tend to swell and rupture (hemolyze) the cells, spilling hemoglobin into the surrounding solution in a brief period of time. The hemoglobin colors the solution and its concentration can be measured with a spectrophotometer.

The experiment consisted of 10 runs, scheduled on 10 successive days (not including weekends). Each run involved rate of hemolysis measures on 10 blood samples. Five of these were control samples and five were samples which M.M. attempted to influence so that hemolysis would be retarded...

> Each of 10 spectroscope tubes was filled with 6.0 ml of a 0.34 percent saline solution at room temperature (20° C)... all samples of both blood and saline came from the same 'stock solutions'... A trial consisted of measurement of percent light transmittance at 540 m.microns... through

a tube 0 min and 5 min following the addition to the tube of three drops (measured by a Pasteur pipette) of human blood...

During the 5 minute period between measurements, the tube remained in the holder of the Spec 20. For control trials, M.M. rested and attempted not to think of the tube. For influence trials, M.M. placed his hands above but not touching the closed holder of the Spec 20 and attempted to decrease the rate of hemolysis of the tube's contents. The experimenter (W.B.) sat next to M.M., observed him constantly, and made the two readings for each tube. M.M. attempted to accomplish his goal by imagining the erythrocytes as intact and resistant to the hypotonic saline. Sometimes he mentally projected a "white light" around the cells. The sequence of the five control and five influence tubes was randomly determined by the order of 10 cards shuffled 20 times (as in the above experiments). This was the procedure for nine of the 10 runs. For these runs, since M.M. preferred to sit with his hands above the apparatus, the experimenter was aware of the nature of a trial and the measurement could not be performed blind. However, for Run 2, a different protocol was used. M.M. sat in a distant room and attempted to influence the tubes at a distance. The experimenter signalled the beginning and end of each influence and control period by ringing a bell. When M.M. heard one ring, he turned up a card from the deck of 10 cards which he had shuffled 20 times. If the card was blank, M.M. rested and tried not to think of the blood sample. If the card contained the word, 'Influence', M.M. attempted to decrease the rate of hemolysis of the sam-ple. When M.M. heard two rings of the bell (5 minutes later) he stopped and rested until the next trial began. Under these conditions, the experimenter was able to make his measurements in a blind fashion, unaware of whether M.M. was attempting to influence the tube or not. At the end of the run, M.M. came into the experimenter's room with a copy of the trial (card) sequence which he had prepared before seeing the Spec 20 measurements.

The results were highly significant ($p < 0.00096$). The test run with the most significant results was the one in which Manning sat apart from the experimenter.

The authors also briefly report on a study on *MANNING* by KMETZ:

Cervical cancer cells are cultured in specially prepared plastic flasks. 'Healthy' cancer cells adhere to the plastic surface of the flask by means of an electrostatic force. Changes in metabolism, the injury, or the death of the cells disturb their normal positive charge, causing them to lose their attraction to the negatively charged flask wall and to slough off into the surrounding fluid medium. Microscopic counts of the number of cells in the medium provide measures of the 'state of health' of the cultures. M.M. was able to exert quite dramatic influences upon these cancer cell cultures, ranging in magnitude from 200 to 1,200 per cent changes, compared with appropriate controls. Most of these effects followed M.M. 'laying on of hands' on the experimental flask for a 20 min period... However, strong effects also occurred when M.M. never touched the flasks, but attempted to influence the cultures at a distance, while confined in an electrically shielded room.

In one experiment with 38.02 percent deviation from chance statistical significance reached p < .00002.

Discussion
A. The highly significant study of BAUD ET AL. suggests that cell membranes of the red blood cell may be strengthened with healing. This may be a site of action for healing in general. Cell membranes are both barriers and gateways between cellular environments.

Manning's abilities to kill cancer cells with near and distant healing are also impressive.

B. The studies by Braud et al. were well-run, adequately described and highly significant.

ARTHUR ELLISON, an emeritus professor of electrical engineering and parapsychologist, attempted with others to replicate this study (personal communication). They found substantial variability between results of hemolysis with blood samples from different individuals and a marked change in red cell susceptibility to hemolysis with passing time. Ellison considers this an unreliable system for demonstration of psi effects. It appears to me that the randomisation of samples from the same stock solution utilised in the study of Braud et al. should have adequately controlled for such variabilities.

The study by KMETZ is tantalisingly interesting, but lacks sufficient detail for proper analysis. (See also a similar experiment by Kmetz with KRAFT, described in Chapter I-5.)

William Braud – Distant mental influence on rate of hemolysis of human red blood cells
(Parapsychological Association Meeting, Montreal, August 1988)

BRAUD'S Abstract:

A formal investigation was conducted in order to determine whether a relatively large number of unselected subjects would be able to exert a distant mental influence upon the rate of hemolysis of human red blood cells. For each of 32 subjects, red blood cells in 20 tubes were submitted to osmotic stress (hypotonic saline). The subjects attempted to protect the cells in 10 of these tubes, using visualisation and intention strategies; the remaining 10 tubes served as non-influence controls. For each tube, the rate of hemolysis was measured photometrically over a 1-minute trial period. Subjects and experimenter were 'blind' regarding critical aspects of the procedure, and subjects and tubes were located in separate rooms in order to eliminate conventional influences. Results indicated that a significantly greater number of subjects than would be expected on the basis of chance alone showed independently significant differences between their 'protect' and 'control' tubes (p = 1.91×10^{-5}). Overall, blood source (i.e., whether the influenced cells were the subject's own cells or those of another person) did not significantly influence the outcome, although there was a trend toward stronger hitting in the 'own blood' condition. Additional analyses of the results were performed by SRI International researchers to determine whether the data were better described by remote action (causal) or by intuitive data sorting (informational) predictions; the results of those mathematical analyses were inconclusive. This research is presented in the context of methodologies for investigating a possible role of psi in self-healing.

Discussion

A. Again we have very highly significant confirmation of abilities of unselected subjects, claiming no healing gifts, to influence a biological system.

The inconclusive aspect of the study related to the methods whereby the healing effect may have been obtained. BRAUD hoped to tease out whether there was a true healing effect or an experimenter effect, by manipulation of the procedures.

B. This was a most carefully performed and meticulously described study. Braud suggests that we must be cautious in interpreting such results. Control of hemolysis in the lab may differ from influence over hemolysis within the body, as body chemistry is far more complex.

Frans Snel – PK influence on malignant cell growth (Research Letter No. 10, Parapsychology Laboratory, University of Utrecht 1980)

FRANS SNEL describes his methods:

Basically a psychic healer attempted to inhibit the growth of mouse leukaemia cells in tissue culture, as compared to controls. One gifted subject was available and the experiment was designed around him. Three experiments were conducted using closely similar procedures.

Experiment 1: The gifted subject was asked to inhibit the growth of cancer cells, which were being incubated in an oven. The healer was never allowed closer than two meters from the samples but was given photographs of the bottles containing the cell cultures. He performed the healings (method and duration unspecified) from a distance of 15 kilometers.

Experiment 2: "The same subject co-operated in this experiment. He did not come to the laboratory again. Instead he only received a photograph."

Experiment 3: "On this occasion we used all the available people in the laboratory as subjects (analysts, researchers, students). Generally they did not think it possible to influence the mitosis in this way, but they co-operated."

Experiment 4: "This was a replica of experiment 3. The subject was the natural healer again. He was to try to repeat the results of experiment 2."

An independent staff person measured cell concentrations in blind fashion. The results are shown in Table I-4.

All the bottles in the first experiment contained only dead cells, the targets as well as the controls. There was therefore nothing to count.

The results showed statistically significant differences between cultures remotely treated by a healer and C samples. However, in two of the three viable experiments (2 and 3), results were contrary to the intended direction.

Snel notes that methodological artefact is possible. Since the healer insisted on separation of E and C samples, each set was put on a different shelf in the incubator. In checks to determine whether this was significant, no differences were noted in temperature or humidity between upper and lower shelves.

Table I - 4. Snel experiments,numbers 2 - 4

Experiment	% difference target vs control	Mean difference cells/ml	Probability
2	+ 38.93	1946.3	p < .002
3	+ 27.51	780.3	.002 <p< .02
4	- 18.50	641.8	.002 <p< .02

Separate, 'dummy' control runs in which bottles of cells were incubated on upper and lower shelves without healing interventions produced differences of 2.4% –11.9%. Although these differences are clearly smaller, a problem remains. All bottles showing greater values in experiments 2–4 were in higher compartments than the comparison bottles. This leaves room to question whether the observed differences were due to healer effects or to unknown factors associated with the stove that was used.

Discussion

A. The fact that much larger differences were obtained in experiments in which healing was involved suggests that some of the observed differences were a result of healing.

More subjective information on the healer might help us understand why he did not retard cancer cell growth in the second experiment and why he was successful in the fourth.

If healing can kill cancer cells in the laboratory, there is reason to believe it could also do so within the body.

B. This is a meticulously performed and reported study. Despite these positive results, SNEL indicated in personal communication he is now skeptical about the reality of healing because of repeatability problems.

Glen Rein – Quantum Biology: Healing with Subtle Energy (*Quantum Biology Research Labs 1992*)

GLEN REIN explored the effects of a healer upon DNA synthesis of tumor cells in culture. He measured cell proliferation according to the uptake of radioactive thymidine. The rate of cell proliferation was determined relative to the total number of cells, counted in a hemocytometer. The healer was DR. LEONARD LASKOW, an American gynecologist who is now doing and teaching healing.

Leonard Laskow shifted into a specific state of consciousness and mentally and energetically focused on three petri dishes held in the palm of his hand. Another aliquot of cells from the same stock bottle was being held simultaneously by a non-healer in an adjacent room. The non-healer was reading a book to minimise the interaction of his consciousness on the cells. Both sets of petri dishes (n = 6) were brought back to the tissue culture hood where they were labelled (blindly) and scrambled. The author then labelled the cells with radioactive thymidine and processed them after 24 hrs growth to measuring [sic] cell proliferation. The same exact protocol was also followed in another parallel set of experiments done with distilled water contained in a plastic lid-sealed test tube, instead of cells in a petri dish. This water, as well as control water, was then used to make statard [sic] tissue culture medium which was then added to the cells at the beginning of the 24 hr. growth period.

Two series of experiments were performed:

Experiment 1. Laskow explored five different mental intentions... He describes an overall loving state that was maintained throughout all the experiment, which allowed him to be in resonance with the tumor cells. The technique for attaining this non ordinary state is a form of meditation which allows intentional focusing and cohering of energy. Laskow refers to these intentions as different contents of consciousness. He distinguishes the intentions as:

1. returning to the natural order and harmony of the cell's normal rate of growth,
2. circulating the microcosmic orbit [Taoist visualisations after the teaching of Mantak Chia],
3. letting God's will flow through these hands,
4. unconditional love, and
5. dematerialization.

Laskow describes the psychoenergetic state of consciousness as follows: "I shifted to a 'transpersonal healing state' of consciousness by using a balancing breath which balanced and cohered both hemispheres of my brain followed by aligning, centering, and energising techniques. These processes produce, for me, a loving state which allowed my mind to come into resonance with the tumor cells as I focused on them. While in this transpersonal loving state I varied the content of my consciousness to specifically evaluate the differential influence of changes in mental content on tumor cell growth. We evaluated five different intentions while I was holding petri dishes containing tumor cells in my hands for each of the mental intentions."

"We were interested in varying what I was intending in my mind for these tumor cells. The first intent was the focused instruction that the tumor cells return to the natural order and harmony of their normal cell line. By normal I meant that the cells should grow at a normal rate, rather than their present accelerated tumor cell rate. Another intention was let God's will flow through my hands, so (in this case) there wasn't a specific direction given. Unconditional love was giving no direction at all. When I do healing work, I shift into an unconditionally loving transpersonal state. While in that general loving state, superimposed unconditional loving intent without giving specific direction to the energy." [sic]

"I had two forms of dematerialization, one was dematerialised into the light and the other one was dematerialised into the void. I wanted to see whether there was a 'reluctance' on the part of the cells to go into the unknown. Or is it better to give them a direction into the light. Obviously, this has import for people who are doing healing work in terms of giving direction to tumor cells and energy forms that you want to release. Is it easier to release them giving them a direction or releasing them into their potential, but without the light."

Experiment 2. ...We were then interested in determining to what extent intention, as a focused mental through, might contribute to the healing response. This was achieved by Laskow intending and instructing the cells to "return to their normal order and rate of growth", while holding no visual image, thus separating intent from imagery. This experiment can be directly compared with the previous one, since the microcosmic orbit state of consciousness was maintained throughout and the previous experiment involved no consciously focused intent.

REIN then proceeded to study the efficacy of water as a vehicle for healing.

Experiment 3. ... Specifically, we wanted to determine whether there were differences in the energetic patterns associated with different states and contents of consciousness and whether these patterns could be transferred to water. If the energetic patterns could be detected in water using absorption spectroscopy, it might indicate that specific spectral patterns are associated with different states and contents of consciousness. The rational [sic] for this hypothesis is based on the reported ability of healers to change the spectral patterns of water (S. Schwartz et al). Preliminary experiments with Laskow indicated he could non-specifically alter the Raman spectra of water charged holoenergetically (W. Gough). In our approach to this question, we studied whether changing the content of consciousness, while in a nonordinary state, could be used to alter tumor cell growth when culture medium was treated psychoenergetically.

Rein then reports on the results:

Experiment 1. ...the different contents of consciousness could be distinguished in terms of their biological responses. Of the different intentions studies, only three showed a significant effect on inhibiting the growth of the tumor cells. The most effective intention we tried with tumor cell cultures was "return to the natural order and harmony of the normal cell line" (39% inhibition). Allowing God's will to manifest appeared to be only half as effective (21% inhibition). Under the same experimental conditions, unconditional love neither stimulated or inhibited cell growth. Its effect was neutral and seemingly accepting of the present condition...
... different biological effects could be observed by just changing the intent or the imagery associated with the healing process but non-focused thought has no effect. Thus, while Laskow was in the microcosmic orbit state of consciousness, the mental image of visualising only three cells remaining in the petri dish after the experiment caused an 18% inhibition of cell growth. On the other hand, switching the mental image to one where many more cells were visualised in the dish resulted in an increased growth of tumor cells (15%). The results are remarkable since not only could a different biological response be observed by changing the mental image, but an actual reversal of the biological process of cell growth was achieved.

Experiment 2. ...Focused intent for the cells to return to the natural order of their normal growth rate produced the same inhibitory biological response (20% inhibition) as did imagery alone. When we included the intention for the cells to return to the natural order of the normal cell line together with the imagery of reduced growth, the inhibitory effect was doubled to 40%. These results suggest that imagery and intent each contributed equally in inhibiting the growth of tumor cells in culture.

...These results have important implications for healers. The results suggest that certain healing states and contents of consciousness are more effective than others. As mentioned above, however, we do not know to what extent these effects are target specific. It is possible that other interventions would have been effective if other biological endpoints were chosen. For example, treating the tissue culture medium with microcosmic orbit (41% inhibition) was equally as effective as treating it with returning the natural order, although the two focuses of consciousness were significantly different when treating the tumor cells directly. Alternatively, the content and states of consciousness that were effective in this experiment for Laskow, may not have been optimal for another healer treating the same tumor cells. Thus the results may be healer specific. These questions, however, are amenable to study using cultured cells in the protocol followed in this study. Future studies will in fact compare different states of consciousness with different biological experiments, albeit with one healer Leonard Laskow.

Experiment 3. The results indicated that water was in fact capable of storing and transferring the information associated with different contents of consciousness to the tumor cells. Thus water treated with the intention to return the cells to their natural order and harmony resulted in a 28% inhibition of cell growth, quite similar to that obtained when the cells were treated directly. Even more surprising, however, was the fact that two other focuses which were ineffective when the cells were treated directly, were effective when the water was treated. Thus unconditional love caused a 21% inhibition of growth and dematerializiation caused a 27% inhibition.

These results suggest that the efficacy of different focuses of consciousness depends on the target being healed. The data also suggest that water may be a more universal target. It is possible that pure water is more capable of picking up certain types of energy and information than cells. In other situations, with different environmental energy influences present, water may not store or release information. The practical application of this observation is that healers can give their clients water to drink which has been previously charged with their healing energy. This may also be the basis for blessing food and wine.

REIN demonstrated that non-Hertzian fields can have marked effects directly on biological systems (1988;1989:1991), on water (1990) and on biological systems via the water as a vehicle for the effect (1991).[3]

Rein also demonstrated that *LASKOW* could generate a specific magnetic field pattern from his hands when he was in a particular state of consciousness.[4]

Rein speculates that non-Hertzian energies may be a mechanism explaining some or all healing effects.[5]

Discussion

A. Rein has not published the data from Experiment 3 in his monograph, as he intends to submit them for publication in a refereed journal. The results appear highly significant.

It is fascinating to have a healer who can demonstrate different effects on biological systems with different states of consciousness and intent.

The studies of SPINDRIFT[6] appear to support this observation, which is often stressed by healers (e.g. LeSHAN 1974a).
B. Without the data to permit independent assessment of the significance of the results, one must suspend judgment upon these experiments.

REIN's experiments also bear replication, in his laboratory as well as in others, before conclusions may be reached on his hypotheses that states of consciousness or non-Hertzian waves are involved in healing. The differences observed in the various experiments may have reflected different moods or other states of being in Laskow or in the experimenters, as well as such extraneous factors as geomagnetic field fluctuations, sunspot activity, etc.[7] This is especially relevant because the experiments were conducted on one day weekly over many weeks, due to limitations on Laskow's availability to participate in the studies.

S. Baumann, J. Lagle and W. Roll – Preliminary results from the use of two novel detectors for psychokinesis *(Research in Parapsychology 1985)*

Pacemaker cells in the giant marine snail, *Aplysia californica*, are morphologically similar to human nerve cells. At regular intervals they emit action potentials at a steady rate.

Piezoelectric crystals connected to charge amplifiers have been used to test PK abilities of subjects in psi experiments (HASTED 1982; ISAACS 1982). Two crystals were used, one as the ostensible target for PK and the other as a control (hidden from view). A third, shielded capacitor (also hidden) was employed to detect random 'noise' from electric fields.

Both detectors were mounted side by side on a laboratory-grade vibration-damping table to decrease mechanical artifact. Subjects were asked to perturb the firing rate of the pacemaker neurons so there would be a statistically significant difference between interval lengths during target and control periods, or to perturb the piezoelectric target crystal so detectable signals would appear on the stripchart record.

Experiments were performed with seven individual subjects and two groups of subjects who attempted to influence the detectors, but preliminary analysis of the results has been completed on work done with only four subjects...

Experimental sessions with the pacemaker neurons were divided into target or control periods following an ABBA format in which either A or B was randomly selected as the target period.

Two different statistical methods (Student's t-test and the non-parametric Mann-Whitney U-test) were used for technical reasons to analyze the results. Where results were similar, only one 'p' value is mentioned.
Subject 1 (a parapsychologist): One out of three series with the pacemaker detector was significant ($p < 0.002$), with an *increase* in firing rate of the neuron despite the subject's aim to decrease it.
Subject 2 (a trance medium who claims she

Table I - 5. Healing effects on cells in the laboratory

Subject of Healing	Researchers	T/N/D*	Duration	Healers	Results	Significance
Red blood cells	Braud, Davis & Wood	9N; 1D	5 mins	Manning	Decreased rate of hemolysis 10 runs, 5 samples each	p< .001
	Braud (1988)	D	1 min	Unselected	32 volunteers each visualized protection to 10 tubes vs 10 controls	p< .00002
Mouse leukemia	Snel	N	?	Manning	1. Inhibiting growth: experimental and controls: all cells died	
		D	?		2. +39% Experimental vs control	p< .002
		N	?	Many people	3. +27.5% experimental vs control	.002 <p< .02
		D		Manning	4. -18.5% experimental vs control	.002 <p< .02
Cervical cancer cells	Kmetz (from Braud, Davis & Wood)	N&D	20 mins	Manning	Cells adhere to plastic surface of flask electro-statically: 200 -1,200% change	?
Snail pace-maker cells	Baumann, Lagle & Roll	N	?	Parapsy-chologist	1. 1/3 series: increased firing rate, despite intent to decrease it	p< .002
				Healer	2. 1/2 series: decreased rate	p< .01
				Healer	3. 1 series: decreased rate	p< .01
				RSPK agent	4. 4/4 series: decreased rate	.002 <p< .01
Chlamydo-monas engameba	Alexandrov (Zhukoborsky)	?	5 mins	6 healers	Protection from heat stress, perhaps tolerating 46 degrees vs 43 degrees)	?

* T/N/D: Touch/Near/Distant

can *'channel energy through her hands'):* One of two experiments with pacemaker cells was significant (p < 0.01).

Subject 3 (a woman claiming to channel energy through her hands): Her one experiment was significant (p < 0.01; p < 0.00006).

"The experiments on the piezoelectric detector were negative, although the same individual had apparently produced persistent, large-amplitude oscillations recorded on a prototype detector during pilot sessions two years earlier."

Subject 4 ("a teenage girl who had been the focus of ostensible RSPK activity for several months"): Four out of four experiments were significant:

Experiment 1: p < 0.01;   p < 0.000006;
Experiment 2: p < 0.002; p < 0.011;
Experiment 3: p < 0.002; p < 0.0000006;
Experiment 4: p < 0.01;   p < 0.009.
… The most striking instance of cell slowing occurred during a target period toward
the end of the first experiment when the
cell actually stopped firing for 23 seconds
and then recovered, to continue emitting
APs at its normal rate of about 1 Hz for another five minutes before it stopped firing
altogether.

Subject 4 also attempted four experimental sessions with the piezoelectric detector. She sat on a stool about two to six
feet in front of the detector, often with
both hands resting quietly on her legs. Although none of the sessions produced any
clear-cut effects isolated to the target
channel, large-amplitude oscillations on
both channels occurred when the subject
attempted to affect the detector. No such
oscillations ever occurred naturally, but
we could replicate these effects by tapping
in a certain orientation directly on the vibration-damping table. However, we have
no evidence to indicate that the subject
committed fraud during any of her time
spent in our laboratory.

Subject 4 was also the source of over 30
incidents of putative RSPK in the laboratory, most of which occurred between experimental sessions while the subject was
attempting to stay 'charged up' for the
next experiment.

Discussion

A. This paradigm seems most productive. If
healers can affect single cells significantly in
the laboratory they may equally be able to influence nerve cells in intact organisms. This
would provide access to a subject's nervous
system whereby far-reaching alterations in
psycho-physiological processes could be
produced.

The concomitant testing for subjects' abilities to influence living and nonliving systems is of great interest. Several healers have
also been noted PK adepts (e.g. KULAGINA;
MANNING).

B. This study was well done and well reported.

The experiments on cells are summarized in
Table I-5 (see page 143).

Healing Action on Fungi/Yeasts

Jean Barry – General and comparative study of the psychokinetic effect on a fungus culture *(Journal of Parapsychology 1968)*

Journal Abstract:

The objective of this research was to discover the effect of thought on the growth of a fungus. The fungus was cultured in petri dishes in a laboratory incubator, each subject being assigned five experimental and five control dishes. At each session, the dishes were placed 1.5 meters from the subject, who tried for 15 minutes to inhibit the growth in the experimental dishes while disregarding the controls. The results were measured by outlining the boundaries of the colonies on thin paper, cutting them out, and weighing them. If the total of the experimental dishes was less than that of the controls, the trial was a hit.

There were 10 subjects. Three to six subjects worked during a session, and there were nine sessions. Out of 39 trials, 33 were successes ($p < 0.001$). This success was consistent to an extra-chance degree: out of 11 subjects or combinations of subjects, 10 scored above chance ($p < 0.01$); and out of 194 experimental dishes, 151 were hits ($p < 0.001$).

Discussion

A. This highly significant study suggests yet another mechanism whereby healing might occur. Diseases may be cured if healers inhibit growth of infectious agents. The mechanism for inhibition of the disease agents needs further elucidation. Perhaps it is via inhibition of fungus enzyme activity. Other possibilities exist, such as alteration of cell membrane permeability, interference (other than enzymatic) with the use of nutrient media, and possibly other, unknown mechanisms.

B. This study appears sound. Barry gives us no clues as to the nature of healing employed.

William H. Tedder and Melissa L. Monty – Exploration of long distance PK: A conceptual replication of the influence on a biological system *(Research in Parapsychology 1980)*

These researchers studied effects of distant PK on the inhibition of growth of fungal cultures. One author handled the cultures and had no knowledge regarding the subjects or choice of experimental and control targets.

The other organized the PK subjects. Two groups of subjects participated. The first consisted of people familiar with the author; the second were volunteers who at best infrequently interacted with him. All were shown pictures of the target location. All were told to concentrate on the cultures in any way they wanted for at least 15 minutes daily, from a distance of up to 15 miles from the target area.

In examining overall results, Group 1 had 16 hits and no misses, producing a highly significant p = 0.00003... Collectively, the seven subjects produced a mean growth differential of −9.81 mm per trial, or almost −2 mm per dish over a total of 80 dishes ... This was ... highly significant ... (p = 0.00006) ... Group 2 finished with four hits, eleven misses, and three ties over the two series (p = 0.08) ... while the mean growth was non-significant.

The authors note that subjects concentrated consciously for 15 minutes daily. Assuming that growth inhibition occurred only during those periods and knowing the normal fungal growth rate to be 0.65 mm per hour, this would not account for the observed growth inhibition of −1.96 mm per trial. This suggests that either inhibition continued unconsciously between periods of conscious effort or that the fungus was appreciably 'affected' during the periods of conscious concentration by an unknown psi-induced mechanism and required a latency period before resuming a normal growth rate. Alteration of growth rate might have occurred by: extreme temperature change, enzyme degradation, chitin breakdown, etc.

The authors note that the second experimenter could conceivably have acted as the true agent in the PK effect. They express skepticism on this point because, if she were

the agent, she would have had to use super-psi to detect the above factors and then would have had to use her own PK to produce the observed results. The greater effectiveness of the first group may have been owing to greater rapport within the group or to an experimenter effect.

Discussion

A. This study demonstrates that distant healing can produce significant effects.

Aspects of the study require explanation. First, no mention is made of preclusion of approach by experimental subjects or by the second experimenter to the target area during the three days of fungal culture incubation. As the authors themselves note, unconscious PK may have been working during intervals between periods of conscious concentration. This places in question the magnitude of the distance effect under study, as one or more subjects may have at some time approached quite close to the target area. Second, the authors assume that the first experimenter (in charge of culture handling) would have had to perform a difficult psi task, probably of impossible complexity, in order to act as agent for the observed effects. SOLFVIN (1982) demonstrated that PK of the complexity required for the second experimenter to be the PK agent is possible.[8] Alternatively, the agents may have used the first experimenter as an auxiliary agent to themselves. That is, the distant agents may have telepathically directed the energies of the first experimenter to act locally on the cultures near her. Healers occasionally report they will do this, using friends, family and/or chance observers as 'proxies' to relay or augment their own healing powers. **B.** Excellent study, but again too scantily reported to permit independent analysis of the results.

Erlendur Haraldsson and Thorstein Thorsteinsson – Psychokinetic effects on yeast: An exploration experiment *(Research in Parapsychology 1972)*

Seven subjects were asked to increase the growth of yeast in a group of ten test tubes, without touching them. They were stored in the same place for 24 hours along with 10 control tubes. An experimenter who was 'blind' regarding the experimental and control tubes measured yeast growth in a colorimeter. In 12 sessions, 240 test tubes were run, half E and half C. "For purposes of analysis, each experimental tube was paired with a control tube used in the same session, and the yeast growth in the two tubes was compared."

Results were significantly in favor of the experimental tubes (p < 0.02). "Three of the subjects were engaged in healing, two as mental healers and one as a physician. The bulk of the positive scoring was done by these subjects (p = 0.00014) whereas the non-healers gave chance results."

Discussion
A. Significant increases in yeast growth were demonstrated with healing. The finding that practitioners of healing achieve better results than non-practitioners is common.
B. This report is too brief to permit proper evaluation. (See SNEL review in this chapter for a much better report on a similar study.) Many questions can be asked: Were precautions taken to ensure similar temperature for control and experimental tubes? Were tubes paired randomly? What accuracy of measurement was achieved? What range of error in measurements existed?

Bernard Grad: PK effects on fermentation of yeast *(Proceedings of the Parapsychological Association Meeting 1965)*

GRAD reports:

Eighteen bottles with sterile, vacuum-sealed 5% dextrose and normal saline solutions were arranged in six sets of three bottles per set. Five sets consisted of one bottle 'treated' by a man, another by a woman, and the third was untreated. The sixth set, the 'control', consisted of three untreated bottles. Treatment involved holding the bottles between the hands for 30 minutes. Each set was investigated as a separate experiment on a different day. A multiple-blind system was devised for scoring the results. This not only kept the experimenters ignorant of which bottles were treatment and which were controls, but in five out of six sets, which were treated sets and which, controls. In each experiment, 20 milliliters (ml) from each bottle were placed in each of 16 randomly selected fermentation tubes to which 5 ml of 20% yeast in solutions of 5% dextrose and 20 ml saline were added, and the rate of carbon dioxide production was measured 8 times over the next 5 1/2 to 6 hours. Statistically significant differences were observed in four out of five sets, three of these being significant to the level of p < 0.0005. In two cases, the differences were produced by female-treated solutions, and the third, by male. In the latter, 12 days elapsed between the time of treatment of the solution and its testing; in the other two cases, 5 and 23 days. The smallest difference in carbon dioxide production between the three bottles of any one set was observed in the control set.

Discussion

A. A highly significant effect was obtained, perhaps from a healing energy. The direction of the healing effect is not noted. (In personal communication, GRAD clarified that it was an increase in carbon dioxide.)

Again, information regarding subjects' objectives in conducting the experiment and also the experimenter's expectations would be worthwhile.

B. Insufficient data are presented in this brief report. Specific numbers are not cited for summarized measurements.

The next study on the influence of healing examines whether psychotics might have a *negative* effect on yeast growth via the mediation of water that they have held.

Carrol B. and Catherine S. Nash – Effect of paranormally conditioned solution on yeast fermentation *(Journal of Parapsychology 1967)*

The researchers state:

Each of 19 psychotics held a separate sealed glass bottle containing an aqueous solution of dextrose and sodium chloride for 30 minutes. Six ml of the solution in the bottle held by the psychotic was placed in each of 12 fermentation tubes, and 6 ml of a similar solution in a control bottle (held by no one) was placed in each of 12 other fermentation tubes. To each of the

24 tubes, 4 ml of a yeast suspension was added. The total amount of carbon dioxide produced in the 12 experimental tubes during an interval of approximately two hours was compared with the amount produced in the 12 control tubes.

The bottles were divided into groups on the basis of how long after they were held by the psychotics they were tested, i.e. within two weeks and from two to six weeks. While the results are only marginally significant and have not been corrected for selection, they suggest the inhibition of yeast fermentation by a solution when held by psychotics, the deterrent effect of the solution lasting for approximately two weeks after being held.

Discussion

A. This brief report hints at many interesting points. Assuming there may be some legitimacy to the trend noted, one must look for answers to such questions as: (1) Can emotional states of humans affect life system processes in organisms outside themselves? (2) Can an aqueous solution of dextrose and sodium chloride be a vehicle for negative energy to bring about (1) above? (3) Are there agent-factors other than the participants' emotional state that could account for the results? (See GRAD 1967, on the effects of saline held by depressed people on plant growth, reviewed below.)

B. This study also presents insufficient detail. One would want to know exact numbers or units of measurements observed; specific statistics used and what the authors consider 'marginally significant'; diagnoses of the psychotics; information on the degree and nature of understanding and co-operation of the participants in the study; attitudes and expectations of subjects and experimenters; and more.[9]

Harold A. Cahn and Noel Muscle – Toward standardization of 'laying-on' of hands investigation *(Psychoenergetic Systems 1976)*

The researchers describe a technique in which a culture of baker's yeast, *Saccharomyces cerevesiae,* is poisoned with cyanide. This inhibits oxygen consumption and thus provides a system which a healer can influence. Connecting the flask of yeast to a manometer allows one to observe changes in oxygen uptake, with feedback on healing effects obtained within seconds.

CAHN/MUSCLE prescribe precise procedures for setting up this apparatus.

In a pilot study with a female 'psychic healer' they write:

> ... The overall effect is clear: both the slope and cumulative ten minute readings for the 'hands on' interval is greater than for either the pre-run or post-run controls. Statistically, only the difference in cumulative uptake between the pre-run and 'hands on' run is significant ... (p < 0.02).
>
> Examination of the graph will reveal an interesting anomaly. The first four minutes of the post-run series is nearly identical with those of the 'hands on' series. Could this be due to a residual effect of 'laying-on' of hands? ...

Discussion

A. While showing a significant influence of psi healing, this report presents a method

wherein immediate feedback of in-vivo effects of healing can be obtained. This could prove valuable in showing the effectiveness of healing; exploring further some of the biochemical mechanisms involved in healing; providing feedback to student healers; and testing whether someone has healing abilities.

For more on 'linger effects' of healing (on anaesthetized mice) see studies of WATKINS/WATKINS/WELLS; WELLS/WATKINS, reviewed below.

B. Well-done study, but raw data again not provided in sufficient detail.

Savely Zhukoborsky – An experimental approach to the study of psychic healing *(Parapsychology in the USSR, Part III, 1981)*

SAVELY ZHUKOBORSKY, a Soviet engineer, now lives in the United States. He reports several experiments on healers performed in Leningrad in 1975-1977. NINA KULAGINA, one of the healers studied, is highly gifted with a variety of PK abilities.

1. DR. TONU RIKHOVICH SOIDLA at Leningrad State University discovered that some yeast cultures appeared to be sensitive to the influence of the hands of laboratory personnel who worked with petri dishes with the cultures.

> During the tests, the quantity of spores in the field of vision of the microscope was calculated. (As is known, yeasts propagate themselves in two ways – sporulation and mitosis.) The increase in quantity of spores due to the influence varied from 20% to 80% depending on the kind of culture and on the person who held the dishes in his hands... I proposed to Dr. Soidla to

conduct experiments with Kulagina using this culture to find out the kinetics of the influence. Twelve petri dishes were prepared. Three were used as controls, one was treated by Alexander Sh. (20 seconds), one by the author (20 seconds), and seven were treated by Kulagina during various periods of time – from 15 seconds to 1.5 minutes. A subject held a petri dish with the culture between his palms trying to exert some energy influence. Afterwards samples from all 12 dishes were analyzed by the usual method – calculating the average quantity of spores in the field of vision.

Three control dishes showed 11 +/- 3. The dish which was influenced by Alexander Sh. showed 18, and treated by the author – 20.

Kulagina's graphed results show a peak of 26 in 20 seconds, returning to baseline at 40 seconds, and slightly below baseline thereafter. The following conclusions were made:

* For the given yeast culture, which is notable for its high mutability, the effect of the bioenergy influence does exist.

* The optimal time of influence for Kulagina is 20–30 seconds.

It was an impression that Kulagina's influence intensified both mechanisms of reproduction, although first sporulation increased more actively then mitosis. However, our methodology did not permit us to verify this assumption.

With another culture which had less mutability, in which verification of re-establishing the lysine synthesis function was attempted, the effect was not found.

2. Dr. Vladimir Yakovlevich Alexandrov of

the Botanical Institute of the *Academy of Sciences of the U.S.S.R.* studied the recovery of bacterial and cell cultures after trauma of heat stress.

Before these tests, the laboratory studied the influence of a temperature shock (5-minute influence of temperature from 34 to 43 degrees C) on biological organisms *Chlamydomonas engameba* and epidermal cells of *Tradiscentia flaminensis* leaves. As a result of the study, the time duration for re-establishing the moving activity of the organism after the temperature shock within the previously stated temperature limits was well known. The duration varied from 10 to 20 minutes when the samples had been subjected to a temperature of 34 degrees C, to 48 hours when the shock was produced by a temperature of 43 degrees C. When the higher temperature was applied, the moving activity was not re-established, and the organisms died.

The tests were conducted as follows: Samples of the organisms in water subjected previously to a temperature shock under various temperatures, were divided into test and control samples. There were 20 test samples which were subjected to biofield influence by 6 individuals who possessed healing abilities (Yuri Linnik, Anatoly Shimansky, Alexander Sh., David Flaks, Savely Zhukoborsky, Lyubov Zhukoborskaya). The influence (with mental concentration or laying on of hands on a flask with the organisms) varied from 3 to 20 minutes. Afterwards the time of recuperation of test samples was recorded and compared to that of control samples.

Significant differences in time of recuperation between test and control samples

Table I - 6. Healing effects on fungus and yeasts

Subject of healing	Researchers	T/N/D*	Duration	Healers	Results	Significance
Fungus	Barry	N	15 mins	10 healers	5 dishes each - to decrease growth	
					Decreased in 33/39 trials	p< .001
					Decreased by 10/11 subjects	
					(some combined efforts)	p< .01
					Decreased in 151/194 dishes	p< .001
Fungus	Tedder & Monty	D	Minimum 5-15 mins/day	7 healers	3 sess/wk, 3 X/sess, 5 cultures/trial	
					Grp. 1. Familiar with researcher - 16/16 with 80 dishes,	
					decreased almost 2 mm/dish	p< .00006
					Grp. 2. Unknown to or infrequent interactions with researchers -	
					4 hits; 11 misses; 3 ties	p< .08
Fungus	Soidla (in Zhukoborsky)	T/N	20 secs	Kulagina	Increased nos. of spores:	
					26 vs. control: 11+/-3	?
			40 secs		Return to baseline	?
			20 secs	Alex. Sh.	18 spores	?
			20 secs	Zhuko-borsky	20 spores	?
Yeast	Haraldsson & Thorsteinson	N	?	3 healers, 4 'others'	10 test tubes each, 12 sessions:	
					Combined results	p< .02
					Healers	p< .0004
					Non-healers	NS**
Yeast	Grad (1965)	T/N vehicle	30 mins	2 healers	CO_2 production in 16 test tubes; 3/5 sets	p< .0005
Yeast	Cahn & Muscle	T/N	10 mins	Healer	Oxygen production after cyanide poisoning of yeast culture:	
					Rate increased with healing	p< .02
Yeast	Nash & Nash	T/N	30 mins	19 psychotics	12 fermentation tubes each to inhibit	Marginal

* T/N/D: Touch/Near/Distant **NS: Non-Significant

were not found. The only surprising fact for physiologists was that both treated and control samples appeared to be resistant to a temperature of 46 degrees C, i.e., 3 degrees higher than was ever observed.

A few comments should be mentioned in relation to this negative result:

a) One cannot exclude that the temperature influence which causes direct denaturation of protein molecules, is not a typical (natural) case of disruption of physio-logical functions, and therefore, the human biofield appeared to be non-specific for intensifying the recuperative function.

b) The samples of organisms were located in a large amount of water which could prevent direct influence of the human biofield.

c) It is quite possible that the biofields of human beings and unicellular organisms do not interact with each other due to large homologous differences.

Discussion

A. The use of yeast budding as a measure of healing effects is unique. Yeast budding has been extensively studied in connection with *mitogenetic radiation*[10] It is unclear as yet just what this effect represents. The growth curve of Kulagina's effects on yeast buds can be interpreted in many ways. Excessive healing could create a negative effect. (*KULAGINA* produced a skin burn with her healing during an experiment, reviewed in Chapter I-2.) Alternatively, the yeast culture may simply be

exhausted from exceeding its capacity to reproduce without overextending certain metabolic processes or using up nutrients in the culture medium needed for growth and reproduction.

Again in these experiments it would be useful to know the intention of the healers in their activities. If Kulagina's purpose was primarily to increase budding, the implications could be different from those where she intended to heal or help the yeast, or where she was merely 'turning on the energy'.

Procedures in the second experiment are insufficiently described to evaluate the results. The survival of cell cultures in higher than usual temperatures during the experiment suggests that there may have been a general healing effect on all samples. (See SNEL experiment, this chapter, for comparison.)

B. Specific numbers are not provided in the summaries of these experiments for independent evaluation of the significance of the effects.

The experiments on fungi and yeasts are summarized in Table I-6 (see page 151).

Healing Action on Bacteria

Carroll B. Nash – Psychokinetic control of bacterial growth (*Journal of the Society for Psychical Research 1982*)

Journal Abstract:

The experiment was conducted to determine whether the growth of the bacterium *Escherichia coli* can be psychokinetically accelerated and decelerated during a 24-hour period with subjects not known to be psychically gifted. Each of 60 subjects was tested in a single run consisting of a set of three tubes of bacterial culture to be growth-promoted, a set of three to be growth-inhibited, and a set of three to serve as controls. The growth was greater in the promoted tubes than in either the controls or the inhibited tubes... $p < 0.05$. Post hoc correlations between the three treatments for the 60 subjects yielded the following results... between promoted and inhibited tubes... $p < 0.001$... between inhibited and control tubes... $p < 0.02$. Post hoc analyses showed that the intersubject variance in growth was (1) greater between the three treatments than within them... $p < 0.05$, and (2) greater in both the promoted and the inhibited tubes than in the controls, with $p < .01$ in each case.

The results are interpreted to indicate that bacterial growth was psychokinetically accelerated in some of the tubes intended for growth promotion and psychokinetically retarded in some of the tubes intended for growth inhibition.

Discussion
A. It is particularly interesting that the subjects who were not known to be healers produced highly significant healing results. This supports the belief generally held by healers that most people possess a modicum of healing ability.
B. This is an excellent study, rigorously performed and adequately reported.

Fong Li-Da – The effects of external Qi on bacterial growth patterns (*China Qi Gong Magazine 1985*)

Researchers studied the ability of a *Qi Gong* master, adept at producing external *Qi*, to enhance or retard the growth of bacteria. The master was handed sets of three test tubes with cultures of *Escherichia coli* bacteria. He held the control tube without intending to do anything with it, then placed it aside. He attempted to kill all the bacteria in the second tube by projecting *lethal Qi* for one minute.

He projected *health-promoting external Qi* to the bacteria in the third tube.

Results in 'over forty repetitions' of the experiment reportedly showed:

1. *Lethal Qi* reduced the numbers of bacteria by 50% or more.
2. *Health-promoting Qi* increased the numbers of bacteria by 700 – 1,000%.

Discussion
A. This study is in line with western research.
B. It is regrettable that insufficient details are provided to allow proper independent evaluation of the study.

William C. Leikam – A pilot study on the psychic influence of E. coli bacteria
(Unpublished report)

WILLIAM LEIKAM trained 23 high-school students 'to enter light trance through a standard relaxation response'. Using double-blind procedures, he studied their abilities to influence the growth of *E. coli* bacteria psychically.

> In all there were three sets of bacteria with twelve cuvettes per set for a total of thirty-six. One set was used as the control, a second used as the visual experimental set, and the third as the remote experimental set. In the case of the visual set subjects were allowed to directly view the *E. coli* bacteria, while with the remote set the subjects did not know where the bacteria were located, save that it was in the science laboratory some fifty meters distant.
>
> Each cuvette was numbered from one through thirty-six. Each subject was assigned a specific cuvette, except in one case where a subject influenced two. The control

> set went unassigned so that there could be no influence subjected to that set... Five of these subjects formed the visual group who were able to see the bacteria in the cuvettes...
>
> The process of influencing the growth of the bacteria proceeded for a period of four days. Each day at the same time a laboratory assistant took readings of all thirty-six cuvettes and recorded the data. Readings were taken on a Spectrometer 20... Taking into account the standard deviation of each set the calculations showed that in the remote set there was an increased growth over the control set of 3.2%, and in the visual set an increased growth of 7.5% over the control.

Leikam claims that the results were statistically significant, though he does not provide data to back this claim.

Discussion
A. Again it is nice to see that healing can apparently be taught.
B. It is unfortunate that this report is so brief, precluding a better assessment of its results. It is also perplexing to read that there were five students in the visual group but 12 cuvettes and that each cuvette was influenced by one student.

Elizabeth A. Rauscher and Beverly A. Rubik – Human volitional effects on a model bacterial system
(Psi Research 1983)

RAUSCHER/RUBIK studied the effects of the laying-on-of-hands by the well-known healer, OLGA WORRALL, on the growth and motility of *Salmonella typhimurium* bacteria.

Worrall held her hands near the bacteria for two minutes but did not touch them. The bacteria had been treated with chemicals to retard either their growth or their motility. Motility was measured under a microscope and growth of cultures with a spectrophotometer.

The results

1. Motility was totally inhibited by phenol in C sample after 1-2 minutes, while 7% of the healer-treated samples remained motile after 12 minutes.

2. Healing treatments of bacteria growing in normal (untreated) cultures showed enhanced growth if the treatment was given in the bacterial life phase of active growth (mid-logarithmic growth phase). There was no difference between treated and control samples if healing was carried out in an earlier growth phase (lag phase). RAUSCHER/RUBIK speculate that this could be explained in the following way:

> … in lag phase, conditions are optimal for growth, i.e., no bacterial wastes have accumulated; in logarithmic phase, the culture medium may be less than optimum, since bacterial wastes have accumulated. Thus, the difference in the results obtained between these two different experiments may be significant, indicating the possibility of an optimum state of health for bacteria beyond which healer intervention has little or no effect.

3. In bacteria inhibited with antibiotics a consistent dose-response effect was found. Healing produced a greater differential in the growth rate between E and C samples when the dose of antibiotics was lower. The aim of the healer was to protect the bacteria from the antibiotics.

4. To rule out warming of the cultures by the healer's hands as a factor in the results, a non-healer held test tubes of bacteria. No difference was noted between C and E samples.

5. An analysis of the results with different antibiotics may provide clues regarding mechanisms for healing.

> … the validity curve characteristics differ for the two different antibiotics. For tetracycline, at all times the healer-treated cultures have more bacterial survivors than controls, but for chloramphenicol, at small generation times the control cultures have apparently more bacterial survivors. Then, at large generation times in chloramphenicol, the healer-treated cultures have more bacterial survivors than controls. The chloramphenicol viability curves exhibit a 'cross-over' effect that is not observed for the tetracycline viability curves. The specificity of these results assures that the phenomena are real and may lead to the elucidation of a mechanism of healer action on the bacteria in the presence of the antibiotics. Since both chloramphenicol and tetracycline inhibit protein synthesis (by somewhat different mechanisms, however), the cross-over effect is especially significant.

6. The researchers further explored possible mechanisms for healing.

> Several experiments conducted using bacteria in the presence of 0.05 M sodium nitrate, a chemical mutagen which attacks DNA and leads to mutant bacteria, were performed. Olga Worrall's treatment of cultures with mutagen led to a decrease in viability over control cultures. Healer treatment of cultures with mutagen and antibiotic present led to an enhancement of culture growth over controls, both for chloramphenicol and tetracycline treated samples.

These results may be reconciled by the fact that mutagens have mostly a neutral or negative effect upon bacteria unless they are under stress to survive, as for example in the presence of antibiotic. Then, a mutagen may provide a possibility for generating resistance to the drug, by accelerated production of resistant mutants. From this limited data, it appears that Worrall's treatment accelerates the mutation rate of the bacteria in the presence of nitrite. However, a study was conducted to observe whether Worrall's treatment upon a methionine auxotroph (bacterial mutant unable to synthesize the amino acid methionine, necessary for growth) would lead to mutations enabling the strain to survive in the absence of methionine. No significant growth of this mutant was observed for the treated samples over controls. Thus, the simple explanation that the healer treatment accelerates the mutation rate seems insufficient. Further work is needed to clarify the role of mutability in the healer intervention process.

Discussion

A. These experiments begin to tease out possible mechanisms for aspects of the healing process.

Worrall related that she had been asked to kill bacteria as part of the experiment. She refused to do so, feeling that a negative use of healing on her part could have unknown consequences, possibly extending to negative effects on healees receiving distant healing from her.

B. Unfortunately, the published report lacks details of data, procedures and statistical analyses to allow readers to evaluate the results independently. Drawing more than very tentative conclusions from these experiments prior to their replication is premature. The variability of healer effects or other factors may have contributed significantly to the results in addition to (or rather than) the proposed differences in bacteria or antibiotics.

The next study demonstrates yet another possible mechanism for healing: alteration of genetic factors in bacteria. CARROLL NASH explored the possibility that healing might alter the rates of bacterial mutation. This is a logical possibility according to STANFORD's conformance theory, which postulates that PK may work better on systems with elements in a state of random flux.[11]

Carroll B. Nash – Test of psychokinetic control of bacterial mutation *(Journal of the American Society for Psychical Research 1984)*

Journal Abstract:

Three experimenters each tested 20 subjects not known to be psychically gifted. Because of procedural errors, results were obtained for only 52 subjects. Each subject was tested in a single run with a separate set of nine tubes of a mixed culture of lac-negative and lac-positive strains of *Escherichia Coli* (bacteria). Mutation of lac-negative to lac-positive was mentally promoted in three of the tubes, mentally inhibited in three, and three of the tubes served as controls. The mutant ratio of lac-positive to total bacteria was greater in the promoted than in the inhibited tubes, with... $p < 0.005$; less in the inhibited tubes than in the controls, with ... $p < 0.02$; and greater in the promoted tubes than in the controls, although not significantly so. The results are inter-

Table I - 7. Healing effects on bacteria

Subject of healing	Resear-chers	T/N/D*	Dura-tion	Healers	Results	Signifi-cance
Bacteria E. coli	Nash (1982)	D	?	60 subjects	9 test tubes each 3 to increase vs controls vs decrease 3 to decrease vs controls 3 controls - left alone	p< .05 p< .001 p< .02
	Fong	?	?	Qi Gong masters	Healing increased growth 700-1,000 % Killing decreased growth 50%	? ?
	Leikam	N	?	23 students	Near: Increased 7.5% vs control Distant: Increased 3,2% vs control	? ?

Salmonella typhimurium	Rauscher & Rubik	T/N	2 mins	Olga Worrall	**1.** Phenol inhibition of motility
					     Healed: 93% inhibited in 12 mins
					     Controls: 100% inhibited in 2 mins
						
						?
						?

					2. Increased growth during active
					     (mid-log.) growth phase
					     NR of growth during inactive
					     (lag) phase
						
						?
						
						?

					3. Protecting bacteria from antibiotics
					     (by dose)
					     Tetracycline 1mcg: +121%
					                              10 mcg: +28%
					     Chloramphenicol10 mcg: +70%
					                              100mcg: +22%
						
						?
						?
						?
						?

					4. Controls hand-warmed by non-healer: + 0%	

					5. Tetracycline:
					     more survivors at all times
					     Chloramphenicol: at small generation
					     times, Controls grow better; at large
					     generation times, healed grow better
						
						?
						
						?

					6. Sodium nitrate .05 M.
					     (mutagen attacking DNA)
					     decreases viability: - 50%
					     Sodium nitrate + antibiotic increases
					     growth:
					     Tetracycline: $\pm$ 50 %
					     Chlormaphenicol: + 75 %
						
						?
						
						?
						?

Bacterial mutation (growth?) E. coli	Nash (1982)	D	?	52 ungifted volunteers	Promotion of mutation from lac negative
					to lac positive; inhibition of same;
					Controls: 3 test tubes each
					   Promoted vs inhibited
					   Inhibited vs controls
					   Promoted vs controls
						
						p< .005
						p< .02
						NS**

* T/N/D: Touch/Near/Distant   **NS: Non-Significant

preted to suggest that the rate of bacterial mutation was psychokinetically affected.

Careful blinds were instituted to preclude sensory awareness of lab workers to which tubes were selected for which conditions. One experimenter told the subjects to open the envelope instructing them on which tubes were particular target tubes after they left the laboratory, while the other two experimenters asked the subjects to open their envelopes in the laboratory. The latter subjects had greater success in promoting the mutant ratio, while the former performed better at inhibiting the mutant ratio in the appropriate tubes.

NASH points out that another explanation for the overall observed effects could be a differential in the growth rates of the two strains rather than in the mutation rates. The results are therefore only suggestive of a PK effect on bacterial mutation.

Discussion
A. This study suggests how healing could help the body fight off infections of pathogenic organisms as well as promote growth of benign organisms that normally grow in the body.
B. This is a carefully designed, executed and reported experiment.

The experiments on bacteria are summarized in Table I-7 (see page 157).

Let us now proceed to the controlled studies on plants.

Healing Action on Plants

L et us digress briefly to set the stage for the review of healing effects on plants. To appreciate these we should consider recent research suggesting that plants are more than passive organisms responding automatically to water, light and other physical factors in the environment. There are indications that plants may possess a measure of sentience which overlaps that of animals.

PETER TOMPKINS/CHRISTOPHER BIRD present the broadest summary of reports that look at plants as more than inanimate objects. They include LUTHER BURBANK's work, which seemed to demonstrate genetic changes in a cactus that led to the development of a specimen without spines (BENOR 1988).

CLEVE BACKSTER explored the responsiveness of plants to animal and human actions and thoughts. He used a lie-detector apparatus to measure electrical resistance in plant leaves. Plants reacted to the presence of their owners, to intense human emotions, mental threats by humans, the death of brine shrimp in the room and other emotional situations.

ROBERT BRIER and MARCEL VOGEL each repeated these experiments with positive results, while KENNETH HOROWITZ ET AL. and KMETZ (1975; 1977) replicated them with negative results. Others have done such studies, with mixed results.[12]

LYALL WATSON describes some loosely performed experiments he carried out several times, demonstrating sentience in plants (1975). He arranged for one of six persons to destroy one of a pair of plants. Using a polygraph-type measure of the surviving plant's electrical potential, he found that it reacted to the presence of the 'murderer' but not to that of the other five individuals.[13]

VOGEL (1974) reviews a series of 38 such reports, including non-controlled studies. He comments on his own experience in such investigations, noting the difficulty in obtaining stable electrical baselines for plant recordings until the experimenter establishes a thought-link with the plants. Once this is done, either by concentrating or meditating, the plant seems to respond more to the experimenter than to random environmental variables.[14]

SHEILA OSTRANDER/LYNN SCHROEDER include a chapter on plants in a general review of psi discoveries. They provide qualitative descriptions of Burbank's work with plants, including his conversations with cacti and his reassurances to them that they had nothing to fear – as he was coaxing them to grow without spines. They also mention a practical application of plant psi-receptivity. A plant can be used as a transducer to translate telepathic messages to the plant into electrical impulses, thus allowing an experimenter to turn on an electrical switch mentally.

HOYT EDGE placed plants close to a RNG,

which was in turn hooked up to a series of lights in such a way that they were lit randomly half of the time (1976). She found that when the plants were present the lights were lit either more or less of the time by a very significant margin from the expected 50 percent demonstrated by the RNG when not connected to lights in the presence of plants.

Discussion   The studies conducted by Backster, Vogel and Brier suggest that plants have sentience and respond to animal and human actions, emotions and thoughts. They demonstrate responsiveness in altered surface electrical activity. This is very similar to how humans react physiologically to emotional factors, with a change in electrical skin resistance.

Why Horowitz et al. and Kmetz obtained negative results with similar studies is a mystery. As psi powers of telepathy and/or PK are involved, a possible explanation is that some plants do not demonstrate such abilities, just as some humans do not. Experimenter effects may be present here, although in some studies attempts were made to preclude them by the experimenters' absenting themselves from the vicinity of the apparatus during the experiment. Super-ESP combined with 'sheep' vs. 'goat' attitudes might be relevant. Whether such effects might have been present to produce the positive or the negative results is not clear because critical details of experimenters' attitudes to psi are not reported. Both are possible. Watson's game of 'murder' with plants seems to confirm and extend the findings of the above studies.

Edge adds a dimension to our appreciation of plant sentience. Her experiment indicates that plants can affect their environment, producing favorable conditions for their growth in some instances. Why they would selectively evoke apparently unfavor-

able conditions of darkness is unclear.

I am personally impressed that the weight of the evidence above is in favor of plant sentience.

The implications for healing research are important. We must be aware that plants can be participants in their responses to healings just as animals can. We cannot assume their responsiveness reflects solely the healers' inputs. The reports by Burbank and Sauvin of apparent genetic engineering by PK suggest another area where psi may be effective. According to Stanford's conformance theory, the genetic pool would be a reasonably random system which the subject's intention could affect through PK (Benor 1988). Carroll Nash (1984) and William Cox conducted studies that seem to support this conjecture.

We must heed the words of Luther Burbank:

In pursuing the study of any of the universal and everlasting laws of nature, whether relating to the life, growth, structure and movements of a giant planet, the tiniest plant or of the psychological movements of the human brain, some conditions are necessary before we can become one of nature's interpreters or the creator of any valuable work for the world. Preconceived notions, dogmas and all personal prejudice and bias must be laid aside. Listen patiently, quietly and reverently to the lessons, one by one, which Mother Nature has to teach... She conveys her truths only to those who are passive and receptive. Accepting these truths as suggested, wherever they may lead, then we have the whole universe in harmony with us. At last man has found a solid foundation for science, having discovered that he is part of a universe which is eternally unstable in form, eternally immutable in substance.

well controlled, with procedures and data reported in satisfactory detail.

Bernard Grad – Some biological effects of the 'laying on of hands': A review of experiments with animals and plants *(Journal of the American Society for Psychical Research 1965)*[15]

Barley seeds, damaged by watering with 1% saline solution, were divided into E and C groups. Saline was used to damage the plants so that there would be a greater chance that a healing effect would be evident. The healer could significantly mitigate the subsequent retardant effect of the saline on plant growth by holding the beaker of saline with which the plants were initially watered ($p < .001$).

The experiment was repeated three times, with results in the same direction: $p < .05$ and $p < .02$. The E group of plants were a darker green, suggesting higher chlorophyll content.

Discussion

A. These significant plant experiments suggest the healer either influenced the saline solution in a manner that mitigated its damaging effect on seeds; affected the water in such a way that the damaging effect was counteracted with a positive result (separate and distinct from the negative effect), which was transferred as healing energy in the water; or made a connection between himself and the seeds via the water and then acted by distant healing on the plants. It is unclear whether this is an example of a healing effect or a prevention of injury. (I have termed the water a 'vehicle' for healing on the table.)[16]

B. Grad's studies are carefully done and are

Tony Scofield and David Hodges – Demonstration of a healing effect in the laboratory using a simple plant model *(Journal of the Society for Psychical Research* 1991)

TONY SCOFIELD/DAVID HODGES, lecturers in animal physiology at Wye College, London University, studied the effects of healings by *GEOFF BOLTWOOD* on cress seeds. The seeds were stressed by soaking overnight in half saturated saline solution, which ordinarily lengthens the time required for germination. Six experiments were performed. In each, a number of seeds were placed in Boltwood's right hand after he washed his hands. He held them either with or without the intent to heal, covering them with his other hand, for two minutes. Seeds were washed before and after his intervention.

In each experiment, 120 seeds from each of the E and C treatments were selected and placed on damp filter paper, 15 seeds to each of 8 covered plastic dishes. A regular pattern of placement permitted ready assessment of growth over 5-6 days, until leaves were pressing against the dish covers. The 16 dishes were kept under controlled conditions. Assessments were made daily, using a 9 point rating scale, including half-point scorings. (See Table I-8.) The average of ratings for the 15 seeds in each plate were used in calculations.

Careful blinds were instituted. The healing was supervised by Scofield, who took care to observe Boltwood constantly to prevent substitution of seeds. This would have been difficult in any case, as the wet seeds formed a sticky clump. Assessments were made by Hodges. A third experimenter randomized seeds and coded the plates.

In addition to the stressed, treated control, control sets of seeds soaked in distilled water and others soaked in saline were run in parallel with E sets. In some experiments Boltwood held the E seeds first, in others the C seeds first.

In a seventh experiment treatment was for two minutes to water which was used to soak the seeds for two minutes, rather than treating the seeds directly. In a final experiment the entire procedure was filmed.

... In the healing group, the seeds generally germinated quickly and then grew and developed steadily in a balanced way, such that an initial rapid root growth was followed by an even development of both root and shoot. By Day 5 the majority of seedlings in the healing group possessed cotyledons at Stage 8—9 and roots

3–4 cms long or even longer... the non-healing group was much more irregular both between separate seeds within a dish and between subsequent assessment days with individual seeds.

... abnormalities that manifested regularly in the stressed, non-healing group seeds, other than simply a slower rate of germination and development, were as follows:

1. Short stumpy roots...
2. A difficulty in releasing cotyledons from the seed coats in some later-germinating seeds resulting in leaves... and sometimes roots... being trapped and even distorted.
3. Deep green cotyledons, blue- to purple-green rather than a true 'leaf-green', supported by a shortened shoot.

... difficulties of assessment in the non-healing group resulted in a positive bias in favour of these seedlings.

... in the non-healing group in all the experiments there was a higher rate of infection.

Table I - 8. Rating scale for seed sprouting

0	Dry seeds prior to soaking / stressing. Colour dark brown.
1.	Seeds swollen to about three times original diameter, seed coat coloured pale brown. Well-developed, transparent mucilaginous coat. Overall dimensions about 5 x 6 mm.
2.	Root swollen to the point where it splits the seed coat along its length and extends 0.5-1 mm beyond the end of the seed.
3.	Root about 2-3 mm long, turning downwards and splitting out of a surrounding sheath.
4.	Root about 4-6 mm long or even longer. Root hairs developing.
5.	Pale green cotyledon leaves breaking out from the seed coat.*
6.	Shoot plus leaves fully released from the seed coat and beginning to grow upwards. Leaves tightly folded together and bent over in the form of a 'crook'.
7.	The stem has straightened out; the leaves are deep green but are still partly folded together.
8.	The seedling growing with the leaves well open.**
9.	Seedling leaves fully opened and growing in size.

* After Stage 5 the assessment concentrates upon shoot and leaf growth. However, the root continues to grow, often to a length of 3 - 4 cm.

** At about Stage 8 the upward growth of the seedlings was often impeded by the Petri dish lid. Because of this, assessments were not continued beyond Stage 9.

The normal appearance of a fully-hydrated seed, after soaking in either saline or distilled water... appears to be plump and smooth-surfaced and is surrounded by a well-developed mucilaginous coat. Details of the root, shoot and cotyledons are clearly visible through the seed coat... After healing many of the seeds were dried up, closely resembling dry seeds from a freshly-opened packet; others retained a developed mucilaginous coat, whilst the remainder seemed to be partly, patchily dried...

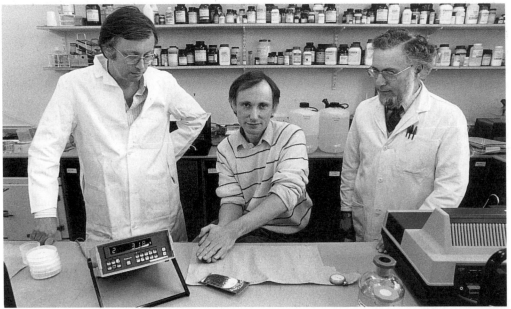

Fig. I-6. Tony Scofield, Geoff Boltwood and David Hodges study the sprouting of cress seeds, which may commence within minutes of a healing treatment.

Photographs by Barry Marsden

The rate of germination of treated seeds was often nearly double that of the control seeds. In Experiment 1 this reached statistical significance at p < 0.05; in the Experiments 2–6, p < 0.0001 or less.

Unstressed seeds grew more rapidly and more robustly than stressed, healed seeds. Unstressed seeds which were given treatment germinated significantly more rapidly on the first day than unstressed, untreated seeds. Thereafter the differences were not significant.

Temperatures in Boltwoods' hand were measured during two non-healing and two healing sessions. Variations were in the range of 2 degrees Celsius.

In non-controlled demonstrations, Boltwood was able to markedly accelerate the germination of unstressed cress seeds by holding them in his hand for two to five minutes. Roots up to 2 cm and sometimes shoots with leaves appeared. This would normally require 24–48 hours or longer.

Discussion

A. This study was rigorously run and the results were highly significant.

I have myself observed Boltwood sprouting cress seeds in his hand. I took care to watch that his hand was always in view from the time he grasped the seeds until he opened his hand to show the sprouted seeds, and I am convinced this is a genuine phenomenon.

The finding that significant results were not obtained when the experiment was videotaped has been reported in other psi studies.

The drying out of some of the seeds may be similar to the dessicating effects with fruit, fish and meat reported by CASSOLI; GRAD, reviewed in Chapter IV-3.

B. This study was rigorously performed with the exception that seeds were not marked to preclude substitution by Boltwood with sleight-of-hand techniques. The fact that no significant results were obtained when videotaping was introduced suggests caution in accepting the results.

R.G. MacDonald, H.S. Dakin, and J.L. Hickman – Preliminary physical measurements of psychophysical effects associated with three alleged psychic healers (Research in Parapsychology 1976)

Three well-known healers were studied: REV. JOHN SCUDDER (J.S.), DEAN KRAFT (D.K.), and OLGA WORRALL (O.W.). Under double-blind conditions, sterile saline in sealed bottles was treated by the healers, then used to water 16 identical sterile peat pots, each containing five rye grass seeds. An identical number of pots and seeds was watered with untreated saline. All pots were randomly distributed close together to ensure equivalent conditions of ambient air and sunlight. Following the initial watering with saline, each pot was daily watered with 15 ml distilled water.

The results of the experiment were as follows:

With D.K., only data from days 9, 10, and 11 were analyzed. On the previous days the plant growth was too scarce for comparison, and on the following days the plants had grown so tall that the shoots began to break. Data from the plants treated by O.W. were analyzed only on days 15, 16, 17, and 18 for the same reasons. On some of the days analyzed, the total and mean heights of the plants treated by D.K. were significantly less than those of the control group: total height on day 9 $p < 0.05$; mean height day 9 $p < 0.02$; mean height day 10 $p < 0.001$. The total end mean heights of the treated group were on the average 15 percent and 17 percent less than the heights of the control group, respectively. There was no difference between the number of sprouted seeds in each pot on the three days analyzed.

The total and mean heights of O.W.'s experimental plants were sometimes significantly greater than those of the control group: total height day 15 $p < 0.05$; total height day 16 $p < 0.05$; mean height day 17 $p < 0.05$; total height day 18 $p < 0.05$. The total and mean heights of the treated group were on the average 27 percent and 18 percent greater than the heights of the control group, respectively. She had little influence on the number of sprouted seeds in each pot...

No significant differences were noted with plants of J.S.

Discussion

A. The language and content of the report suggest the authors are skeptical regarding healing. Despite this, significant effects were found. Kraft's negative results with plants warrant questioning of Kraft as to his attitudes towards plants. (He is the healer who killed a rat in attempting to influence its heart rate.)
B. Data are too scanty to permit independent judgment of these results.

Alok Saklani – Psi-ability in shamans of Garhwal Himalaya: Preliminary tests *(Journal of the Society for Psychical Research 1988)*

ALOK SAKLANI performed the following experiments:

Experiment 1: Saklani asked an Indian shaman to treat randomly selected wheat seeds by holding them in her hands for 45 seconds. Another experimenter planted E and C seeds in separate pots (coded 'A' and 'B'), and a third experimenter, blind to which were E and C, watered them for seven days with equal amounts of water. From the eighth day water treated by the healer for 20 seconds was used for the E plants by the experimenter who knew which were A and B plants but was blind to which were E or C and to which was the treated water. Growth was determined by measuring plant height to the 'longest leaf. "... the mean length of the treated group as compared to the control group was significantly greater $(p < 0.01)$ on days 15–18, and of borderline significance $(p < 0.05)$ on days 14 and 19."

Experiment 2: Saklani arranged for the same shaman to treat a group of randomly selected wheat seeds and a bottle of saline which was subsequently used to injure the seeds, per Grad's design. Untreated control seeds and saline were used for comparison. A second experimenter planted the seeds in pots labeled A and B and a third experimenter, blind to which were E and C seeds, watered them with the saline from bottles marked A and B. "The total number of seeds germinated per pot was... significantly greater in the treated group as compared to the control group $(p < 0.01)$. Also, the number of plants per pot was significantly greater on day 12 $(p < 0.01)$ and of borderline significance on days 7, 9 and 11 $(p < 0.05)$..."

Discussion

A. The results of these experiments suggest that, through influence either directly upon the seeds and/or on the water, the healer was able to enhance plant growth significantly.

In personal communication, SAKLANI adds:

> Two experiments ... have shown that mere treatment of seeds does not influence growth of plants in E group significantly. Also, a third experiment showed that treatment of water alone (seeds not treated) influences growth of E group significantly ...

The latter findings contradict those in SCOFIELD / HODGES.

B. Well run and well reported experiments.

Alok Saklani – Psychokinetic effects on plant growth: Further studies *(Research in Parapsychology 1989)*

In this series of experiments SAKLANI studied wheat seeds which were undamaged by saline. Four experiments explored whether random variations in growth of two groups of plants might produce significant differences which could account for differences observed when healers treat plants. Saklani selected the seeds, divided them into packs of 50 each, coded them, and handed them to an assistant, who assigned them (by drawing lots) to pots filled with earth from the same source. All were given identical water and ambient light and temperature conditions in the laboratory. "Light intensity measured at rim level on each pot was uniform." Only plants germinating on the same initial day were considered. Plant height above earth was the only measure of growth. The first reading in each experiment was taken when plants reached a height of 5–6 cm. (Variations between experiments in days elapsed till readings were taken probably reflected season-

al differences in temperature.) A final reading was taken when plants began to bend and develop cracks.

Results:

> *Experiment 1:* 200 seeds, Days 9, 19 differences non-significant
> *Experiment 2:* 200 seeds, Days 11, 17 differences non-significant
> *Experiment 3:* 1,200 seeds, Day 10 – $p < 0.001$; Day 18 – $p < 0.05$
> *Experiment 4:* 1,200 seeds, Days 10, 15 differences non-significant

In a fifth experiment, two shamans treated one pack of 300 seeds each by holding the sealed packs in their hands for 90 and 150 seconds, respectively, with the intent to influence them to grow better. These packs, along with three packs of untreated seeds (totaling 900 seeds), were coded as A and B and given to an experimenter. These were randomly assigned to 30 pots and treated as above.

> *Experiment 5:*
> Treated vs. controls,
> Day 7: A and B $p < 0.001$;
> Day 13: A $p < 0.001$; B $.1 < p < 0.05$;
> 3 Untreated, each vs. the other,
> Day 7: – 1 vs. 3 $p < 0.05$, others non-significant;
> Day 13: – all non-significant

Saklani notes that "... had the pots been differently grouped in the control runs, a few more significant differences would have emerged."

Discussion

A. Under the conditions of Experiment 5, the effects of the healer were more highly significant than the those found between two of the controls.

B. Experiment 3 and the control finding in

Experiment 5 caution us against hasty conclusions in healing research. Some of the results obtained might be due to chance variations in the results rather than to healers' influence.

Although in one control-only experiment a difference of p < 0.001 was obtained, in Experiment 5 the control vs control difference was not as significant. One cannot compare with any confidence results obtained from separate experiments.

As Saklani selected the seeds and sorted them by hand, it is possible that he produced the results by intuitive sorting of seeds into groups with better or worse growth potentials.

Other studies included further measures, such as the numbers of plants germinating in each pot, days till initial germination, etc. Inclusion of these data might shed further light on what occurred in this experiment

Chris Nicholas – The effects of loving attention on plant growth (New England Journal of Parapsychology 1977)

Journal Abstract:

The purpose of this experiment was to test the possibility that a human subject by his thought processes can affect living plant tissue. There were two groups of plants used in the experiment. Each group contained 19 subjects which were radish plants. One group was termed the ignored group. Both groups had the same physical environment, except that the experimenter sent loving, caring vibrations to the love group and simply ignored the other group. He did this for ap-

proximately 15 to 20 minutes each day for 30 days. After 30 days the experimenter measured the height and weight of each plant in both groups. He then performed a test to compare the differences in weight and height of both groups. The results showed that there was no significant difference in *height* between the love group and ignored group. There was, on the other hand, a significant difference in *weight* between the two groups which was p = 0.02.

Discussion

A. Despite the small numbers of plants, a significant effect of healing seems evident.

B. This appears at first glance to be a carefully run experiment. Procedures are adequately described regarding weight measurements, though whether height was measured to include the roots or only the sprouts is not specified. However, neither blinds nor randomization are described for selection of plants, nor in distribution between E and C groups. This leaves open a possibility of unconscious experimenter bias in distributing the plants.

Mary Rose Barrington – Bean growth promotion pilot experiment (Proceedings of the Society for Psychical Research 1982)

MATTHEW MANNING, the noted British healer, was challenged to treat half of a group of mung beans to make them grow faster. "... four beans were placed in each compartment of ice cube containers, the compartment having been lined with two layers of white blotting paper." Manning was to have treated beans in randomly selected compartments but he objected to this design.

He was therefore given three entire trays to treat and three were kept as controls. Because of further problems only 48 beans were ultimately treated, with another 48 as controls. Appearance versus nonappearance of radicles and plumials within seven days was taken as the measure of success or failure.

Significantly more radicles and plumials were found in the promoted than in the control trays, $p < 0.02$ (see Table I-9).

Table I - 9. Bean Growth Results

	Succeeded	Failed	Total
Radicles promoted	42	6	48
Control	32	16	48
Plumials promoted	34	14	48
Control	21	27	48

In another experiment MANNING was given a sample of beans in a sealed container and asked to retard their growth. "The retarded beans did slightly worse than the promoted, but better than the controls, in neither case to any significant degree."

Discussion

A. A significant healing effect on plants is demonstrated by this experiment. It would be interesting to know whether Manning has reservations about using his healing to retard plant growth.

B. Procedures are too meagerly described to be certain these experiments were properly run. For instance, experimental and control samples were given to a third party for nurture and observation, presumably to ensure blinds, but BARRINGTON does not specifically mention whether or not he was blind as to which tray was experimental and which control.

Robert Miller – The Relationship Between the Energy State of Water and Its Physical Properties *(Research paper, undated, Ernest Holmes Research Foundation)*

ROBERT MILLER reports:

Tests were conducted to determine the effect of energized water on the growth rate of rye grass. Exactly 25 rye grass seeds were placed in each of six plastic cups filled with potting soil. Holes were punched in the bottom of the cups and each cup was placed on a saucer. The seeds were watered by placing the water in the saucers. This permitted the water to reach the seeds at a uniform rate by capillary action.

Two of the cups were watered every day with measured amounts (50 ml) of Atlanta tap water, two with tap water which had been energized by an individual who could produce large changes in surface tension by the standard test, and two cups were watered with tap water which had been exposed for 16 hours to a horseshoe magnet having a field strength of 1500 gauss. At the end of four days 8 per cent of the seeds in the control cups had sprouted, 36 per cent of the seeds in the cups watered with the subject-energized water had sprouted, and 68 per cent sprouting occurred in the cups watered with the magnet-energized water.

After eight days the length of each blade of grass was carefully measured. The average height of the control blades was 2.8 inches, the blades watered with the subject-energized water averaged 2.9 inches, and the grass blades watered with the magnet-energized water had an average length of 3.6 inches – 28.6 per cent more than the control blades.

Discussion

A. An effect of healing on plants is suggested.

It seems that magnets may impart to water the equivalent of a healing influence, and that in some instances this might be better than the effects of a healer. This study adds to those of SMITH and EDGE with enzymes and magnets.

MILLER does not mention who the healer was. It may be that the healer was not a particularly potent one or that he had an off day or was not gifted with a green thumb. We have no basis to assume that all healers will be equally successful with plants as with animals or people.

B. No blinds were used, statistical analyses were not done and data are not presented to permit independent assessment of the significance of the results.

G. F. Solfvin – Studies of the effects of mental healing and expectations on the growth of corn seedlings (*European Journal of Parapsychology 1982*)

GERALD SOLFVIN performed six experiments of healing by a healer and by botany students (who did not claim healing abilities) on the growth of corn seedlings. As with his study of malaria in mice (SOLFVIN 1982a), he included in the design false expectations. In this plant experiment he led the laboratory workers to believe that some of the seeds were damaged by immersion in saline and that some were normal, although in actuality all were damaged.

He made every effort to select seeds randomly and to see that conditions for each seed were as equal as possible. Seeds were hand-picked by the experimenter without looking at them and assigned in alternating fashion to damaged and (alleged) undamaged groups. A planter was used with individual cups which isolated each seed, while watering them by capillary action from a common pool of water below the cups. Experimental and control seeds were placed in randomized checker-board fashion to minimize any possible positional bias for factors of which the experimenter might not have been aware. Seeds were carefully planted, "...assuring that they are the same depth (0.3 cm) and orientation (pointed end down, longest cross-sectional axis parallel to the long dimension of the planter). The sand is levelled over the seeds, adding extra sand as needed ..."

No consistent significant effects were found, although occasional suggestive effects were noted.

Solfvin concludes that this model is so riddled with problems that he does not recommend it for studies. He suggests that mature plants might prove less problematic, and makes several further observations about variables which might need more careful controls.

Discussion

A. There may be a problem in the checker-board fashion of distribution of the various groups of seeds. This might make it difficult for a healer to focus his attention on seeds to be healed as opposed to those to be ignored such that healing might mistakenly be directed toward the wrong seeds or such that 'leakage' or scattering of healing energy might occur. In other studies healers objected to this design.

B. Though not producing significant effects, this report is a model for the careful observations and reports required in plant experiments. Such reporting allows a reader to appreciate the details attended to by the experimenter; permits other investigators to point out possible extraneous factors which might have influenced the results; and makes possible the replication of an experiment. This study points out the care needed in evaluating similar reports (e.g. LOEHR's review of plant experiments, discussed in Chapter I-5) which might not consider important extraneous factors that could contribute to the observed effects.

SOLFVIN himself noted that despite his best efforts to provide the same environment for each seed, some cups were drier than others. He suspected that there may have been some variation in the tightness of the packing of the sand around the seeds which could have produced these results.

Solfvin's randomization procedures may have been faulty. His methods could permit the experimenter to select seeds in non-random fashion via subtle sensory cues, clairsentience and/or precognition. This might account for some of the suggestive results he obtained rather than healer or expectancy effects. Solfvin noted that the weights of a particular group of seeds were heavier than those of the comparison group. This supports a possibility that some such selection bias could occur.

I disagree with Solfvin about the usefulness of the seed model for future study. I would recommend that:
1. randomization be instituted with procedures less open to experimenter bias;

2. larger numbers of seeds be used;
3. seeds be planted in separate rows, at least, and perhaps better in separate trays, with proper alternation of their placement in the lab to ensure the randomization of extraneous factors; and
4. watering be done from above, with measured amounts of water for each tray.

Alberto Barros et al. – Methodology for research on psychokinetic influence over the growth of plants (Psi Comunicacion 1984)

Journal Abstract:

A series of PK studies with plants as targets were conducted to show that this type of PK effect has a physical basis and is not a nonphysical process. The following factors were controlled: (1) distance of target from subjects, assistants, and experimenters, and (2) different persons planted the seeds of each target to avoid PK effects of specific planters. Some trials were done at a distance and with the Ss having no contact with the target, while in other trials Ss planted and influenced their own seeds. In general, more significant results were obtained with the group without such contact. This is not presented as proof of the energetic nature of PK, but it is considered consistent with the concept.

Discussion   This abstract is too brief to permit serious evaluation of the results. It would be helpful to have some figures, such as the numbers of plants in each of the experimental and control groups, and some indication of statistical methods employed.

Joseph Michael Wallack – Testing for a psychokinetic effect on plants: Effect of a 'laying-on' of hands on germinating corn seeds *(Psychological Reports 1984)*

Journal Abstract:

A possible psychokinetic effect on plants from the 'Laying-on' of hands of a self-claimed 'psychic healer' was studied in 3 procedures. The 'healer' treated a sealed petrie dish containing germinating root growth-retarded corn seeds. In Procedure 1 randomly drawn corn seeds were pre-soaked for 12 hr. in a 2% NaCl solution. Seeds were then randomly assigned to 3 prepared petrie dishes: healing, control, and a control for the temperature of the healer's hands. Root growth was measured after 96 hr. Procedure 2 tested for a possible transitory healing effect following the same procedures as Procedure 1 but measuring the roots after 48 hr. In Procedure 3 the pre-soaking period of the corn seeds was reduced to 8 hr. to test the possibility that the 12-hr. pre-soaking period was too severe to allow a 'healing effect' to be manifest... [statistical analyses] yielded nonsignificant effects in all 3 experiments. Additional studies are needed to avoid a Type II error, i.e., to rule out possibility of a psychokinetic effect on plants by the 'laying on' of hands.

Discussion
A. The author probably correctly speculates that further testing (especially observation) might provide different results and notes that root growth may not be the best measure for healing effects. Also, the soaking time and concentration of salt may be variables contributing to negative results.

Other plant experiments that measured growth for longer periods have shown better results, examining root, stem, and shoot length as well as dry and wet weights. The use of a limited number of plants (15/-group) may also restrict the information garnered.

Further descriptions of the healer would be welcome.

In particular, the experimenter's attitude to healing would be of interest, although by his quotation marks around key words in his paper one may well assume him to be skeptical.

B. Though the experiment appears well designed, run and reported, it seems unreasonable to use an unduly brief study in evidence for or against healing.

Sandra Lenington – Effect on holy water on the growth of radish plants *(Psychology Reports 1979)*

Journal Summary:

Mean growth of 12 radish seeds in peat pots watered with holy water were not significantly different from that of 12 watered with tap water.

Plants were measured at three weeks' growth. Differences between groups of plants were not statistically significant, although the mean of those watered with holy water was slightly longer.

Discussion   This is too small a sample on which to base reasonable conclusions.[17]

Enrique Novillo Pauli – PK on living targets as related to sex, distance and time
(Research in Parapsychology 1972)

ENRIQUE PAULI, a Jesuit priest, reports on 20 experiments in which a variety of subjects, mostly school children, were requested to enhance the growth of Fescue Kentucky grass seeds planted in laboratory petri dishes. All were watered equally from the same source; light and temperature were uniform; position of the dishes was rotated daily; and the experimenter and his assistants were blind as to experimental and control plant assignments. Experiments lasted 10 to 14 days. Growth was measured from the seed pod to the tip of the blade.

The whole group was given the task of influencing the entire batch of plants. Positive results were noted when male and female subjects had separate group targets. When male and female subjects were focusing on the same targets, the results were not significant. In one experiment, significant results were obtained when subjects and plants were separated by eight miles; in another when they were continents apart. In some experiments, males outperformed females; in another the reverse was true. "…magnitude of the effect seemed to be independent of the number of subjects participating…"

Discussion
A. It would appear that distant healing was demonstrated and that sex of healers may have been an influence in the group healings. One can only guess at the biases of the researcher and wonder whether this isn't an experimenter effect. Healers commonly gather in mixed groups for distant healings and I have found no other reference to negative effects with mixed sexes in healing.

B. These studies appear to have been performed with proper attention to rigorous procedures. Unfortunately, specific numbers and statistics are not given to support the claimed results.

Bernard Grad – The laying-on of hands: Implications for psychotherapy, gentling and the placebo effect (Journal of the American Society for Psychical Research 1967)

GRAD examined the possibility that depression might produce a negative healing effect on the growth of plants. He postulated that if depressed people hold water which is then used to water plants, the plants might grow more slowly.

A study was set up to test the effect on plant growth of the laying on of hands conducted by three individuals (not including O.E.) as compared with an untreated control. The three subjects included J.B., who had previously been used in the goiter experiment and who had a "green thumb"; a woman with a depressive neurotic reaction (R.H.); and a man with a psychotic depression (H.R.). The latter two subjects were patients in a psychiatric hospital.

The hypothesis was that there is a direct relationship between the mood of the persons doing the treatment and the subsequent growth of plants watered by these untreated solutions. Thus, it was hypothesized that a solution held for 30 minutes in the hands of an individual in a confident mood would permit plants watered by this solution to grow at a faster rate than plants watered by identical solutions, but held for the same length of time by persons with a depressive illness or not held by anyone (the control group). The experiment also tested whether solutions held by depressed persons would inhibit plant growth relative to the control group.

In essence the procedure consisted of having each person hold a sealed bottle of normal saline between his hands for 30 minutes. The solution was then poured on barley seeds embedded in soil which was then dried in an oven for 48 hours. Following this, the pots containing the seeds were removed from the oven and watered at suitable intervals with tap water not treated by anyone. When the seedlings appeared above the soil their number was counted and their height measured. The determinations were continued until seedling growth reached a plateau, which occurred seven to nine days after they first appeared above the soil surface. The results obtained with the hand-treated and untreated saline solutions were then compared. The watering with saline, the subsequent drying, and the restricted watering with tap water were used as forms of experimental stress to the plants. This experiment was carried out under multi-blind conditions, the information necessary to identify the treatment of each potted plant being divided among five individuals.

The results showed that the seeds watered by the saline held by J.B. (who was in a confident mood at the time of hand-treatment on the saline) grew significantly faster than those in the remaining three groups. Thus, this part of the hypothesis was supported by the experimental data. However, the plants treated by R.H., who had a neurotic depression, had a slightly higher growth rate than that of the controls, and this was contrary to expectations.

This difference in the growth of the plants treated by the two depressed persons relative to the control group might be explicable as follows: The growth rate of H.R.'s plants was slower than that of the controls because he was agitated and depressed at the time he was holding the saline solution in his hands; in so doing, something associated with his depression might have been transferred to the solution, which then inhibited the growth of the barley seeds. He never inquired as to why he was given a bottle to hold, and therefore he was not told.

On the other hand, when R.H. was given a bottle of saline to hold for 30 minutes, she inquired as to the reason for the procedure, and when told, she responded with an expression of interest and a decided brightening of mood. Also, it was observed that she cradled the bottle in her lap as a mother would hold her child. Thus, the important fact for the purpose of the experiment was not what her psychiatric diagnosis was, but what her mood was at the time she was holding the bottle, and she did not appear to be depressed at that time. Therefore, the growth of the plants was not inhibited when watered with the solution she held at that time. In short, it would appear that a positive mood while holding the bottles favors a change in the solution which leads to a stimulation of cell growth compared with other solutions not held by anybody, or held by persons in a depressed state. Also, it would seem that a negative mood such as depression, while holding the solution, results in an inhibition of cell growth when such cells are watered by these solutions. Further studies are indicated here.

Discussion

A. This study suggests that emotions may influence healings.

B. Data and statistics are presented adequately. However, in view of 'green thumb' and 'brown thumb' people identified and demonstrated by LOEHR (see Chapter I-5), GRAD's research on single cases of depression are only hints, at best, regarding a possible connection between emotions and healing on plants. Grad may have had one green-thumb and one brown-thumb subject. Further clarification is needed.

Radionics deals with the diagnosis and cure of illness with the help of various devices with dials and/or calibrations (affectionately called *black boxes)* designed to aid the user to tune into *vibrational frequencies* of the target. It is similar to dowsing in that the operator of the device is a part of the diagnostic/ treating system. The device is probably a feedback mechanism aiding the user to apply his psi diagnostic and healing abilities, though many radionics specialists insist the devices themselves have psi powers.[18]

Radionics is a recognised and accepted subsection of dowsing and healing in the U.K. In the U.S., the Food and Drug Administration (F.D.A.) takes strong exception to these devices and actively prosecutes radionics practitioners.

Edward W. Russell – Report on Radionics: Science of the Future, the Science Which Can Cure Where Orthodox Medicine Fails

EDWARD W. RUSSELL presents a concise history of the development of radionics along with descriptions of numerous experiments that demonstrate its efficacy. Summaries of two experiments follow:

1. *Enhancement of plant growth with radionic treatments:* Increased yields were noted for potatoes (see Table I-10).

2. *Pest control in fields with various crops:* The radionics device is tuned first to a particular field, usually by a photographic negative of that field. It is then tuned to vibrations noxious to pests infesting crops in that field. Counts are made of damaged plants in sample rows in the E field and in adjacent C plots. For example, an E plot of seed corn was radionically treated for a corn borer infestation. The C plot included 50 rows at the northern end of the field.

Six hundred individual plants in both check and treated plots were checked for incidence of European corn borers above the ear spike in each stalk.
* Lengthwise
   (i) 100 stalks in each of second rows on each side of field (200 altogether)
   (ii) 100 stalks in approximately centre of field.
* Crosswise– same procedure as lengthwise count, direction only difference.

The experiment is detailed in Table I-11.

In 1950 four out of six trials were significantly positive in one year. In 1952 when the targets were Japanese beetles and European corn borers, 78,360 corn stalks were inspected on 81 farms, covering 1,420 acres. Significant results were obtained in 92% of the cases for Japanese beetles and 58% for European corn borers. In 1953, 13 out of 14 tests against European corn borers produced significant results.

Discussion

A. If these experiments can be verified, radionics might provide methods for enhancing crop growth and for controlling pests, neither of which would contaminate the environment. Moreover, both would be far less expensive than existing methods. Variations not studied include whether radionics plus fertilizers and/or pesticides is even more potent.

If healers can protect seeds from chemical damage, enhance their growth and control plant pests, they may be able to help humans in similar fashion.

B. No blinds or randomization are mentioned in these experiments. However, the fields were planted by various farmers, so randomization may have occurred for specimens planted. This still leaves the possibility of experimenter bias in counting infested stalks. Statistical analyses are also lacking.

The plant experiments are summarized in Table I-12.

The next series studies movements of single-celled organisms. I am not sure whether they should be included under healing, as they seem more to represent telepathic instructions to the organisms to move in a particular direction. Theoretically, this could be of assistance to immobilize infesting parasites so that the body could more easily attack and eliminate them.

Table I - 10. Increases in potato yield with radionic treatment (1949 - camp potato - Potter Co., Penna.)

	Rate yield per acre	% Increase over check	% Increase over conventional spray
Check (no treatment)	340.3 bu.		
Conventional spray treatment*	394.7 bu.	15.9	
Radionic treatment	446.5 bu.	32.2	13.1

* Seven sprays during 1949

Table I - 11. Pest control with radionic treatment (1950 - Host plants: Field and sweet corn. Insects: European corn borer, sweet corn borer - second brood)

Check plot			Radionically treated plot		
No. stalks	Direction	No. stalks infested	No. stalks	Direction	No. stalks infested
100	L.W.	19	100	L.W.	8
100	C.W.	21	100	C.W.	10
100	L.W.	21	100	L.W.	13
100	C.W.	25	100	C.W.	15
100	L.W.	24	100	L.W.	11
100	C.W.	22	100	C.W.	12
600	Totals	132	600	Totals	59

Table I - 12. Healing effects on plants

Subject of Healing	Researchers	T/N/D*	Duration	Healers	Results	Significance
Barley seeds	Grad (1965)	T/ vehicle	15 mins	Estebany	Barley seeds, damaged by 1% saline solution; decreased damage with healing to the solution	$p < .001$
					Repeated X 3 with careful blinds, sealed jars of water	$.05 < p < .02$
Rye grass	Macdonald, Hickman & Dakin	T/ vehicle	20 mins	Kraft	Seeds damaged with healer-treated saline. Day 9: total height less than control	$p < .05$
					9: mean height less than control	$p < .02$
					10: mean height less than control	$p < .001$
				Worrall	Day 15: total height greater than control	$p < .05$
					16: total height greater than control	$p < .05$
					17: mean height greater than control	$p < .05$
					18: total height greater than control	$p < .05$
Wheat seeds	Saklani (1988)	T	43 secs	Shaman	Treated seeds - mean length greater than control: Days 15 - 18	$p < .01$
					14, 19	$p < .05$
		T+ T/ vehicle	30 secs		Total no. germinating/ pot greater than control	$p < .01$
					Mean length greater than control: Days 12	$p < .01$
					7, 9, 11	$p < .05$
	Saklani (1990)	T	90, 150 secs	2 shamans	Treated seeds of both shamans - Mean length greater than controls: Day 7	$p < .001$
					Treated seeds of one shaman vs controls: Day 13	$p < .001$
					Control seeds, group 1 vs group 3: Day 7	$p < .05$

* T/N/D: Touch/Near/Distant   **NS: Non-Significant

(Table I-12 is continued on page 177.)

Table I - 12. Healing effects on plants (cont.)

Subject of healing	Researchers	T/N/D*	Duration	Healers	Results	Significance
Radish seeds	Nicholas	N	15 - 20 mins x 30 days	Nicholas	Weight treated greater than controls Height treated greater than controls	p< .02 NS**
Mung beans	Barrington	T/N	?	Manning	More radicles and plumials vs controls by 7 days	p< .02
Cress seeds	Hodges & Scofield	T	2 mins	Boltwood	1. 120 seeds saline-damaged vs undamaged seeds 2.- 6. Repeat as in (1)	p< .05 p< .0001
Rye grass	Miller	T/ vehicle	?	?	Sprouting Blade growth Controls 8% 2.8ins Healed 63% 2.9ins Magnet- 60% 3.6ins Treated (avg.)	? ? ? ?
Corn seeds	Solfvin	D	?	Healer	Checkerboard distribution	NS
?	Barros, et al.	T&D	?	?	Greater growth with distant than touch healing	`more sig.´
Corn seeds	Wallack	T/N	30 mins	?	15 seeds at 48, 96 hours root growth	NS
Radish seeds	Lenington	vehicle	?	Holy water	12 seeds	NS
Grass seeds	Pauli	D	?	School children	Greater growth when males, females worked apart	?
Barley seeds	Grad (1967)	T/ vehicle	7 - 9 days	Depressed	Seeds oven-dried, watered with saline 1 person with psychotic depression vs control 1 person with neurotic depression vs control 1 person with 'green thumb' vs control	 slightly 1. more NS significant
Potatoes	Russell	D	?	?	Increase vs untreated control 32.2% Increase vs sprayed control 13.1%	? ?
Corn	Russell	D	?	?	59 treated vs 132 control infested with borers	?

* T/N/D: Touch/Near/Distant **NS: Non-Significant

Healing Action on Single-Celled Organisms

Nigel Richmond – Two series of PK tests on parameci (*Journal of the Society for Psychical Research 1952*)

NIGEL RICHMOND reports:

The following experiments were designed to test whether an ability of PK exists which would influence the behaviour of protozoa. Paramecia were chosen as suitable subjects for these tests because they are very common, are easily recognized, and usually swim about in random fashion.... The purpose of the experiments was to influence, by thought alone, the direction in which a chosen animalcule would swim during a selected period.

The method of assessing the success of each attempt, which was made under a low-power microscope (magnification x 75), was to divide the field of view of the microscope into four by cross wires in the eye-piece of the instrument. The attempt was timed by a stop-watch for a given period, and the quadrant containing the paramecium at the end of this time was noted. The quadrant into which the paramecium was to be willed was selected by turning up cards from an ordinary pack of playing cards, each suit indicating one of the four divisions.

A series of 794 experimental trials was run. A control series of 799 trials was conducted in which 'no conscious effort was made to influence the paramecia and the card was not turned up until the end of the 15-second period'.

Richmond adds:

Although the field of view of the microscope is divided into four, the chance expectation is taken to be one half. This is because I suspected that influence applied in one direction would sometimes have its effect in the diametrically opposite direction, according to the kind of mental work employed. The experimenter may either influence the paramecium according to his conscious will, or alternatively he may set up an unconscious resistance which will strengthen its direct opposite, in this case the equivalent of scoring in the diametrically opposite quadrant.

As it was not possible to ensure that the thought process was controlled correctly, both the chosen quadrant and that diametrically opposite were, for assessment purposes, counted as targets, although during the experiment only the selected quadrant was treated as such. It should be remembered, however, that the experimenter was aware of a success in the opposite quadrant even though he would will towards the selected one.

A second series of 701 E and C trials was run, employing minor improvements in techniques. There were 444 successes in E trials (253 in the desired direction; 191 opposite). Richmond states his results are highly significant.

Discussion

A. In the second experiment, where successful chosen-direction trials are tabulated, there was a significantly positive result for that category alone.

B. The inclusion of 'opposite-direction' movement with 'chosen-direction' movement seems questionable. 'Opposite' can be defined in any way convenient, and could actually include all non-chosen quadrants. Richmond does not provide comprehensive data to permit full evaluation of his results.

RICHMOND reports his statistical analyses in the form of "Critical Ratios" which appear to be in the range of high significance (over 7) but does not provide sufficient data to allow independent derivation of probability levels.

J. L. Randall – An attempt to detect psi effects with protozoa (Journal of the Society for Psychical Research)

J. L. RANDALL repeated Richmond's experiment, using *Stylonychia mytilus,* a protozoon similar to the *Paramecium.*

These creatures are in the habit of making sudden darting movements about the slide, and it was thought that they might be amenable to psi influences. The targets were [randomly] chosen... For convenience, the experiments were performed in runs of 20 trials, the mean chance expectation (M.C.E.) being 5 hits per run. Each run was followed by a control run in which the cards were not turned up until the conclusion of the run.

...560 trials were completed, of which half were controls. The direct hits amounted to a total of 72 on the 'attempt' runs and 75 on the 'controls' (M.C.E.=70). Richmond included hits in the opposite quadrant in his scoring, since he felt that PK could sometimes operate in the reverse direction to that intended. If this is done with the present data we have 146 for the 'attempt' runs and 145 for the 'controls'... There is thus no evidence for psi, either of the direct or reverse variety. The writer did not embark on these experiments in an attitude of disbelief; on the contrary, he fully expected to obtain positive confirmation of the Richmond effect, and was somewhat disappointed when he failed to do so. The fact that no such effect was detected does not necessarily prove that Richmond's results were faulty, since we know that psi effects are extraordinarily elusive; however, the work of any experimenter cannot be regarded as more than suggestive until it has been confirmed by others.

Discussion

A. Numerous questions remain: Does *Stylonychia mytilus* respond differently from *Paramecium*? Was Richmond more gifted with psi than Randall? Did other factors account for the disparity in results between the two studies?

B. Details of this study are adequately reported. It is a pleasure to find a researcher who mentions his attitudes and intentions – variables that may influence the results in a variety of ways. KNOWLES also reports an attempted replication of Richmond's experiment with no positive results, though he does not provide details (1954).

Charles M. Pleass and N. Dean Dey – Using the Doppler effect to study behavioral responses of motile algae to psi stimulus (*Parapsychological Association Papers 1985*)

PLEASS/DEY developed a highly sophisticated, mechanized and computerized model for observing the motility of marine algae *Dunaliella tertiolecta* in laboratory test-tube culture. They used a light-scattering spectrometer, which measured the velocity and vector of algae motion. They were able to calculate the speed of movement of algae with approximately one percent accuracy, taking up to 75 measurements per second. Data samples represent averages of 200 individual records of swimming speed. Fifty such measurements can be accumulated in four- to five-minute trials. The vertical axis was monitored because of the tendency of the microbes to move vertically in daily rhythms.

Participants were told to "be with the algae" during E periods compared with C periods. This was chosen rather than instructions to influence algae movement in specific directions because "... natural changes in the vectors of the microbes due to endogenous rhythms were sufficiently pronounced to make the result of a command such as 'go high' or 'swim faster' ambiguous." Calmness and relaxation of the participants, without ego involvement in the outcome, seemed to be very important in their success.

Great care was taken to insure that temperature, pH (acidity) of culture solutions, extraneous light, time in algal life cycle and laboratory sound and humidity levels were equal in E and C measurement periods.

In 251 trials with 18 subjects, the results were highly significant (p < 0.000000005).

C. M. Pleass and N. Dean Dey – Conditions that appear to favor extrasensory interactions between Homo sapiens and microbes (*Journal of the Society for Scientific Exploration 1990*)

A second series was run, taking into account radio frequency shielding, more careful controls for ambient temperature, physical isolation of the vessel holding the microbes, and "control data taken from uninterrupted time series data acquired on a different occasion". Under these conditions, 118 trials with 14 participants did not reach significant levels (p < 0.059).

PLEASS/DEY also ran experiments where they measured the response of algae to the killing of a portion of the culture which had been removed from the main batch. Pilot trials produced significant results, while results of formal trials did not differ from chance.

The authors propose that the initial enthusiasm of participants is an important element in producing significant effects in psi research.

Discussion
A. The very highly significant results in the early series suggest that microorganisms may be influenced to move in particular directions.

The decline effect has been noted in numerous psi studies. The authors' hypothesis to explain it appears reasonable. Healers state that their powers are activated by real needs in healees. The presence of a need factor may explain why studies of healing have produced more significant results than most other types of psi studies.
B. One must be cautious in accepting evidence which cannot be replicated. There is always the possibility that unrecognized chance factors might have produced the results.

Louis Metta – Psychokinesis on Lepidoptera larvae (Journal of Parapsychology 1972)

Journal Abstract:

The subjects in this exploratory experiment tried by PK to influence Lepidoptera larvae to crawl into specified sectors of an experimental box. The box was a petri dish provided with a hole in the cover through which the larva was dropped. The dish was placed on a background marked into 12 sectors. Half of the sectors were designated "good" and half, "wrong". The subject tried to influence the larva to go to the "good" sectors. There were two experimental subjects. Subject 1 obtained a significant negative deviation in his overall scoring (p = 0.012). The negative effect was weakened by inconsistency in the individual run scores; of the four runs, run 2 was comparable in size but opposite in direction from the other three runs. An analysis which considers only size of deviation yielded p = 0.0006. It appeared that this subject demonstrated a strong psi influence but could not control its direction. Subject 2 gave insignificant results.

Discussion

A. The importance of this significant study is that a subject could influence the larvae to move in a given direction. Similar studies have been run on telepathic control of animal movement (with cats and rats).[19] I do not see such experiments as being directly relevant to healing except in demonstrating telepathy or PK with animals, which lends credence to healers' reports that they are effective in healing animals.[20]

B. Technically, the study is sound and produced significant results. The fact that the movement was in a direction opposite to that intended is a problem if this mechanism is suggested as a manner in which healing could be effective with parasitic infestations.

Table I - 13. Healing effects on movement of organisms

Subject of healing	Researchers	T/N/D*	Duration	Healers	Results	Significance
Paramecia	Richmond	N	15 secs	Richmond	**1.** 794 Experimental (E) vs 799 control (C): Motility measured in predicted and opposite directions **2.** 701 E vs 701 C	'Highly significant'
Stylonychia mytilus	Randall	N	?	Randall	280 E vs 280 C	NS**
Algae	Pleass & Dey	N	4-5 mins	?	Motility, speed influenced	Significant
Lepidoptera (moth) larvae	Metta	?	?	1 subject 1 subject	4 series: 3 significantly positive; 1 negative : Mean Negative series	 p< .012 p< .0006 NS

* T/N/D: Touch/Near/Distant   **NS: Non-Significant

Healing Action on Animals

Among studies of the effects of healing on animals, the work of BERNARD GRAD is a classic. He was the first to study healing on animals in the laboratory in a scientific manner. He did this on his own time, at great risk to his professional standing and to his continued employment at McGill University.

Bernard Grad – Some biological effects of the 'laying-on of hands': A review of experiments with animals and plants (Journal of the American Society for Psychical Research 1965a)

BERNARD GRAD anesthetized ninety-six mice and created similarly sized wounds on their backs by the removal of a piece of skin approximately one-half by one inch. The wounds were measured daily by tracing their shape on paper, cutting out the tracing, and weighing the cut-out. A healer (OSCAR ESTEBANY) held the cages of half of the mice for fifteen minutes twice daily. At fourteen days, the treated group had healed significantly more rapidly than the untreated group (p < 0.001).

This experiment was repeated, with similar results. As no blinds were employed, no further details were provided.

B. Grad, R. J. Cadoret, and G.I. Paul – The influence of an unorthodox method of treatment on wound healing in mice (International Journal of Parapsychology 1961)

This study repeated the above, with 300 mice, careful controls and blinds. Additional cages were placed in closed or open paper bags during healings to prevent any physical intervention by the healer. On days 15 and 16 of the study (by which time nearly all wounds had healed) E group had healed more rapidly than C group (p < 0.01).

Discussion

A. These are the first controlled experiments on mammals. They suggest that psi healing helps heal wounds.

In personal communication GRAD reported that Estebany had to hold the cages of mice twice daily over the course of the experiment in order to obtain these noted effects. This was more intensive effort than usually necessary for Estebany to obtain results.

The most useful part of these experiments is that mice do not respond to suggestion. It is impossible to claim this is a placebo effect. (See the parallel study of WIRTH, 28 years later, on human dermal wound healing.) **B.** Nicely designed, performed and reported studies.

Bernard Grad – Some biological effects of the 'laying-on of hands': A review of experiments with animals and plants (Journal of the American Society for Psychical Research 1965)

Goiters were produced in mice by withholding iodine from their diets and by giving them thiouracil, a goitrogen. The rate of thyroid growth was measured by weighing the thyroids of mice, which were serially sacrificed over 40 days. Seventy of these mice were divided into the following groups:

1. baseline-control: no treatment;
2. healer-treated: held in groups for 15 minutes twice daily in special boxes, five days per week, and once on Saturdays.
3. heat-control: mice were kept in heated cages for the same length of time as group 2, with the temperature adjusted to the same heat attained in the treatment of that group.

The thyroids of the healer-treated group of mice grew significantly more slowly than those of both of the controls ($p < 0.001$). The thyroids of group 3 did not grow significantly more slowly than those of group 2.

In a second experiment, 37 mice on a goiterogenic diet were divided into C and E groups. This time the healing was not done directly. The healer held some wool and cotton cuttings in his hands for 15 minutes, once on the first day and twice on the next 24 days of the experiment. Ten grams of cutting (treated for E mice, untreated for C mice, with blinds) were placed in each cage with four or five mice, for one hour, morning and

evening, six days a week. Mice in contact with the healer-held vehicle developed goiters significantly more slowly than the controls ($p < 0.001$).

Upon return to normal diet the thyroids of goitrous mice receiving direct or indirect healing returned to normal more quickly than those of the C group. (No numbers or statistics are cited for this last portion of the study.)

Discussion
A. These studies once more demonstrate a significant healing effect in mammals. As with water for plants, we have in cotton treated by a healer a vehicle which appears to convey healing. We should also note this may be preventive rather than curative healing.

It is ironic and sad that mice had to be sacrificed in these and later studies to demonstrate effects of healing. GRAD, in personal communication, explained that he could find no doctors willing to study Estebany's healing on humans. His choice was either to do this or nothing. As it took 24 years to repeat the skin wound experiment in humans, and as this study has not yet been repeated, his point is understandable.
B. This is an excellent study. Details are adequately reported.

Frans Snel and P. R. Hol – Psychokinesis experiments in casein induced amyloidosis of the hamster (European Journal of Parapsychology 1983)

Amyloidosis is a disease in which amyloid protein deposits are formed around cells in various organs, eventually compromising their function. This usually occurs in late life, with no known etiology. It is currently thought to be the possible cause of Alzheimer's disease. Several animal species may also develop amyloidosis, providing a basis for this experiment with hamsters.

Experiment 1: 42 hamsters were randomly divided into healing and control groups (from amongst 200 animals in groups of five per cage). Starting weights were 80–100 grams. The hamsters were injected with 2 ml of casein 5% subcutaneously five days per week. Every third day animals were sacrificed and weighed, with blood samples taken for analysis of hemoglobin, red and white blood count, lactate dehydrogenase, gamma-glutamyltransferase, total protein, cathepsin-D, electrophoreses and serum amyloid A. Experimenters were blind to which were E and C cages and blood samples.

Four natural healers received photographs of seven target cages with five hamsters in each. "One healer tried to prevent the onset and severity of the disease during the entire experiment (30 days); three others worked for one week prior to the expected appearance of amyloid (day 16 till day 23). The animals were treated by the healers once a day, at a time that suited them best."

Experiment 2: 50 hamsters, in groups of 5 per cage, received casein injections daily for 50 days (except for day 27, when no injection was given). Starting weights averaged 123 grams. Samples were taken every 10 days for hemoglobin, gamma-GT and LDH, and body weight was recorded when they were sacrificed.

Three professional healers and "two persons who acted as healers (acquaintances who when asked were enthusiastic and interested in the idea of trying to heal the hamsters in this way)" participated. Two photographs of five hamsters were given to each healer. Absent healing was given once daily.

There were ten photographs of five hamsters, two for each healer. Cages were numbered 1 to 10. The photographs were randomized and distributed to the healers by an otherwise uninvolved person. Every sampling day, one hamster was taken from each cage. When the code was broken after the experiment was finished, it showed that on each sampling day 8 hamsters were designated as experimental animals and two as controls. So after all the healers could only have known this in a clairvoyant way. All photographs were coded twice to prevent any possibility of a clue.

… Subjects were to get feedback only if the results were in the predicted direction…

Three parameters from the first experiment were studied in this second one: hemoglobin, LDH and gamma-GT. We did not repeat the differentiation of the white blood cells because we considered the results too dependent on the varying daily interpretations of the analyst.

Prediction indicators of health would be:
1. a higher weight, hemoglobin and red blood count;
2. lower white blood count (especially of band forms which indicate infection) and platelet counts, LDH, gamma-GT and Cathepsin-D levels;
3. total protein and electrophoreses as close as possible to normal values.

Results were reported as follows:
Experiment 1: Significant effects in predicted directions were noted for differentiation of bandforms ($p = 0.017$), lactate dehydrogenase ($p = 0.036$), and suggestive effects for hemoglobin ($p = 0.057$) and gamma-GT ($p = 0.069$).

Experiment 2: On day 4 the level of hemo-globin was significantly lower in the treated animals (p < 0.05)...

Snel/Hol note that some of the healers disapproved of the animal experimentation and that in the second experiment the ran-domization ("designating which were to be the experimental and control animals after the experiment was finished") and daily in-jections may have limited the lack of oppor-tunity to 'get through' to the animals. They deplored not being allowed to touch or see the animals in their surroundings.

They also state that "none of the experi-menters thought it possible to influence in-duced disease, as distinct from a natural dis-ease..."

Discussion
A. The significant positive effects in Experi-ment 1 support claims of healers that they can ameliorate the progression of illnesses. The lower number of bandforms in E group suggests their reactions to the casein were not as severe as those of C group. The higher hemoglobin in E group is consistent with the studies of Krieger showing elevations of he-moglobin in humans with Therapeutic Touch healing (reviewed below).

The significant reduction in hemoglobin on day 4 of Experiment 2 is worrisome but is not sustained and may have been due to chance factors.

The design of the Experiment 2 seems to place hurdles in the way of the healers. One might speculate that the experimenters were seeking to confirm their disbeliefs, especial-ly when they also eliminated study of band-forms, the parameter which provided the most significant results in Experiment 1.
B. In Experiment 1 the results could have

been produced by intuitive (psi) selection of the mice by the experimenters rather than a healing effect. The significantly lower band-forms could be a *negative* effect of healing.

One would want to have further tests to see whether this is repeated and whether negative effects on hemoglobin might occur.

The next study is an extremely important one. It reveals how experimenter effects may creep into healing and other research, in addition to showing how healing may influ-ence infectious disease in animals.[21]

Gerald F. Solfvin – Psi expectancy effects in psychic healing studies with malarial mice (*European Journal of Parapsychology 1982*)

Gerald F. Solfvin set up a revolutionary, though complex study of several experimen-tal variables. He hypothesized that animal handlers' expectancies could produce diffe-rentials in rates of illness of mice in their care. In addition, he studied the effects of healing expectations in the animal handlers without use of any designated healer(s) and without knowledge on the part of anyone during the experiment as to which mice were designated to be healed.

The manipulations in the experiment were of the expectations of the student as-sistants. All the mice were inoculated in-terperitoneally with 0.1 milliliter of 1:10 stabilate (Babesia rhodaini), the rodent version of the malarial blood parasite. Each student was assigned 12 mice housed in a single cage and was told that half of them would be inoculated with babesia while the other half would receive a sterile injection. The students themselves randomized and marked their mice with either yellow (babesia) or black (non-babesia) markings to indicate which were which, thus this condition remained non-blind to them. In addition, the stu-dents were led to believe that half of each of these two groups would be receiving distant healing from a psychic healer, when in fact there was no such healer in the study. These expectations formed a balanced two-way analysis of variance that was fully randomized.

The students were not aware of which mice were supposed to be healed and which not, these being randomly assigned to the healing and control conditions by the author.

This allowed evaluation of cross-correlations amongst the conditions according to the possibilities in Figure I-7.

A picture was taken of each mouse. Randomization procedures were elaborate.

The first randomization was to assign the mice to specific colors and numbers within their cages. For each student a set of 12 address labels with sticky backs was prepared with one of the twelve possible combinations of the two colors (yellow, black) and six numbers (1–6) written on each. These were sealed in 12 identical envelopes, shuffled well, clipped together and inserted into the notebook for the students to use during the randomizing procedure.

The second randomization was to assign the photos of the mice to the supposed 'healing' and 'non-healing' groups so that exactly half of the black and yellow marked mice from each cage would be assigned to each condi-

tion. When the photos of the mice were collected from the laboratory (day 3 of the experiment), E returned to his office and conducted the following procedure. For each student, the large envelope was opened and the photos, still in their separate envelopes, were placed in two piles according to the color marked on the outside of the envelopes. Each photo was inserted into a new envelope and sealed and each pile was shuffled ten or more times. Another person was brought into the room and, after E left, re-shuffled the piles and dealt out two groups of 3 from each pile of 6. E returned to the room, placed the subpiles on the left side into a large envelope and labeled this 'H' (healed) and the subpiles on the right side into an envelope labelled 'NH' (non-healed). These envelopes were sealed and placed in a drawer in E's desk which remained locked until the results of the experiment were all in E's possession.

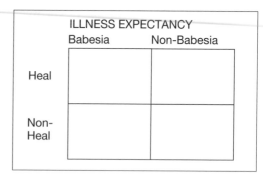

Fig. I-7. Solfvin's experimental conditions.

In *Experiment 1* Solfvin had three handlers. Two were clearly 'sheep' and one was clearly a 'goat'. The sheep produced random results. The goat produced significant results ($p < 0.021$) on the dimension of illness expectancy and a suggestive trend ($p < 0.092$)

for healing expectancy, *both in the direction opposite to that predicted by the experimental hypothesis.* That is, the results were strongly in the direction a 'goat' would predict.

SOLFVIN discusses how the illness dimension effects could be produced without psi.

> The only significant results in this experiment were contributed by the group handled by J. The significant illness expectancy effect suggests that the expectancy treatment had an effect on this student which resulted in differential babesia infestation in the mice which he handled. Although we cannot exclude the possibility that this occurred parapsychologically, it can be most parsimoniously explained as a social psychological (Rosenthal) effect mediated by the physical handling of the mice. This is further supported by the fact that handler J's mice showed generally higher babesia levels (significantly so) than those of the other two handlers and the unhandled control group.
>
> A number of studies have demonstrated the deleterious effects of stressful handling on laboratory strains of rats (e.g., Weininger, 1953; 1954). In the current experiment the illness model employed may be particu-larly susceptible to such stressful handling effects. The blood parasite babesia rhodaini is a very effective agent. It spreads rapidly through the bloodstreams of all the mice and, if left untreated, will inevitably result in their deaths. The natural mechanisms in the body of the mouse are stretched to their limits and still are wanting. Any additional stresses on the mouse, such as being handled by humans, can only tax the system further and will result in the more rapid spreading of the parasite. In the current experi-

ment, for example, we see that the unhandled control group showed lower babesia levels than any of the handled groups. Apparently the best thing that one can do for the mice is to leave them alone.

In *Experiment 2* Solfvin had five handlers. "The babesia and non-babesia designations (used for inducing expectancies in handlers) were changed to high or low babesia." The results were uniform across the five groups.

> The results show a significant main effect for the healing expectancy factor (p < 0.05) and a marginal trend for the illness expectancy factor (p between 0.05 and 0.10). Both of these are in the direction of the induced expectancies.
>
> This healing expectancy effect is definitely a parapsychological one in the sense that it cannot be entirely explained in terms of known sensory processes, since the 'target' animals were not known by anyone until the end of the study. We have therefore produced a paranormal healing effect, or something that resembles a healing effect, in a well controlled laboratory study which cannot be attributed to a specific psychic healer or healing treatment. It must therefore be attributable to something else and that something else may be operating in other psychic healing situations as well.
>
> In experimental studies of psychic healing treatments the experimenters may have reason to expect positive results. The healer may have performed well in pilot or screening trials, may have brought an impressive anecdotal case history of successful healings, or may make a strong personal impression on one of the experimental staff members. The results of the current study, modelled after this situation, sug-

gest that the expectation structure may be an important contributor to the results, regardless of what the healer does.

Discussion

A. Though no *known* healer participated in the study, one must postulate that one (or more) of the experimenters was responsible for the significant healing effects.

This is a key study for understanding possible errors of interpretation that might arise even in controlled studies. Mice in this study were all inoculated with the same dose of malarial parasites, yet some became sicker than others. On the surface this seems to indicate a healer effect. SOLFVIN points out that this need not be so in all cases. Differentials in the handling of mice in the various groups in line with handler expectations (perhaps augmented by clairsentient or precognitive perceptions of mouse group assignments) could have produced portions of the results.

Healing effects were clearly noted in addition to the presumed handling results. This was so even without the intervention of anyone designated as healer and without anyone knowing by sensory means which animals were assigned to healing and non-healing *groups*. This is reminiscent of STANFORD's (1974b) report of a successful PK experiment in which a subject "just hoped everything would go well", without even comprehending what was requested.

The implications of this study are truly revolutionary. They indicate that *psi influence can be produced despite apparent totally controlled, double-blind conditions.* If substantiated by repetitions under a variety of circumstances this will force science to reevaluate one of its most valuable tools in research, the double-blind experiment. It will throw into question many assumptions based

on previous studies of this type. The expectations of experimenters should be clearly stated in future studies, as this may be one of the variables affecting the results.

B. The experiment was designed well and reported adequately. The levels of significance are too modest for any far-reaching conclusions to be made without further replications.

P. Baranger and M.K. Filer – The protective action of collars in avian malaria *(Mind and Matter 1967)*

In many parts of the world, various collars, bracelets, anklets, and earrings are recommended for protection against illness. Their potency is usually attributed to the substance of the materials used, which may include gold, silver, copper, iron or plant materials. This study examined the effects of such collars on the progress of avian malaria.

… Six-day-old chicks were given an intravenous injection of the strength of 40 million parasites *(Plasmodium gallinaceum)*, taken from a highly infected bird. Five days later a count was made of the parasite content of the blood corpuscles, and in addition the average number of days which the chicks lived after infection was noted.

The effect on the parasites elsewhere in the system was also measured… The six-day-old chicks were given an intravenous injection of sporozoites in a suspension of the mosquito *Aedes Aegypti*, carrier of the sporozoites, macerated in blood diluted with Ringer's Solution… On the 16th, 23rd and 30th days respectively the numbers of birds free from parasites were counted; on the 30th day the number of birds still alive was count-

Table I - 14. Effects of metal collars on parasites in chicks
Experiment 1
The effect on the parasites in the system (other than in the red blood corpuscles)

No. of birds	Type of collar O = open C = closed S = spiral	% of birds parasite free on		% of birds alive on day 30	Avg. no. of days of survival
		day 16	day 23		
8	Gold (O)	40	--	--	20
5	Gold (O)	60	40	60	29,6
8	Silver (O)	--	--	--	18
4	Copper (S)	50	--	--	22,5
5	Copper (O)	40	--	--	26
5	Copper (O)	60	--	20	28,5
8	Copper (O) + rubber sheath	37	--	25	27,4
4	Copper (O) varnished	50	--	--	27,4
5	Copper (C)	33	--	16	28
6	Iron (O)	70	17	--	23
7	Iron (O)	50	--	20	22,7
6	Iron (C)	50	--	--	23
6	Iron (C)	70	--	--	23
8	Tin (O)	14	--	--	21
8	Zinc (O)	--	--	--	13,2
8	Aluminum (O)	--	--	--	12,2
8	German Silver (O)	--	--	--	14,2
8	Brass (O)	--	--	--	14,5
8	Nickel (O)	--	--	--	14,3
8	Nickel Chrome (O)	--	--	--	12
8	Lead (O)	--	--	--	15
8	Magnesium (C)	--	--	--	11,6
8	Lead (S)	--	--	--	11,5
8	Manganese (S)	--	--	--	11,6
6	Cotton (C)	--	--	--	11
6	Chloroquine	66	--	33	24
6	Quinine	83	33	50	30
13	Controls	--	--	--	11,6
196	Total				

ed, and in addition the average survival time of the chicks was noted.

The metal collars were 1 mm in diameter, of either open, closed or spiral design, measuring about 20 mm across. The materials used included: aluminum, brass, copper, gold, iron, lead, magnesium, manganese, molybdenum, nickel, nickel alloy (nickel, iron, chromium and manganese), silver, German silver (copper, nickel and zinc), tin and zinc. Plant fiber collars, also about 20 mm across, were made from twisted threads of cotton, linen, nylon, rayon, silk, sisal and wool. In one experiment copper and iron were twisted together; in another a rubber sheath completely encased a copper collar; in a third, a coat of varnish was applied to a copper collar. Chicks were acclimated to the collars for two days prior to the injection of parasites.

Groups of six to eight birds were used in repeated trials, until more than 350 birds were included in the studies. Birds in control groups were either given nothing or had 12 doses of either 1mg of chloroquine or quinine.

Gold, iron and copper appeared most effective. The average survival of the birds wearing these collars was 20–30 days compared with only 11.6 days for the controls. The ap-

Table I - 15. Effects of metal collars on parasites in chicks
Experiment 2
The effect on the parasites in the red blood corpuscles

No. of Birds	Type of collar O = open C = closed S = spiral	% cells infected by the 5th day	Avg. no. of days of survival
6	Gold (O)	26	20
6	Silver	27	15
6	Copper (O)	27	17,6
6	Copper (S)	27	15,3
6	Copper (C)	30	16,6
10	Iron (O)	28	14
6	Iron (S) (claws)	44	15
4	Iron & Copper (O)	33	17
7	Nickel	46	13
8	Nickel Chrome (O)	45	15
8	Magnesium (O)	54	10
8	Zinc (O)	62	14
8	Aluminum (O)	50	11
8	Lead (O)	48	14
8	Molybdenum (O)	50	14
8	Brass (O)	48	12
6	Wool	68	14
6	Cotton (C)	73	13
6	Linen (C)	64	14
6	Sisal (C)	64	13,3
6	Nylon (C)	68	14
6	Silk (C)	68	14
6	Rayon (C)	61	13,6
4	Quinine (1mg 7 times)	9	16
12	Controls	80	13,5
171	Total		

pearance of the parasites in the blood of birds with collars of these metals was delayed dramatically relative to the controls. In the second experiment the results were comparable to or exceeded the results obtained with quinine or chloroquine. Tin and silver increased slightly increased the average length of survival or had no effect. Results were not related to collar shape, nor were they altered by the sheathing with rubber or varnish. Fiber collars produced only a slight lowering of the percentage of parasite count. Cotton had no effect. (See Table I-14, on page 189.)

All the metals decreased the percentage of cells infected with parasites. Gold, silver, copper and iron were particularly effective. (See Table I-15.)

In several instances birds lost their collars. Their infections increased markedly by the next day. In one case an iron spiral around the claws replaced an iron collar, resulting in a parasite infection of only 44%.

Discussion

A. The effects of metal collars on prolonging survival with malarial infection seem clear. How to explain the findings is a problem. I have deliberately placed this study following Solfvin's study, as the experimenter effect seems a likely explanation. One might also postulate that the presence of the metal or fiber collar alters an energy field around or within the body so that the defense mechanisms of the organism function more efficiently. This seems a possible explanation since particular metals appear to have greater influence than other materials. Again, however, the differential responses could be an experimenter effect.

This study is to be differentiated from studies of bracelets with knobs worn in order to activate acupressure points relevant to various ailments.

B. Randomization is not described and no statistical analyses are presented. Blinds could be easily arranged with coated materials.

The next studies explore healing for tumors in mice.

Brenio Onetto and Gita H. Elguin – Psicoquinesis en la tumorogenesis experimental (Psychokinesis in experimental tumorogenesis) *(Journal of Parapsychology 1966)*

This is a translated abstract based on a thesis presented for Professional Degree in Psychology, University of Chile 1964, by Gita H. Elguin.

ONETTO/ELGUIN state:

That PK ability may be effective in inhibiting tumoral growth in living organisms is suggested by a preliminary study in which the area, weight and volume of such growth in one group of 30 tumorogenic mice showed significantly less growth (p less than 0.01) than that of 30 untreated control mice after 20 sessions of treatment with 'negative PK'. A second group of 30 mice were treated for an equal period of time with 'positive PK' in an attempt to increase the tumoral growth, but these mice did not differ from the untreated control animals. All mice initially had been inoculated subcutaneously with a tumoral suspension and then had been assigned randomly to the three groups.

ANTHONY CAMPBELL (1968) adds, regarding those treated with positive PK by Elguin, that

... the average tumour area was significantly smaller at 16 days and 22 days (p < 0.001 in both cases), and when the animals were killed (at 23 days) this difference was confirmed by direct measurement and weighing of the tumours (p < 0.01). The animals ... lost significantly less body weight than did the controls (p < 0.05).

The experimenter suggests that her failure to influence tumour growth ... may have been owing to her partly unconscious dislike of this part of the study.

Discussion

A. This appears a sound, significant study. We have a more complex situation here. The healer may be affecting the target cells or their enzymes as in previous experiments. In addition, the healer may be influencing the host animal's own defense mechanisms to act on the cancer cells. Host antibodies against cancer might be increased; blood supply to tumors might be diminished, thus 'starving' the tumors; or other processes may be activated.

The fact that attempts to increase the rate of tumor growth failed is interesting. This is in line with many healers' claims that a *native intelligence* in the healing process guides healing to act only in directions that are beneficial to the healee, in line with the intentions of the healer.

B. This appears to be a good study, but insufficient raw data are provided for evaluation of procedures or independent confirmation of statistical analyses.

FRANS SNEL, whose studies are reviewed earlier in this chapter, observes: "... the report does not suggest a careful handling of the material: her preparations suffered from infections which have an influence on the tumor growth, and she used an unreliable method for measuring tumors." He does not elaborate on these criticisms.

Gary Null – Healers or hustlers (Self-Help Update 1981)

GARY NULL sought to understand healing when his brother had a stroke at the age of 35. In this, the fourth of a series of articles, Null details his explorations of healers, the healing process and subjective aspects of the healing experience.

Fifty healers were screened for demonstrable ability to prolong the lives of mice injected with cancer cells. Healers were assigned one mouse for touch healing and one for distant healing, with another two as controls.

Each mouse was inoculated with a highly lethal strain of cancer. Healers were allowed to employ whatever methods they felt would prolong the lives of their mice.

Only one of the fifty healers was consistently successful. *RABBI ABRAHAM WEISMAN* produced total tumor regression in one of his mice and the other survived longer than average.

Rabbi Weisman then participated in further studies.

The second and third experiments began on July 14, 1977. In each experiment 20 mice were inoculated with cancer; 10 of them were to be treated with healing energies and 10 were to serve as controls.

A double-blind procedure was used throughout the experiment. The scientist who evaluated the results of the evolution of the tumors and survival times of the animals was not aware of whether the respective animal was from the control group or the treated group. Nor did the scientist know who selected and marked the animals.

... Weisman was able to extend the average life of the treated mice to 12.8 days, compared to 8.9 days for the control group.

The increase amounted to 43.8 percent.

In the second experiment the mice were inoculated with half the cancer cells of the first experiment. Weisman was able to extend the average life of the treated mice to 14.9 days, compared to 12.9 days for the controls. The increase amounted to 15.5 percent.

Rabbi Weisman commented:

> As I became adept at working with the energies I began to realize that, although I believe I am channeling from God, you might believe you are channeling from Buddha, the wind or the sun and it would still be the same energy source.
>
> I also found that you cannot impose a healing on anybody. People create their illnesses for their own reasons, and there is a lesson for them in it. Each person is as powerful as any other, thus each person must choose health over sickness. Only then will the healing take effect.

Discussion

A. This is the first broad scientific screening of healers to determine healing ability. The use of only two mice each seems likely to lead to Type II errors in all but the very best healers. Some healers may be squeamish regarding mice or in other ways unprepared or inexperienced for working with animals in general, or uncomfortable in a laboratory.

B. Randomization is not mentioned, raw data are not provided and no statistical analyses are reported.

The following is an exploration of animal gentling. FREDERICK KNOWLES, a healer, assumes that healing may be involved in the observed effects.

Frederick W. Knowles – Rat experiments and mesmerism *(Journal of the American Society for Psychical Research 1959)*

FREDERICK W. KNOWLES very briefly reviews eight experiments exploring the effects of stroking on young rats' rate of growth. He notes that five of the eight reported a positive effect of enhanced weight gain. He suggests that differences in personality between strokers may be an important variable. He was unable to produce weight gains when he himself was a stroker, observing that rats rarely purred for him when he stroked them but that they did so regularly for his two-year-old daughter.

Knowles considers alternative hypotheses to account for observed differences in some studies, including poor temperature controls, defecation and urination of unstroked rats during handling prior to weighing and unconscious bias of experimenters in choosing rats for E and C groups.

Discussion

A. The assumption in these studies is that healing might be involved in weight gain. Other researchers have also found greater resistance to disease in laboratory animals with stroking (e.g. NEREM, LEVESQUE/CORNHILL; DOSSEY 1982). Generally, such effects are attributed to calming, which then results in beneficial hormonal alterations. Conversely, healing may be involved in calming.

The following would appear to be a more suitable model: control group stroked by non-healers; experimental group by healers.

B. No data or statistical analyses are presented to help evaluate the significance of the findings in the series of studies.

The effects of healing on animals are summarized in Table I-16 (on page 194).

Table I - 16. Effects of healing on animals

Subject of healing	Researchers	T/N/D*	Duration	Healers	Results	Significance
Mice Skin wounds	Grad (1965)	N	15 mins x 2 days	Estebany	**1.** 48 mice, more rapid wound healing: Day 14	p< .001
	Grad, Cadoret & Paul	N	x 14 days	Estebany	**2.** 150 mice, double blinds: Days 15, 16	p< .01
Retardation of goiter growth	Grad (1965)	1. N	15 mins x 2/day x 5 d/week x 8 weeks	Estebany	**1.** 23 mice, slower thyroid growth, with baseline and heat controls	p< .001
		vehicle	1 hr x 2/day x 6 d/week	Estebany	**2.** 37 mice, same	p< .001
Malaria	Solfvin	D	?	3 + (?)	**1.** 2 believers, 12 mice each 1 non-believer, opposite direction from the expected for malaria healing	NS** p< .02 p< .09
				5 + (?)	**2.** 12 mice each: malaria healing	.05<p< .10 p< .05
Chicks Malaria	Baranger & Filer	Collars	Constant	Metal, vegetable materials	368 chicks wore collars of various metals or plant fibers. Gold, iron, and copper were most effective against malaria	Significant (?)
Mice Tumors	Onetto & Elguin	?	?	Elguin	**1.** 30 Tumorogenic mice, healer to decrease tumor	.001<p<.01
					2. Same, healer to increase tumor growth	NS
	Null	T&D	?	50 healers	**1.** 1 mouse each for E and C: 12.8 days (E) vs 8.9 days (C) - 44 % longer	?
				Weisman	**2.** 20 mice, 1/2 dose cancer cells: 14.9 days (E) vs 12.9 (C) - 15.5% longer	?
Rats Growth	Knowles	T	?	?	Enhanced growth in 5/8 experiments	?

* T/N/D: Touch/Near/Distant   **NS: Non-Significant

The following is a series of studies in which the objective of the healing is to hasten recovery from anesthesia. Many healers report that they can appreciably reduce the morbidity of surgery by adding healing to the routine medical care of the surgical patient. Healing may lessen anxiety, pain, swelling, infections, and hasten wound healing. Healing is often given prior to, during and after hospitalisation.

Reducing the amount of time patients spend under anesthesia could reduce all sorts of complications which accrue the longer the anesthesia is applied.

This series also demonstrates how experimenters hone their methods to focus with increasing clarity on possible mechanisms of healing.

G.K. and A.M. Watkins – Possible PK influence on the resuscitation of anesthetized mice (Journal of Parapsychology 1971)

Journal Abstract:

Twelve subjects (nine of them professed 'psychics' or known to be exceptional performers on PK or ESP tests) were tested for their ability to cause mice to arouse more quickly from ether anesthesia than normally would be expected. Pairs of mice (Swiss-Webster) were simultaneously rendered unconscious in identical etherizers charged with 10 ml USP ether. The pairs were of the same sex, comparable size, and were litter mates. After both mice were unconscious, they were removed to plastic pans and taken to the area in which the subject was seated. The lids of the pans were then removed and the subject was told to attempt to awaken his or her mouse. The other mouse was used as a control.

For all experiments, 24 pairs of mice were serially anesthetized in each 'run'. Care was taken to randomize mice which were more easily anesthetized between the experimental and the control conditions.

Experiment 1: Of 10 runs, 8 were by talented subjects. Subjects and experimental mice were in one room, control mice in another.

The mean sleep time for the controls was 32.63 seconds, that of the experimentals, 28.72 seconds...$p = 0.03$. There were 157 hits in the 240 trials...[$p < 0.01$ or < 0.001, depending on statistical methods used]...

Experiment 2: Of 7 runs, 6 were by talented subjects. Subjects and both mice were in the same room. Mice were on a table, separated by a wooden screen. Subjects could see only the experimental mouse, while experimenters could see both. Separate experimenters timed experimental and control mice.

Overall, the mean control time for all subjects was 27.90 seconds, as compared with the mean experimental time of 21.54 seconds...$p < 0.001$. There were 116 hits out of 168 trials...[$p < 0.01$ or 0.001, depending on statistical methods used]... There were no negative runs in Experiment 2...

Experiment 3: All 15 runs were by talented subjects. Both mice were in the same room, with the subject in an adjacent room, viewing them through a one-way mirror.

...all of the subjects who participated in this phase of the experiments expressed discomfort at being asked to shift sides more than once in the course of the run and even protested one side change unless a brief rest period could be provided between the two halves of the run. Such a period was provided in all four runs of the last part of Experiment 3. The subjects also noted that they felt more at ease with the experiment during those trials in which A.W. was timing the experimental animal and the target side was the left; and this is the situation which produced the most consistent scoring...

* In 4 runs the experimenters had full knowledge of the subjects' location.
* In 7 runs the experimenters were completely blind.

The mean control time to arousal was 24.79 seconds, and the mean experimental a little greater, 26.01 seconds. There were 88 hits from 168 trials. None of these values differs significantly from chance. Moreover, none of these seven individual runs is independently significant in either direction...

...c) In four runs, five variables were randomized through a factorial design to control for E and C mice; left/right side of table viewed by subjects; experimenters timing mice; ease of mouse-anesthetization; and type of mouse (male, female or juvenile). The experimenters were 'partially blind'...

... the subject being randomly assigned the right or left side at the start, without the experimenters' knowing which side had been chosen, and remaining there for 12 trials.

After a 15 minute break, the subject would concentrate on the mouse on the opposite side for the remaining 12 trials... all four of these runs were independently significant.

For Experiment 3, overall, the mean time to arousal for the controls was 30.14 seconds... for the experimentals... 24.91 seconds... $p < 0.001$. There were 237 hits in 360 trials... $p < 0.001$... [by both statistical methods].

A possible experimenter effect is suggested by the negative results under blind conditions. WATKINS/WATKINS propose:

In general, there are three ways in which the experimenters could have biased the study: (1) through unequal treatment of the experimentals and controls in the process of etherization; (2) through direct effects on the time to arousal of the mouse in some direct physical way; (3) through timing or recording errors.

Watkins and Watkins argue that all of these are unlikely.

Discussion
A. Significant accelerations of recovery from anesthesia are demonstrated.
B. This is an excellent study.

Roger Wells and Judith Klein – A replication of a psychic healing paradigm (Journal of Parapsychology 1972)

Journal Abstract:

An attempt was made to replicate the findings of a previously reported experiment by G.K. and A.M. Watkins. In the present experiment, four subjects previously determined to be 'gifted' were tested for their ability to cause mice to arouse more quickly from ether anesthesia than normally would be expected. One mouse of each pair tested was an experimental mouse; the other, a control. The subject's task was to try to awaken the experimental mouse more quickly than the other. Eight experiments, each consisting of 24 trials, were conducted. Seven of the eight were in the expected direction, one being independently significant at the level of $p = 0.01$. There was an average difference of 5.52 seconds between the time the experimental mouse awoke and the time the control mouse awoke ($p < 0.05$). Of the total 192 trials, 110 were hits ($p < 0.05$).

Discussion

A. These are highly significant results in nonsuggestible subjects. A true healing effect seems to be demonstrated.

B. This is another excellent study but, as in the previous example, the experimenters could have caused the observed effects because mice were not randomised thoroughly. Perhaps the experimenters clairsentiently or precognitively selected mice with short waking times to be targets, relative to slow wakers, similarly selected. Perhaps the person timing the waking biased the results.

G. K. Watkins, A. M. Watkins, and R. A. Wells – Further studies on the resuscitation of anesthezized mice *(Research in Parapsychology 1972)*

The previous experiment was replicated seven times with more careful controls and with attempts to rule out possible factors, other than PK, that might influence results. Mice were assigned randomly to E and C groups.

Subjects sat behind a one-way mirror. Experimenters monitored the waking of anesthetized mice in 'blind' fashion. "Sixteen (or 24) such trials constitute a run; the target for the first eight (or 12) is the mouse on one side of the table, and for the second eight (or 12) the mouse on the other side. A 15- to 30-minute break separates the first and second halves of the run."

The results of the various series were as follows:

Experiment 1: Simple replication, using two new 'talented' subjects, ($p = 0.026$).

Experiment 2: Mice pairs preselected according to similar wakening times, anesthetized in the same container ($p = 0.002$).

Experiment 3: 'Non-talented' subjects ($p =$ non-significant in previous tests): subjects' belief in ESP was positively related to scoring ($p = 0.05$). "Those who did not think they would do well in fact did better than those who had a more confident attitude ($p = 0.01$)."

Experiments 4; 5: Subjects were monitored for EEG, ECG, respiration, finger plethysmograph and galvanic skin response (GSR).

The GSR showed no significant changes during the test session, and was therefore dropped from the second series. In both series, the subjects showed significantly increased heart rate, decreased pulse amplitude, increased respiration rate, increased irregularity of respiration, alpha block in the occipital EEG, and muscle tension in the skeletal muscles. The T-wave in the ECG was significantly higher at the end of the session than at the beginning for females; for males, it was significantly lower. Both series yielded significant PK scoring ($p = 0.004$ and $p = 0.00003$).

Experiments 6; 7:

Finally, two series were done to find out why there had been chance results in previous work when the target side was randomly changed from trial to trial, rather than remaining the same for each half of the run. The subjects had complained that they could not shift their focus of concentration fast enough, which led us to hypothesize that a 'lag effect' might exist in which the PK effect exerted on the previous trial would continue to have an influence on the mouse's performance in the current trial. To test for such an effect we had the subjects in these two series do half of a normal run, concentrating exclusively on one side or the other. The subjects then left the room and occupied themselves with other activities while the experimenters, who were of course unaware of which side had been the target, continued the procedure to the end of the run. In the first of these series the same experimenters performed both halves of the run; in the second, as an added precaution against experimenter effects, two different experimenters conducted the second half.

Linear regression analyses showed the two halves of the run to be similar in overall scoring. This was true in both series (p = 0.02 in each). In addition, both halves of the run showed independently significant high scoring levels in each series. In the first series the first half was significant at p = 0.003 and the second half at p = 0.002. In the second series the significance levels were p = 0.04 for the first half and p = 0.05 for the second half.

In one of the series timing was also done manually with a stopwatch. No significant difference was found between the two methods, attesting to the reliability of each.

Discussion

A. This is a demonstration of work carefully done to tease out alternative explanations. Series 2 rules out the possibility that the results were due to biased selection of mice.

Series 6 and 7 try to clarify an apparent 'lag' or 'linger' effect of a healing. The researchers feel that the healing directed to a given side of the table seems to linger after a given trial so that subsequent mice on that side benefit from the healing sent to the previous mice at that spot. (See also CAHN/MUSCLE'S experiment on an enzyme, described previously, in which a linger effect was suggested.)

Though scantily reported, the meticulous report of WATKINS/WATKINS (reviewed above) suggests it is highly likely this one was equally meticulously designed and run.

B. This is an excellent study, but too briefly reported.

Questions remain. Did the experimenters who monitored the wakening of mice know that mice on one side of the table would always be E (or C) for a number of consecutive trials? How many subjects participated? What were raw scores and physiological measures? It is still possible that the experimenters caused the observed effects. If subjects knew the purpose of the experiment, they could continue to send healing energy from a distance. If animal handlers knew the nature of the study they might sense via psi which side of the table had been the target side and might then cause the observed waking effects themselves.

Roger Wells and Graham K. Watkins – Linger effects in several PK experiments (*Research in Parapsychology 1974*)

WELLS/WATKINS report on further clarifications of their earlier studies:

> In the first series of experiments with this 'healing' effect, we noted that the subjects failed to produce a significant effect when the assigned target side (right or left) was randomly varied from trial to trial. They did well, however, when one side was used as target throughout half of a given run. It is unlikely that this was due to bias in the experimental system. It could be explained, however, if the effect which was causing the accelerated waking of the target mice did not immediately dissipate when the subject ceased to concentrate, but rather lingered on for a certain period of time. This idea was reinforced by the finding that a rest period of approximately 30 minutes was required between halves of the run to insure a successful second half, when the target side was changed from first to second half.

Two experiments were then performed:
1. In eight runs of 24 trials each the target side for each run was randomly chosen. The subjects left the building (from behind the one-way mirror) after the first half of each run. The second half of the run was begun immediately, as though the subjects were still present.

> The first halves showed significantly faster awakening for the mice on the target side...$p < 0.001$, and in the second halves the mice on that side continued to awaken first...; $p < 0.001$.

2. The basic design was the same as that of the first experiment. In eight runs of 16 trials each, one pair of experimenters ran the first half and another pair ran the second half of each run. The second pair was 'blind' with respect to the target side and the outcome of the first half.

> Both halves of this series were significant in the expected direction when tested by analysis of variance ($p = 0.024$ for first halves; $p = 0.015$ for second halves), but only the second halves were significant when analyzed by t-test...$p = 0.05$ for second halves.

The researchers reached the following conclusions:

> This second series of experiments seemed to indicate that the 'linger effect' is not only a reality but may be a more reliable finding than the main effect. Certainly it explains the failure of the subjects in our earlier research to achieve significant results in those runs in which a random side sequence was used rather than one side continuously.

Wells and Watkins then discuss anecdotal reports which may also be relevant. A gifted subject psychokinetically deflected a compass needle, which then remained offset even after she left the area. The needle appeared stuck and was not affected by a magnet or a steel knife.

> When, however, the compass was moved to a distance of approximately one meter away, it returned to North and became normally sensitive to the magnet and blade. When it was moved back, it again moved off North and appeared to lose its normal sensitivity to metal. It is of consid-

erable interest that this effect also took about 30 minutes to decay, over which time the needle gradually moved back to North and gradually regained its sensitivity.

Other possible PK effects of a lingering nature on electronic equipment are also described.

Discussion

A. We continue to see significant healing effects.

B. Again scanty reporting mars otherwise apparently excellent studies. The fact that the experimenters handling the mice appear to have known the purpose and design of the experiments introduces a possibility that experimenter effects might be demonstrated rather than a linger effect. It is also unclear whether subjects knew the experiment was being continued after their departure. Distant healing might also explain the so-called linger effect. Further experiments could be conducted: (1) ensure experimenters and subjects are blind concerning the existence of the second part of the experiment; and (2) assuming the linger effect to be possible, to measure the space within which it appears to function.

Marilyn J. Schlitz – PK on living systems: Further studies with anesthezized mice *(Parapsychology Review 1982)*

In her *Report of the 1982 SERPA Conference* DEBRA WEINER reviews M. SCHLITZ's paper:

A conceptual replication of earlier work by the Watkins team, this experiment tested to see whether or not subjects could use PK to arouse an anesthetized mouse more quickly than a matched control mouse. For each trial two female mice of similar weight were anesthetized and placed over photocells. Television cameras located above the animals were interfaced to a random number generator (RNG) so that one of them could be automatically turned on according to an RNG decision. This procedure determined which mouse was the 'target' animal to be viewed by the subject on a video monitor in a separate room, keeping the animal handler blind to target assignment. Arousal time was measured automatically by the photocells, a methodological improvement over the previous work...

Three subjects participated in 60 trials each, though some data were lost to technical problems. Two measures of success were taken: a rough 'hit/miss' depending on whether the target or control animal awoke first and the difference in arousal times. One subject obtained 33 hits and 24 misses, which was not significant though the difference in arousal times was... ($p < 0.05$...). Subject 2 obtained suggestive psi-missing at the 0.08... level by the hit/miss measure and no psi was produced by the third subject.

Discussion

A. Methodological probelms appear to have been solved and modestly significant positive healing results are evident. Better description of the subjects is desirable.

B. It is reassuring to see persistent research in pursuit of ever refined methods and paradigms. These marginally significant results are encouraging. It would be useful to have further replications with this design.

A full report with raw data is still needed for independent analysis of the results.

The experiments on anesthetized mice are summarized in Table I-17.

Table I - 17. Healing effects on anesthetized mice

Researchers	T/N/D*	Healers	Results	Significance
Watkins & Watkins	D	12 subjects (9 psychic)	1. Experimental mice & healers in one room; control mice in another room: sleep time ***hits 157/240	p< .036 p< .01-.001
			2. All in same room: sleep time hits 116/168	p< .001 p< .01
			3. Healers in one room, both mice in another room, behind one-way mirror: sleep time behind one-way mirror: hits 237/360 Overall results for experiments 1-3	p< .001 p< .001 p < .00001
Wells & Klein	D	4 gifted	Per (3) above; 1 experimenter selecting mice, other experimenters testing: sleep time hits 110/192	p< .02-.05 p< .05
Watkins, Watkins & Wells	D	2 gifted psychics	1. One way mirror, experimenters blind: half-series alternating sides of table, 15-30 minute breaks between halves	p < .026
			2. Mice paired by similar waking times	p < .002
		Non-gifted	3. Believers in ESP vs non-believers. Confident vs non-confident	p < .05 p < .01
			4. Healer physiological paramaters: GSR Increases in pulse; respiration; skeletal muscle tension; female EKG T wave at end Decreases in pulse amplitude; male EKG T wave at end Waking of paired mice	NS**)))) all significant p < .004
			5. Automatic timing of arousal	p < .00003
			6. Lag effect with random sides for 1/2-runs	p < .002-3
			7. Different experimenters for second 1/2-runs, automatic timing of arousal	p < .04-5
Wells & Watkins	N D(?)		1. Sides randomly chosen, constant in runs: First 1/2 - healers present Second 1/2 - healers left building	p< .002 p< .001
			2. Separate experimenters for each 1/2, second one blind to first-1/2 side: First 1/2 - healers present Second 1/2 - healers left building	p < .024 p < .015-.05
Schlitz	D	3	TV monitors; random number generator for target choice; healer in remote room; arousal time by photo cells: Only 1 healer hit vs miss	p < .05

* T/N/D: Touch/Near/Distant **NS: Non-Significant ***hits: successful trials

Healing Action on Electrodermal Activity

The next set of studies examines a more limited influence of one person upon another. They fit the definition of healing in that one person influences another person's physiology via mechanisms that do not involve physical interactions, although healing to improve a problem condition was not the intent.

These reports presume familiarity with the following:

1. Feedback systems have been developed to provide information which an individual can use to alter his internal physiological states. These systems give the individual data on parts and functions of his body of which he normally has no conscious cognizance since they are controlled automatically by the autonomic (unconscious) nervous system. For example, there are feedback systems that monitor electrodermal activity, which correlates with states of tension in the body. When a person can see on a dial or hear by the pitch of a tone his level of skin resistance, he can use this information to alter the instrument reading or tone and thereby to relax his body.[22]

2. REX STANFORD's conformance theory to explain psi (1974; 1978) postulates that the will of a subject can act upon random elements in a system to introduce greater order.[23]

In the first study of this series WILLIAM BRAUD introduced an innovation into the feedback model. He provided an observer (O) with information on the electrodermal activity of a subject (S), who is in another room. O is then told to influence S in order to reduce S's electrodermal activity by PK.

William Braud: Confirmance behavior involving living systems *(Research in Parapsychology 1978)*

WILLIAM BRAUD suggests:

> I would like to state the [conformance] theory in even more general terms than does Stanford, and suggest that under certain conditions, a system possessing a greater degree of disorder (randomness, lability, noise, entropy) changes its organization so as to more closely match that of another system possessing less disorder, less entropy, greater structure. The greater the number of possible alternative states of the random event generator (REG), and the greater the organization of the structured system, the greater should be the probability of conformance behavior.

Braud summarizes 14 experiments investigating this theory. He introduces animate random systems and "firm intention of an observer serves as the more structured system." Each experiment consisted of a randomly distributed series of 10 E and 10 C periods of 30 seconds each. The author, MATTHEW MANNING (a gifted healer) and 10 unselected observers were used.

Experiments 1-4, allobiofeedback modelI: An observer continuously monitors electrodermal activity (EDA) of a subject in another room during the twenty minutes of an experiment. The observer tries to activate recording during the randomly selected 30-second periods. Polygraph records were scored blindly. Observers obtained highly significant results (p = 0.002).

A later report adds details to the above (BRAUD/SCHLITZ 1989). Two types of electrodes are in general use for EDA measurement. BRAUD utilized each type in separate experiments. Silver/silver chloride electrodes with partially conductive gel on the subject's palm were used in Experiments 1 and 3; chrome-plated stainless steel finger electrodes without electrode paste were used in Experiments 2 and 4. Different electronic equipment was used with each type of electrode. EDA was assessed by blind scoring of print-outs of readings.

... In Experiments 1 and 3, the subject was exposed to visual and acoustic ganzfeld stimulation throughout the session...this was accomplished by having the subject view a uniform red light field through translucent, hemispherical acetate covers while listening to moderately loud white noise through headphones. In Experiments 2 and 4, ganzfeld stimulation was not employed; rather, the subject simply sat quietly in the dim room, with freedom to open or close the eyes as desired... The subject was instructed to make no deliberate effort to relax or to become more active, but rather to remain in as ordinary a condition as possible and to be open to and accepting of a possible influence from the distant influencer whom he or she had already met. The subject remained unaware of the number, timing or scheduling of the various influence attempts, and was instructed not to try to guess consciously when influence attempts might be made. The subject was asked to allow his or her thought processes to be as variable or random as possible and to simply observe the various thoughts, images, sensations, and feelings that came to mind without attempting to control, force, or cling to any of them.

The influencer sat in a comfortable chair in front of a polygraph in another closed room. The polygraph provided a graphic analog readout of the concurrent electrodermal activity of the distant subject... The influencer had the option of attending to this polygraph feedback or ignoring it. In most cases, the influencer watched the polygraph tracing throughout a session. In some cases, the influencer closed his or her eyes and ignored the polygraph tracing during the actual 30-second imagery or nonimagery periods... but looked at the tracings following those periods in order to learn of the success or failure of the influence attempts.

Experimental sessions consisted of 20 randomly selected 30-second epochs. During some epochs the influencer was to influence (in some experiments to activate, in others to calm) the subject; in other epochs he was to not think about the subject or the experiment but to concentrate on other matters. Rest periods of 1/4 – 2 minutes were allowed between the 30-second epochs.

Repeated sequences of control (C) and influence (I) were randomly chosen, either CIIC or ICCI for the 12 sampling epochs of each session in order to preclude cumulative extraneous effects of one or the other type of epoch.

Influencer strategies could involve imaging by the influencer of the subject in relaxing or activating conditions; the influencer activating or relaxing himself while imaging the appropriate condition in the subject; or imaging the desired results on the tracings of the recording device.

Table 18 summarizes BRAUD's studies and may be helpful to the reader at this point, as well as in summary of the entire series.

Experiments 5-12, involving movements of animals, are not reviewed.

Experiment 13, prerecorded electrodermal activity ('backwards-in-time' causation model of SCHMIDT 1974): Format was identical to the first four experiments except that the EDA was prerecorded and the observer was unaware of this. The observer attempted to influence the subject's EDA which was electronically displayed for him on an oscilloscope. Experiment 13 produced results close to chance.

Discussion

A. Highly significant effects of healing were found in this series.

Decrease in EDA correlates roughly with decrease in physical and emotional tensions. This would provide a general contribution to well-being in almost any condition of disease or dis-*ease.* It would be specifically helpful with stress-related illness.

Experiments by others on the backwards-in-time model, using random number generators, have produced positive results.

B. Though highly significant results were obtained in what appear to be well-designed and well-executed studies, the descriptive data is somewhat meager. No information is provided on whether consideration was given to the possibility that observers might have been influencing the electronic monitors rather than the living systems. Belief systems of the experimenter and any observers are of interest, especially with respect to Experiment 13, as experimenter effects might be present here.[24]

William Braud and Marilyn Schlitz – Psychokinetic influence on electrodermal activity (*Journal of Parapsychology 1983*)

Experimenters' Abstract:

We conducted a 'bio-PK' experiment to determine whether target persons with a relatively strong need to be influenced (calmed) would evidence a greater psi effect than would persons without such a need. Serving as the influencers, we attempted to psychokinetically decrease the electrodermal activity of distant target persons during certain prespecified periods as compared to an equal number of control epochs in which PK attempts were not made. Sixteen target persons had relatively high sympathetic nervous system activity and thus had a need to be calmed. Sixteen other target persons had moderate or low activity and no particular need to be calmed. A significant PK-calming effect occurred for the active (needy) persons, but not for the inactive persons. The PK-calming effect was significantly greater for active than for inactive persons. Various nonpsychic and psychic explanations for these results are discussed.

For comparison, we conducted an experiment on self-control of autonomic activity in sixteen active subjects (a non-psi experiment). It indicated that the magnitude of self-control did not greatly exceed the magnitude of psychic hetero-influence of autonomic activity.

Significance levels for the calming effects were: p < 0.035 for the 16 active vs. 16 inactive subjects; p < 0.014 for the active subjects vs. chance expectations; p non-significant for inactive subjects.

Discussion

A. A response of EDA to healing is again demonstrated, significant where active subjects were used. This would seem to indicate that healing acts where needed, i.e. where a calming effect might be beneficial.

Activation of self-healing in the healee by the healer appears to be another possible mechanism for healing.

B. Well performed and well reported study.

The experimenters were not blind to the activity type of the subjects and thus an experimenter rather than a subject need effect may have been demonstrated. The authors consider this possibility but dismiss its significance with the observation that this would still demonstrate a need – of the experimenters.

William Braud, Marilyn Schlitz, John Collins and Helen Klitch – Further studies of the bio-PK effect: Feedback, blocking, specificity/ generality (Research in Parapsycholgy 1984)

Utilizing the same experimental arrangements for allobiofeedback as previously (BRAUD/SCHLITZ 1983), three experiments were run:

1. BRAUD/SCHLITZ/KLITCH studied whether 24 unselected volunteers could decrease the spontaneous EDA of 24 volunteer subjects. During half of each session immediate feedback was provided to the influencers; during the other half the influencers simply imagined the desired outcome. Subjects were blind to the sequence of influence and feedback conditions.

Feedback and non-feedback scores did not differ from each other significantly. Combined scores demonstrated a modest significant effect and the non-feedback alone produced a significant effect (each at p < 0.04).

2. BRAUD/SCHLITZ served as influencers, intending to *increase* the EDA of 32 distant subjects. Half of the subjects were told to cooperate and the other half "to attempt to shield themselves, psychologically and psychically, from this attempted psi influence upon their physiological activity". The influencers were blind to the subjects' intentions until the end of each session.

There were no significant differences between the results in the blocking and non-blocking conditions. The combined results of both groups did not reach a significant level. Post-hoc analysis of the individual experimenters' results showed that Braud produced modest significant effects in the cooperation sessions (p < 0.04) but not in the blocking sessions.

3. BRAUD/SCHLITZ/COLLINS explored how specific their focus as influencers might be on seleted physiological variables of subjects. They monitored pulse, peripheral skin temperature, frontalis muscle tension and breath rate. In half the sessions their goal was to calm the distant subjects; in the other half to make their bio-PK influence the EDA alone and not the other measures. In all cases feedback was provided for EDA but not for the other measures.

The only measure showing significant differences was pulse rate, and this differed among the three influencers (p < 0.05). SCHLITZ alone of the three demonstrated significant differences between the general calming and specific EDA focus condition (p < 0.01). BRAUD alone produced a significant deviation in the percent of pulse rate deviation from the expected theoretical average rate. The experimenters conclude:

1. Feedback is not necessary for influence over subjects' EDA.

2. No overall evidence supports the hypothesis that subjects can block a distant influence on their EDA, although there is a suggestion in the post-hoc results that this may be possible.

3. There is a limited indication that some specificity in distant bio-PK influence over various physiological parameters may be possible.

Discussion

A. The experimenters are rigorous in their application of statistical procedures, taking as significant only those findings which were predicted from the start of the experiment.

Experiment 1 is similar to distant healing, with modestly positive results.

Experiment 3 suggests healing may have selective physiological effects.

Blocking is reported anecdotally by many healers. It would be of great interest to pursue this issue further, in light of the suggestive blocking noted here.

B. One would need confirmation of the blocking and specificity effects before one could place much confidence in them.

Marilyn J. Schlitz and William G. Braud – Reiki plus natural healing: An ethnographic/ Experimental Study *(Psi Research 1985;* also in: Weiner/Radin (Eds.) *Research in Parapsychology 1986)*

SCHLITZ/BRAUD studied REV. DAVID JARRELL, who uses and teaches a modification of the *Reiki* healing system, and other *Reiki* healers.[25] He includes spirit guides, etheric bodies, chakras and past lives in his healing. The object of the study was to determine whether distant healing of this sort could alter the skin resistance response (SRR) of a subject, while feedback, consisting of a measurement of SRR, was given to the healer. Healer and subject were in separate rooms, 20 meters apart. Each of three healers had five sessions with one target person for each. In each session, *ten 30-second influence periods were compared with ten 30-second control periods.*

During the influence periods, the healer would attempt to calm the distant person's autonomic activity through various mental strategies. During the control periods, the healer either would do nothing or would attempt to activate the physiological activity of the distant person. The distant participant was blind as to the sampling periods as well as to the influence/control sequence. The magnitude of the distant calming effect was expressed as a percentage and was derived by dividing the SRR obtained during influence (calming) epochs by the total SRR of both epochs (the influence plus control epochs). Mean chance expectation (MCE) in the absence of any absentia healing effect was 50%.

Extensive interviews were conducted with

the healers, using formal questionnaires as well as less structured discussions to identify beliefs, expectations and experiences relating to the study. Volunteer subjects were screened for their beliefs in the existence of psi and healing. Only one of the subjects had ever consulted a healer.

During the experiment subjects were "asked to make no deliberate effort to relax, but rather to remain in as ordinary a condition as possible while listening to computer-generated random sounds through headphones and watching randomly changing patterns of colored squares on a 12-inch display screen about two meters away".

Data were recorded by computer. Ten epochs each for influence and control sessions were recorded. No significant distant healing effect was noted for the healers as a group or for any single healer, although results were in the expected direction.

Subjects reported they experienced a variety of sensations during the experiment, including 'rushes', muscle tremors, tingling, chills, a need to take deep breaths, extreme fluctuations of emotions, relaxation, openness and visual impressions (including memories of childhood).

Discussion

A. This study is seriously flawed, in that the healers were required to function in a fashion inconsistent with their ordinary healing practices.

As the authors themselves note:

> The experiment required that each calming period last only 30 seconds, to be followed, in many cases, by a control period in which the healer either attempted to increase the autonomic activity of the distant subject or to simply allow the subject to regain his or her normal state of autonomic activity. Furthermore, the direct polygraph feedback increased the amount of ego involvement that entered into the healing process...While relaxation is considered to be a healing state, the Reiki practitioners were quick to point out that what was done in the laboratory was not healing. In fact, as one of the participants noted: 'Healing is often an energizing effect.' While the experiment did provide a set-up for the study of an absentia influence on physiological activity, the Reiki practitioners viewed the project more as a game than as a true test of their abilities.

> Further, trying to calm people who were in many cases already calm may have been counterproductive to the healing influence...

B. Methodologically, this experiment was done and reported well.

William Braud and Marilyn Schlitz – Possible role of intuitive data sorting in electrodermal biological psychokinesis (*Research in Parapsychology 1987*)

This study explores the possibility that the observed effects of allobiofeedback may be

> ...contributed totally or partially by an intuitive data sorting (IDS) process in which the influencer or experimenter psychically, yet unconsciously, scans the future electrodermal activity stream of the subject and begins an experimental session at a time that maximizes the degree of fit between the on-going electrodermal activity and the prescribed schedule of influence

and control epochs. Stated somewhat differently, the experimenter might psychically and unconsciously sort the subject's electrodermal data into two bins so that significantly more of the activity in the prescribed direction falls in the influence bins than in the control bins... According to this 'informational' model, psi functioning is still in evidence but is of an informational rather than a causal (psychokinetic) sort.

The present study was designed to test a hypothesis suggested by the IDS model according to which the efectiveness of intuitive data sorting is proportional to the number of opportunities provided for such sorting. It was hypothesized that a single opportunity to psychically sort a future data stream may not be as effective as multiple opportunities for such sorting. On the other hand, according to a causal, psychokinetic interpretation of the bio-PK effect, the scheduling of the sampling epochs should not influence the results; i.e., the PK effect should be the same whether the influencer or experimenter has many or few degrees of freedom in deciding when to initiate sampling epochs.

Each of 8 influencers worked with four subjects (total 32 subjects). The apparatus was modified to include a button the influencer used to initiate sampling epochs. Subjects were watching random light patterns and listening to random sounds (*white noise*).

... The influencer was to press a button at what he or she intuitively felt to be the optimal time for beginning the next sampling epoch. The addition of the IDS option is, of course, accompanied by psychological factors such as beliefs and expectations that might obscure its true effectiveness. Therefore, a procedure was designed that would allow us to control for such psychological factors. This procedure required a contrast condition in which the influencer appeared to be initiating sampling epochs by means of button pressing but in reality was not. In the condition that we expected would optimize IDS, the influencer's button presses initiated sampling epochs after randomly determined variable delays. In this condition (the multiple-seeds condition), the precise times of occurrence of the button presses were crucial in determining the delay periods, since the button presses selected the clock values that served as the different seeds for the pseudorandom algorithm that generated the values of the delays. Thus, button presses actually could be efficacious in determining sampling scheduling. In the contrast condition (the single-seed condition), all random delay periods were determined by the first of the influencer's 12 button presses. The computer's clock value at the time of this first button press seeded the pseudorandom algorithm once and only once, and all other button presses 'fetched' their random delays from the already determined outcome of that first seeding.

Both influencer and experimenter were kept blind by these procedures as to which condition was in effect. The mechanical delays ranged from 30–40 seconds. It was also impossible for the influencer to time his intervention by educated guess from the feedback he had of the subject's EDA. Each subject had both a single-seed and a multiple-seeds trial on a double-blind basis.

For each session, a total score was calculated for all 12 recording epochs (6 calm-aim and 6 activate-aim). This total score was divided into the sum of the mean electrodermal activity scores for the 6 calm-aim epochs; the process was repeated for the activate-aim epochs. In the absence of a psi effect, these two ratios [C/(A+C), A/(A+C)] should approximate 50 percent. A psi effect would be evidenced by a set of calm-aim percentage scores that were significantly lower than 50 percent.

The difference between the ratios was not significant (p = 0.08), nor was a psi effect found in the multiple-seed condition. A psi effect was found in the single-seed condition (p = 0.019).

The authors conclude that this experiment does not support the hypothesis that intuitive data sorting explains their experiment, because the multiple-seed condition offered greater opportunity for IDS to occur but this condition did not demonstrate significant effects.

Discussion

A. The EDA effects observed in these experiments appear to be exerted intentionally by the influencer rather than selected by IDS to match the expectations.

B. The IDS hypothesis is not ruled out by this experiment. There is no way to rule out the possibility that IDS was occurring at the instigation of the experimenters by the influence of super-psi. In line with their investment in producing this long series of experiments, one would anticipate that the experimenters could orchestrate (unconsciously) the entire series of results to be consonant with a preferred hypothesis.

William Braud and Marilyn Schlitz – A methodology for the objective study of transpersonal imagery *(Journal of Scientific Exploration 1989)*

Continuing their series on the allobiofeedback model, BRAUD/SCHLITZ mention very briefly two new experiments (of 30 and 16 sessions) in a summarizing table (incorporated in Table 18). In a footnote they add that the first focused on 'whether increments or decrements in SRR activity might be easier to produce via distant mental influence.' The second studied 'whether the magnitude of a distant mental influence effect could be self-modulated by the influencer.' They promise to expand upon this in a later publication. No significant results were obtained in these experiments.

This article summarizes the entire series of allobiofeedback studies, providing descriptions and data not previously published. There were 323 sessions with 4 experimentrs, 62 influencers and 271 subjects. Of the 15 assessments, 6 (40 percent) produced significant results. Of the 323 sessions, 57 percent were successful (p = 0.000023).

Qualitative information is also provided. Subjects often reported subjective responses correlating closely with influencers' images.

Discussion

A. The overall significance of the series is most impressive.

B. It is disappointing to have so little detail on an experiment which produced no significant results.

The experiments on electrodermal activity are summarized in Table I-18.

Table I - 18. Effects of Healing on Electrodermal Activity

Researchers	No. of sessions	Influ- encer intent [2]	Subject focus [3]	Healers	Electrodes [4]	Results	Significance	
Braud (1979)	10	C/A	G & WN	Braud	S - palm	1. Demonstration, 9/10 sessions significant	.0065	.002 for this series
	10	A	Quiet	Manning	C - fingers	2. Demonstration, 8/10 sessions significant	.035	
	10	C/A	G & WN	10 volunt.	S - palm	3. Demonstration, 8/10 sessions significant	.0077	
	10	Quiet	10 volunt.	10 volunt.	C - fingers	4. Demonstration, 5/10 sessions significant	.736	
	?	?	?	Manning	?	13. Pre-recorded series of EDA	NS	
Braud & Schlitz	16	C	L, WN			1. 16 subjects, active GSR vs Controls inactive	p< .015	
						2. 16 subjects, active GSR vs chance	p< .014	
						3. 16 subjects, inactive GSR vs chance	NS	
Braud et al. (1985)	24	C	L, WN	24 volunt.	C - hand	1. 24 subjects, 1/2 feedback; 1/2 non-feedback: feedback vs non-feedback	NS	
						non-feedback, pre- vs post-intervention	p< .04	
						combined pre- vs post-intervention	p< .04	
	32	A	L, WN	2 'blind'	C - hand	2. 16 subjects cooperating; 16 blocking mental	NS	
	30	C	L,WN	3	S - palm	3. 5 calm subjects each; intention: to decrease EDA without affecting pulse, temperature, respiration. One healer succeeded on pulse.	p< .02	

Significance for entire series (Braud & Schlitz 1989):

(Table I-18 is continued on page 211.)

Table I - 18. Effects of Healing on Electrodermal Activity [1] (cont.)

Re-searchers	No. of sessions	Influ-encer intent [2]	Subject focus [3]	Healers	Elec-trodes [4]	Results	Signifi-cance
Braud & Schlitz (1989)	30	C/A	L, WN	Braud & Schlitz	S - palm	Increasing vs decreasing EDA	NS
	16	C	L, WN	Braud & Schlitz	S - palm	Influencer seeking to modu-late magnitude of EDA	NS
Schlitz & Braud (1985)	15	C	L, WN	3 healers (Reiki)	S - palm	5 sessions/healer	NS
Braud & Schlitz (1988)	40	C/A	L, WN	5 select. volunt.	S - palm	Intuitive Data Sorting (IDS) pilot	NS
	32	C/A	L, WN	8 select. volunt.	S - palm	IDS single seed	.02
	32	C/A	L, WN	8 select. volunt.	S - palm	IDS multiple seed	NS

Significance for entire series (Braud & Schlitz 1989):   p< .00023

[1] All the studies were distant, with 20 or 30 second duration of epochs for influencing subjects; the order of studies in the table follows that of Braud and Schlitz (1989).

[2] Calming (C) or activating (A) of subjects' EDA.

[3] Subjects focused either on a Ganzfeld (G) with or without 'white noise' (WN), or on a display of colored lights (L) on a screen along with white noise.

[4] Electrodes were either (S) silver/silver chloride with partially conductive gel or (C) chrome-plated stainless steel with electrode paste.

[5] Non-significant.

Healing Action on Human Physical Problems

L et us now turn to studies of healing on human illnesses. Unfortunately, very few controlled studies are available in precisely this category which is generally of most concern to those seeking healing in real life.

Dolores Krieger – Therapeutic Touch: The imprimatur of nursing (American Journal of Nursing 1975)

DOLORES KRIEGER was intrigued with BERNARD GRAD's research (1965), which demonstrated increased chlorophyll in plants watered by healer-treated water. Knowing that hemoglobin is similar in chemical structure to chlorophyll, she hypothesized hemoglobin levels could be increased in humans with psi healing. In three separate experiments with *Therapeutic Touch (TT)*, Krieger reports significant effects in E versus C groups ($p < 0.01$ twice, 0.001 once).

OSCAR ESTEBANY, the healer used in Grad's experiments, was the healer in Krieger's first three experiments.

In Krieger's fourth experiment, 32 nurses who were taught methods of TT were the healers. Results on hemoglobin levels were again significant ($p < 0.001$).

Psychological tests on the nurses con-

firmed Krieger's expectations that they were of self-actualized personality type.

Discussion

A. These pioneering studies of healing in humans extend the laboratory work with animals, again showing healing to be effective. They suggest yet another mechanism whereby healing may improve health. With anemia the lack of oxygen-carrying capacity of the blood can weaken an organism. Conversely, increased hemoglobin may help one fight off all sorts of illnesses.

It is unfortunate that more detailed descriptions are not provided regarding diagnoses, e.g., Were the patients anemic to start with? If so, from what causes? What sort of healing touch treatments were used (e.g. duration; whether on- or off-the-body healing was used; whether treatments were global and standardized or focal and individualized)? How long did the effects last? Were the results *clinically* significant?

In personal communication Krieger states that patients in E and C groups were matched for hemoglobin and hematocrit levels. The patients were blind to whether they were in E or C groups. Patients were selected according to willingness to participate in the study, without regard to diagnosis. The healing seemed especially effective in pernicious

anemia, producing results within two hours.
B. Raw data are not provided on specific hemoglobin levels in individual patients. Independent analysis of the data cannot, therefore, be made. Blinds are not described for experimenters.

SCHLOTFELDT adds the following criticisms:
1. Subjects were selected for the experiment according to the healer's intuition that he could help them. This might have biased the results.
2. It was suggested that subjects could meditate to enhance the healing. The meditation and not the healing might have produced the results.
3. Time of treatment was not standardized and varied widely between patients. (This seems to me an irrelevant criticism, considering the nature of healing, which is not administered in arbitrarily 'standardized doses' but rather according to the healer's intuition.)
4. No follow-up was done to check whether increases in hemoglobin were sustained.
5. The demography of the C group is not described. They may have differed significantly from the experimental group.

Wendy S. Wetzel – Reiki healing: a physiologic perspective *(Journal of Holistic Nursing 1989)*

Following the studies of KRIEGER which showed that TT may increase hemoglobin levels, WETZEL studied the effects of *Reiki* healing on this parameter.[25]

A self-selected sample of 48 adults in California were given first degree *Reiki* training after a blood sample was drawn. A second sample was drawn 24 hours after the first. Ten healthy medical professionals who were uninvolved with *Reiki* formed the control group and had two blood samples taken 24 hours apart.

Changes in the hemoglobin and hematocrit values were analysed using absolute numbers to determine the net change without reflecting directionality. Analysis of these data show a significant change in both parameters in the experimental group at the $p < 0.01$ level. The control group remained homogenous and demonstrated no significant change...

Wetzel notes that her study is limited by a lack of randomization, small control group, and lack of blinds for the experimenter who performed the fingersticks and read the hemoglobin and hematocrit values.

Discussion
A. A significant effect is noted for the group undergoing *Reiki* healing training. It is somewhat difficult to assess the significance of this observation because of a lack of clarity between *Reiki training* and *healing treatments*. The implication is that in learning to activate their healing gifts and applying this system, the healers also activate their own self-healing mechanisms.

The combining of increases and decreases in calculating statistical significance points to a dual effect of healing on hemoglobin levels. It is difficult to comprehend the functional benefits of a decrease in hemoglobin and hematocrit to the well-being of normal individuals. This suggests that conventional medicine might re-examine the ancient treatment of bleeding, which was discredited as an effective treatment as the result of a study of an influenza epidemic in the middle of the last century. It may be that there are problems for which bleeding is helpful. It is of course helpful in the condition of polycythemia, where excessive numbers of red blood cells are produced. It may be helpful in other conditions as well, or there may be more people suffering form polycythemia than we appreciate.

In personal communication WETZEL speculates:

> I feel that some individuals have overabundance of hemoglobin, and Reiki simply seeks to bring them to a level most beneficial to each individual...

My sense is that *Reiki* (and most other types of healing) seeks to return us to whatever physical state is most beneficial and in the greatest harmony. The word *healing* derives from the root *heil*, which means whole. Healing is felt by many healers to be a process of returning the healee to a state of wholeness in body, emotions, mind and spirit.

B. To combine increases and decreases in hemoglobin and hematocrit values as a statistical test of the effects of healing seems illogical in terms of conventional diagnoses and treatments.

Furthermore, the prediction one would anticipate following on to the KRIEGER studies is that hemoglobin and hematocrit levels should rise significantly. Wetzel predicted 'a significant change' and is thus within the bounds of legitimate claim to significant results.

Where no blinds are employed, experimenters may bias the results to conform with expectations or to produce significant effects.

The next study parallels GRAD's study of dermal wound healing in mice.

Daniel P. Wirth, – Unorthodox healing: The effect of noncontact Therapeutic Touch on the healing rate of full thickness dermal wounds (M.A. Thesis, JFK University, California; *Research in Parapsychology 1989, 1990; Subtle Energies 1990*)

Author's Abstract:

This experiment examined the healing effect of [5 minutes' treatment by] Noncontact Therapeutic Touch (NCTT) on full thickness dermal wounds surgically administered on human subjects. The wounds were administered at the same depth and diameter by a medical doctor using a local anaesthetic and skin biopsy instrument – this procedure created a relatively consistent...wound...for all subjects. The improvement in the mean wound surface area of the 'treatment' group was contrasted with the improvement in the mean wound surface area of the 'nontreatment' control group on day 8 and 16 of the study. The results obtained showed that there was a statistically significant difference between the 'treatment' and 'non-treatment' groups on both day 8 ...and day 16 (...p < 0.001...).

Subjects were unaware that this was a study of healing.

This study eliminated the influence of suggestion and the expectation of healing, as well as the placebo effect, by utilizing a double blind design and specially constructed laboratory which isolated the TT practitioner from the subjects. Due to the fact that 13 of the 23 'treatment' group subjects were completely healed (full wound closure) on day 16 – whereas none of the 'nontreatment' group subjects were completely healed on this day – as well as in consideration of the statistically significant difference between the two groups on both day 8 and 16 of the study, it was concluded that NCTT is an effective healing modality on full thickness human dermal wounds.

Discussion
A. Excellent, highly significant study. Blinds were carefully maintained, the wounds were created to precise size and depth and were measured by a physician.

It is unclear why 'treatment' should not be designated treatment. The healer was alotted a standard time period for treatment, yet obtained positive results. Other healers (e.g. QUINN 1988; 1989) find a five minute limit discordant with their usual practices.
B. I find no criticisms for this study.

The next series of studies deals with effects of healing on autonomic functions of the body, such as blood pressure. These are generally not under conscious control.

Robert N. Miller – Study on the effectiveness of remote mental healing (Medical Hypotheses 1982)

ROBERT MILLER states in his report:

A statistical study, which involved eight healers and ninety-six patients, was conducted to determine the effectiveness of remote mental healing.

The test subjects were hypertension patients between the ages of sixteen and sixty. The experiment was conducted on a double blind basis where neither the doctor or the patients knew who received the mental healing treatments. Normal medical treatment was continued in all cases. Improvement was judged by changes in the diastolic blood pressure, systolic blood pressure, heart beat rate, and weight.

The statistical analysis showed a significant improvement ($p < 0.014$) in the systolic blood pressure of the healer-treated group as compared with the change in the control group. There were no significant differences in the change of diastolic blood pressure, pulse, and weight of the two groups.

Discussion
A. Healing seems significantly helpful in hypertension. It would be of interest to know the normal medical treatments, since healing may interact better with certain ones than with others. It may be that healing has only a modest contribution to offer hypertensives when given in addition to medications.
B. A serious flaw is that the medications prescribed are not tabulated. It is conceivable that the observed differences between E and C groups were caused by this variable rather than by healing.

This is otherwise a well-designed study. Though randomization is not mentioned in the original paper, in personal communication MILLER clarified that alternate patients were assigned to E and C groups as they were referred by the doctor. The only deviation from this procedure was an effort to maintain male/female balance among the groups. Dropouts of experimental subjects reduced the apparent success of some of the healers.

Though the results are statistically significant and an effect of healing on blood pressure is demonstrated, the clinical efficacy seems minimal. Systolic blood pressure is labile. It is this component of blood pressure that responds most quickly to tensions and anxieties.

Janet F. Quinn – Therapeutic touch as energy exchange
(Nursing Science Quarterly 1989)

JANET QUINN performed this study to clarify effects of TT on anxiety. It is reviewed in greater detail below, along with similar studies. A *post hoc* finding was that diastolic blood pressure was significantly reduced with TT treatments (p < 0.007).

Discussion

A. Healing produced a significant decrease in diastolic blood pressure. It is fascinating that diastolic blood pressure should be affected by TT in patients who were in any case receiving antihypertensive and cardiotonic medications. The diastolic component is usually not greatly influenced by anxiety, so this finding may indicate that healing can reduce hypertension by mechanisms which do not rely solely on reductions in anxiety.

ETHEL LOMBARDI, a *Reiki* Master, reports that iliac pulses transiently disappear periodically during her healings. I have witnessed this phenomenon. Blood pressure changes during and immediately after healing ought to be monitored continuously to clarify this finding.

B. Strict research methodology proscribes acceptance of *post-hoc findings* as more than suggestive, because if one studies sufficient variables one will find a few by chance which demonstrate significant results fortuitously. This finding warrants replication.

Means of data are presented, with pre- and post-treatment differences in the range of only 1 mm Hg. It is impossible to know, without the raw data, whether this finding is *clinically* significant.

Jaap J. Beutler, Johannes T. M. Attevelt, et al. – Paranormal healing and hypertension
(British Medical Journal 1988)

Two hundred patients were chosen out of 587 volunteers who returned questionnaires and consent forms. World Health Organization criteria for hypertension were followed: systolic blood pressure 140 mm Hg or above or diastolic pressure of 90 mm Hg or above, without or despite antihypertensive therapy.

The 120 remaining, after those with complications of hypertension, kidney disease, diabetes, etc. were dropped from the study, participated in the experiment. They were placed in groups of three with comparable diastolic pressures per measurements in the screening visit. Those taking or not taking antihypertensive drugs were grouped into separate triads. Eighty were taking antihypertensive medications.

Patients in each triad were randomly assigned: group 1 – laying-on-of-hands; group 2 – distant healing; group 3 – no healing. Groups 2 and 3 were treated behind one-way mirrors, so that patients and experimenters were unaware whether a healer was present. Twenty-minute treatments were given once weekly over 15 weeks. Twelve healers, members of several Dutch healer societies, provided the treatments.

In the three-week interval from screening to start of the study, all three groups demonstrated a significant reduction in systolic and diastolic pressures (p < 0.05) with average reductions, respectively, 12.6 and 4.7 mm Hg. The difference for each of the three groups in blood pressures between week 0 and week 15 were also significant (p < 0.001). However, there were no significant differences in reductions between E and C groups.

Diastolic pressure increased significantly (p < .05) after each laying-on-of-hands session, by an average of 1.8 mm Hg, although diastolic pressure measured prior to treatment sessions fell over the 15 weeks of treatment in group 1.

> Because of logistic problems only 84 of the 115 patients completed the questionnaire on general wellbeing at the end of the study... After 15 weeks of treatment 30 (83%) of the 36 patients in group 1 felt improved compared with 9 (43%) of the 21 in group 2 and 11 (41%) of the 27 in group 3 (p < 0.005). No patient felt worse... There was no correlation between improved wellbeing and the reduction in blood pressure.

The experimenters conclude:

> In this study no treatment was consistently better than another and the data cannot therefore be taken as evidence of a paranormal effect on blood pressure. Probably the fall in blood pressure in all three groups either was caused by the psychosocial approach or was a placebo effect of the trial itself.

Discussion

A. Subjective improvement in group 1 would seem from this study to be due to psychosocial or suggestion factors related to the presence of the healer. To clarify whether any part of this may be due to healing a study such as that of HEIDT or QUINN, employing mock healing, would have to be done. The blind controls in this study were for distant healing, so that comparisons between subjective assessments in groups 1 and 3 cannot provide answers to such a question.

It is sad that the authors ignore the highly significant finding of greater subjective wellbeing in group 1 in their conclusions.

No mention is made of individual analysis of various healers' efficacy.

B. This appears to have been a carefully performed study. In personal communication, BRIAN MILLAR, a Dutch parapsychologist, indicates that groups 2 and 3 were treated consistently in separate rooms, apparently to preclude a linger effect (see WATSON 1979). This does not appear to have influenced the blinds. See further comments after the next study.

Randolph C. Byrd – Positive therapeutic effects of intercessory prayer in a coronary care unit population (*Southern Medical Journal 1988*)

RANDOLPH BYRD, a physician, summarizes his study:

> The therapeutic effects of intercessory prayer (IP) to the Judeo-Christian God, one of the oldest forms of therapy, has had little attention in the medical literature. To evaluate the effects of IP in a coronary

care unit (CCU) population, a prospective randomized double-blind protocol was followed. Over ten months, 393 patients admitted to the CCU were randomized, after signing informed consent, to an intercessory prayer group (192 patients) or to a control group (201 patients). While hospitalized, the first group received IP by participating Christians praying outside the hospital; the control group did not... After entry, all patients had follow-up for the remainder of the admission. The IP group subsequently had a significantly lower severity score based on the hospital course after entry (p < 0.01). Multivariant analysis separated the groups on the basis of the outcome variables (p < 0.0001)... These data suggest that intercessory prayer to the Judeo-Christian God has a beneficial therapeutic effect in patients admitted to a CCU.

There were no differences between groups on admission in degree of severity of myocardial infarction or in numerous other pertinent variables.

'Intercessors' were 'born again' Christians who prayed daily and were active with their local church. Each patient had 3–7 intercessors praying for him. Intercessors were given patients' first names, their diagnoses and updates on their condition. "...each intercessor was asked to pray daily for a rapid recovery and for prevention of complications and death, in addition to other areas of prayer they believed to be beneficial to the patient." Significantly fewer patients in the prayer group required intubation/ ventilation (p < 0.002) or antibiotics (p < 0.005), had cardiopulmonary arrests (p < 0.02), developed pneumonia (p < 0.03), or required diuretics (p < 0.05).

Despite the differences between groups, the mean times in CCU and durations of hospitalization between groups remained similar.

Discussion
A. This study demonstrates significant effects of distant healing in cardiopulmonary problems. It is curious that duration of hospitalization was not influenced, despite a specific focus on this aspect of recovery by the healers. As Byrd notes, some of the patients in the control group may have had outsiders praying for them, which presumably would have reduced the differences between groups.
B. This appears to be an excellent study. It would be of help to have more details as to how blinds were maintained.

Johannes T. M. Attevelt – Research into Paranormal Healing *(Doctoral dissertation, State University of Utrecht 1988)*

JOHANNES ATTEVELT organized a carefully controlled study of healing for 90 patients with asthma and/or asthmatic bronchitis. Patients were first matched for severity of asthma, measured by the *forced expiratory* [breath] *volume* in one second (FEV1). They were then randomly divided into groups receiving either: (1) 'optimal' treatment in the form of the laying-on-of-hands with subsequent ironing movements ('passes'); or (2) distant healing from behind a one-way mirror; or (3) no treatment. Groups 2 and 3 were treated identically so that the patients could not tell whether healing was given or not.

Patients were treated weekly in 15 minute sessions, eight times in two months, by healers in a laboratory. The FEV1 and the *peak expiratory flow rate* (PEFR l/min.) were measured at various times during the day by the patients themselves in their homes, and periodically by the experimenters in the laboratory. These measures reflect the degree of spasm of muscles, of irritative thickening of linings (due to allergic reaction and infections) and of presence of mucus in the airways to the lungs. Patients also reported on frequency, severity and duration of asthmatic attacks; color of sputum (reflecting presence of infections); use of medication; interference of illness in daily duties and sleep; and subjective assessment of illness.

Group 1 showed the following significant improvements: (1) Increased PEFR of 40 l/min at the academic hospital (p < 0.003); (2) increased PEFR of 21 l/min as measured by the patients themselves at home (p < 0.009); (3) increased minimum PEFR of 28 l/min (p < 0.006) in the morning; (4) increased average PEFR of 22 l/min (p < 0.012) in the morning; and (5) increased subjective improvement in 13 of the 32 patients, with only two reporting worsening of symptoms (p < 0.006). Other measures showed a positive trend but did not reach statistically significant levels. Duration and severity of attacks proved impossible to measure, as patients used medication at the start of attacks. Other measures showed non-significant change.

The C group demonstrated an increase in average: (1) PEFR of 44 l/min measured at the academic hospital (p < 0.002); (2) PEFR of 26 l/min as measured by the patients themselves at home (p < 0.021); (3) maximum PEFR of 29 l/min in the morning (p < 0.015); and (4) PEFR of 29 l/min in the evening (p < 0.027). (5) Eighteen patients out of 33 showed a decrease in the number of attacks of dyspnea (shortness of breath) during the week, and only 2 had an increase (p < 0.001); and (6) 16 showed a decrease in the number of periods per day that they took medication, versus only five showing an increase (p < 0.013).

Most important in this study of healing, there were no significant differences between the three groups. Attevelt concludes that because no healing effects greater than placebo could be demonstrated in group 2, which received distant healing, no aspect of the positive results in group 1 can be attributed to healing. He suggests that improvements in all groups were related to attention given by healers and/or research staff; to patients' expectations regarding treatment results; and to the initiative generated by the patients in participating in the study.

Attevelt also found that patients' subjective evaluations correlated with some of the objective clinical measurements of improvement: average PEFR l/min in the morning (p < 0.003) and in the evening (p < 0.004).

Discussion
A. ATTEVELT seems biased that contact healing is 'optimal', in contrast with distant healing, which – by inference – he must view as less than optimal treatment. The experimental results may in part represent experimenter effects. His insistence that only distant healing can demonstrate healing effects seems likely to lead to a Type II error.

There may also be a negative healer effect related to the 15-minute duration of the healing treatments. One ought to question the healers regarding their usual practices for distant healing. In my experience with numerous healers, distant healings are usually done in about five minutes, while touch healings may take 15–45 minutes. The experimental requirement for standard 15-minute treatments may have introduced a negative element in both types of healing.

Some positive effects of healings in humans may be placebo responses. That is, suggestion in humans may activate healees' self-healing.

The confirmation that subjective reports

correlated with objective findings is an important one. This adds credence to the various other healee surveys which found high percentages of positive results. (See Chapter I – 5.)

No mention is made of analysis of treatment by individual healers.

B. This study is meticulously designed and described, except that effects in group 2 are not clearly delineated. It seems flawed by the lack of blinds for the experimenters.

Ankun Kuang et al. – Long-term observation on Qigong in prevention of stroke *(Journal of Traditional Chinese Medicine 1986)*

ANKUN KUANG ET AL. report on 244 out of 266 hypertensive patients who were treated with *Qigong* (frequently written *Qi-gong*; a Chinese form of exercises for self-healing) and responded to a mail questionnaire. Patients ranged in age from 21 to 69 years (mean 46.1), with hypertension followed for 0.5 to 30 years (mean 5.8). Prior to treatment mean blood pressures measured 175 +/- 13.8 mm Hg systolic and 108 +/- 11.9 mm Hg diastolic.

KW classification placed 48, 176 and 20 cases in stage I, II and III respectively. Highest values of systolic and diastolic blood pressure, daily blood pressure, urine routine examination, BUN, serum cholesterol and hypertensive classification, complications, cause of death, drugs used, Qigong practice, recent ECG and KW stage were recorded...

Qigong was the main therapy in the Qigong group, with drugs as adjuvant. Qigong... consisted mainly of tranquil mind, relaxed body and smooth breath-

ing...done for the most part in sitting position, though occasionally the patients stood. Massage was at times added once or twice a day.

Patients were considered consistent in therapy if they practiced *Qigong* or took their western medicines for more than three-quarters of the follow-up period. Thirteen were excluded because of death from illness unrelated to a stroke. A control group comparable in age, course of disease and blood pressure prior to treatment was used.

Total mortality was 19.3% (47/244) in the *Qigong* group and 41.7% (130/312) in the control group (p < 0.01). Mortality in the consistent *Qigong* group was 11.2% (23/162) versus 29.3% (24/82) in the non-consistent *Qigong* group (p < 0.001). The difference in mortality between the non-consistent *Qigong* and the control group was non-significant. Consistent *Qigong* and drug therapy correlated with prevention of stroke (respectively p < 0.01 and 0.05).

Discussion
A. This study is included in the review because *Qigong* is the Chinese equivalent to western healing. It appears that self-healing was the primary mode of therapy. This may be primarily relaxation techniques and/or meditation, though *Qigong* healer-healing appears to be more than that. Even *Qigong*-self-healing is usually boosted with the master's absent healing. 'Massage' is not described. This may be a euphemism for *Qigong* touch healing by a *Qigong* master.

The clinically significant effects of these methods is impressive.

B. This study appears to have been carefully performed, providing significant evidence for the effectiveness of *Qigong* therapy. Unfortunately the description of selection of patients, randomization and therapy is incomplete. Medications used are not described, nor is there comparison between E and C groups on the medication variable.

Guo and Ni – Study of Qigong in treatment of myopia (Cited in: David Eisenberg with Thomas Wright – Encounters with Qigong)

Eighty myopic (nearsighted) children aged 12–15 were randomly selected from an ophthalmology clinic. Each had measurements of vision, corneal curvature and anterior chamber dimension. They were divided into four groups of 20 each: (1) no treatment; (2) placebo eye drops; (3) instruction in the practice of *Qigong* meditative exercises (similar to those used for hypertensive patients); (4) treatment by a *Qigong* master who spent twenty minutes a day with one hand in front and one hand behind each child's head "emitting external Qi" in the direction of the eyeballs.

The results were as follows: (1) and (2) No improvement in vision after two months; (3) two improved; (4) sixteen improved;

The authors speculate that group (3) showed few improvements because the children may have been too young to concentrate in the meditative exercises.

Discussion
A. Myopia is a condition which almost never improves and quite often worsens with time until late in life. A healing effect seems evident, as there is no other known treatment for childhood myopia. *Qigong* healers claim myopia responds frequently to healing.
B. Unfortunately, few details are reported. It would be important in replicating this study

to know which measurements were altered by the treatments and by how much. As reported, the research is unconvincing.

Ewa Purska-Rowinska and Jerzy Rejmer – The effect of bioenergotherapy upon EEG tracings and on the clinical picture of epileptics *(Psychotronika 1985)*

Bioenergotherapy was used with 42 epileptic patients. There was a definite reduction in the severity of epileptic attacks, with no change in frequency. No distinct alterations in the EEGs were noted. Some improvement was seen in mood, with increased loquacity in adult patients.

Discussion   Though this report is too brief for proper assessment, it is encouraging to learn that healing may be a helpful adjunct for treatment of epileptics.

P.J. Collipp – The efficacy of prayer: A triple-blind study *(Medical Times 1969)*

Ten out of 18 leukemic children were randomly selected for treatment by a prayer group at a church (in addition to routine medical treatment). At the church, 10 families were asked to pray daily for the children and received weekly reminders of their obligation. Treating physicians and patients did not know they were subjects of this study. The praying families did not know their prayer was part of a study.

Evaluations by doctors and parents (apparently focused on global changes – criteria not mentioned) were performed at unstated intervals. Table I- 19 summarizes the results.

Discussion

A. It is sad to have a study of cancer in humans, one of the most serious challenges to healing, and to find it so seriously flawed that it is useless.

B. Although the author feels the data support the hypothesis that prayers are efficacious, the results are not statistically significant.

Weaknesses in this study include: (1) the small numbers of patients studied; (2) control group biased with inclusion of two patients with myelogenous leukemia – a more malignant, rapidly fatal, form of leukemia; (3) a patient in the control group who lived more than 11 years after diagnosis, biasing the results by chance; (4) criteria for 'improvement' unstated; (5) different chemotherapies for different patients – possibly accounting for variability in responses between groups; (6) intervals for measurements of improvement unspecified; (7) no checks made to see whether families actually prayed for the patients, and if so, how often; and no specifications mention types of prayer, whether this was a regular healing prayer group, etc. Because of these problems no conclusions can be drawn from this study

Effects of healing on human physical problems are summarized in Table I-20.

Table I - 19.
Data on 18 children with acute leukemia who participated in a prayer study

Age at diagnosis	Sex	Type of leukemia	Drug* therapy	Survival after diagnosis (months)	
19	M	lymphatic	a - d;g	14	
12	F	lymphatic	a - g	23	
8	F	lymphatic	a - e;g	36+	(alive)
6	F	lymphatic	a - d;f;g;	23	
4	M	lymphatic	a - g	36	(alive)
5	M	lymphatic	a;c;d	15+	(alive)
3	F	lymphatic	a - e	41+	(alive)
3	F	lymphatic	a;b;d	54+	(alive)
3	M	lymphatic	a - e	21+	(alive)
3	F	lymphatic	a - f	17+	(alive)
3	M	lymphatic	a - e	21	
2	F	lymphatic	a - d	130+	
2	M	lymphatic	a - f	22+	
3	M	lymphatic	a - d;h	15	
19	M	lymphatic	b - d	4	
14	F	myelogenous	b - d	2+	
7	M	lymphatic	a - d;f	14+	(alive)
1	M	myelogenous	a - e;g;i	5+	

*a: methotrexate; b: 6-mercaptopurine; c: vincristine; d: prednisone;
e: daunamycin; f: bis-chlorethyl-nitroso-urea; g: cytosine-arabinoside;
h: tryptophane mustard; i: fluorinated progesterone

Table I - 20. Effects of healing on human physical problems

Subject of healing	Researchers	T/N/D*	Duration	Healers	Effects	Significance
Hemoglobin (Hgb) increase	Krieger	T/N	15 mins	Estebany	1. 19 patients, pre- vs post - healing Hgb levels	p< .02
					9 Controls, pre- vs post-time Hgb levels	NS
					Healed vs controls Hgb levels	p< .01
					2. 43 healing vs 33 controls	p< .01
					3. 46 healing vs 33 controls, matching for diet, breathing exercises, medications	p< .001
		T/N	?	32 nurses TT	4. 2 patients each, one healing and one control Healed: pre- vs post treatment Hgb levels	p< .001
					Controls: pre-vs post-time Hgb levels	NS
Skin wounds	Wirth	N	5 mins	1 TT nurse	23 healing vs 21 controls days 8, 16	p< .001
Hypertension	Miller	D	?	8 Healers	48 hypertensives, healing added to conventional treatments: Decreased systolic blood pressure	p< .001
	Quinn	N	5 mins	Quinn	51 anxious cardiac surgery patients each in TT, MTT and C groups. Diastolic pressure decreased TT vs C	p< .007
	Beutler, et al.	T & D	20 mins	12 Healers	All healing & control patients, pre- vs post-:	p< .001
					Inter-group differences: Diastolic	p< .05
					Touch healing: greater subjective improvement	p< .005
	Kuang, et al.	Qigong (T?)	?	?	244 hypertensives, mortality over 0.5-30 years: Qi gong 19% (47/244) vs control 42% (130/312)	p< .01
					Q. consistent 11% vs Q.non-consistent 29%	p< .001
					Hypotensors alone	p< .05
					Controls vs Q. non-consist.	NS

(Table I-20 is continued on page 224.)

Table I - 20. Effects of healing on human physical problems (cont.)

Subject of Healing	Researchers	T/N/D*	Duration	Healer	Effects			Signifiance
Asthma/ asthmatic bronchitis	Attevelt	T & D	15 mins	healers	30 each, T, D, & controls, pre- vs post-healing No significant differences between groups			All sig. improved
Coronary care	Byrd	D	?	prayer groups		192 healing	201 Control	
					Intubation/ ventilation	0	12	p< .002
					Antibiotics	3	16	p< .005
					Cardiopulmonary arrest	3	14	p< .02
					Congestive heart failure	8	0	p< .03
					Pneumonia	3	13	p< .03
					Diuretics	5	15	p< .05
Myopia	Guo & Ni	T?N?		Qi gong	80 children	Improved		
					20 controls;	NS		
					20 placebo eyedrops	NS		?
					20 self-healing	2		
					20 Qi gong master healing	16		
Epilepsy	Purska-Rowinska & Rejmer	?	?	Healer	42 patients: decreased severity			?
Leukemia	Collipp	D	?	Prayer group	Healing: 10 lymphatic leukemia Control: 6 lymphatic, 2 myelogenous			

* T/N/D: Touch/Near/Distant   **NS: Non-Significant   ***hits: successful trials

Healing Action on Subjective Experiences

Elizabeth Keller and Virginia M. Bzdek – Effects of therapeutic touch on tension headache pain (*Nursing Research 1986*)

ELIZABETH KELLER tested the following hypotheses:

1. Tension headache pain will be reduced following therapeutic touch (TT), and the initial reduction will be maintained for a four-hour period.
2. Subjects who receive TT will experience greater tension headache-pain reduction than subjects receiving a placebo simulation of TT.
3. Subjects who receive TT will maintain greater tension headache pain reduction than subjects receiving a placebo simulation of TT four hours following the intervention.

The patients were 60 volunteers (aged 18–59 mean 30), either students (70%) and staff at the university hospital or from the general public. To be included they had to have tension headache, "defined as dull, persistent head pain, usually bilateral, with feelings of heaviness, pressure, or tightness, which did not involve a prodrome, neurologic deficit, infectious process, or recent head trauma" and to be free of headache medication during the four hours preceding the study. Patients were randomly assigned to TT or placebo touch groups and were blind regarding treatments. The patients' subjective experience of headache pain was evaluated on three scales of the McGill-Melzack Pain Questionnaire (MMPQ). The MMPQ was completed just prior to and five minutes after the treatments.

For the TT group, the researcher centered herself and passed her hands 6 – 12 inches away from the subjects without touching them, "to assess the energy field which extends beyond the skin and to redirect areas of accumulated tension out of the field. She then let her hands rest around, but not on, the head or solar plexus in areas of energy imbalance or deficit and directed life energy to the subject." For the placebo group the researcher simulated the above procedure, omitting the therapeutic components, focusing her mind on subtraction of 7's from 100, while holding no intent to help in her consciousness. Subjects in both groups sat quietly and were asked to breathe slowly during the five-minute procedures.

Initial severity of headaches was comparable between the two groups, which showed a difference of no more than a half-point on the three MMPQ scales. Hypotheses (1) and (2) were supported on all three MMPQ tests (p < 0.005). Hypothesis (3) was not supported on the initial data analysis. However, researchers found that the placebo group had 15 subjects (50%) who "used treatments (unspecified) to relieve their headache during the four-hour interval between posttest and delayed posttest, but only five subjects (16%) in the TT group reported an intervening treatment." Removing data of all who used other treatments from the analysis, significant differences between the groups became apparent (p < 0.005-0.01) on the various MMPQ tests.

Subjects in the TT group reported sensations of tingling, warmth and relaxation, though they had not been told what to expect and had no prior experience with TT. Subjects in the placebo group reported a lesser reduction of pain and more often used other treatments. "Thus it appears that although the placebo intervention did reduce headache pain, the effect did not occur as often, was not as great and did not last as long as the effect of TT."

Discussion
A. This study demonstrates that healing is significantly effective for headache pain.
B. This was a well designed study. However, several factors were not reported which might have influenced the study. How long had the tension headaches been present? Had subjects used medication that was effective for longer than four hours? Either of these factors could have biased the results if present to a greater extent in one group than in the other.

In personal communication, BZDEK added the following:

The intensity, duration and frequency of the tension headaches experienced in this sample varied widely... Fifty percent of the

headaches began less than four hours before the subject's entry into the study, while 20% had been present for at least 24 hours.

Nearly half (26) of the subjects reported they had previously attempted to relieve their headache with some kind of medication with unsatisfactory results, at least four hours prior to entering the study; 27 had tried an aspirin or acetaminophen preparation; the other nine had tried Fiorinal, Motrin, or antihistamines. We do not have information concerning the dosages of these medications that the subjects used. No subjects indicated that they had taken medication with action expected to last longer than four hours. Other attempts to relieve that particular headache included sleep, heat applications, massage, and diverting activities, all of which proved to be minimally or only temporarily effective.

We are left with a possibility that differences between groups may have been due to chronicity of headache.

David Dressler – Light touch manipulative technique (Journal of Alternative and Complementary Medicine 1990)

DAVID DRESSLER recently developed a technique for spinal manipulation which he claims relieves "muscular hypertonicity and vertebral joint motion dysfunction due to muscular and fascial restriction". Light-Touch Manipulative Technique (LTMT) claims to move displaced vertebrae back into position and its conceptualizations and terminology seem to derive from chiropractic or osteopathy. In practice it is clearly a form of healing, as the author notes that treatment may be given with the practitioner holding his finger near the body (up to several feet away). Dressler speculates that this may be explained by interactions of the energy fields of the participants.

LTMT provided marked relief for lumbosacral pain, including pains radiating to distant muscles. It is especially useful when patients are in too much pain to be moved. In addition, race horses with spinal dysfunctions were dramatically improved with LTMT.

...LTMT is a form of joint mobilization or manipulation and of soft-tissue manipulation, employing sustained pressure ranging from just sufficient to begin to dent the skin of the target tissue to pressure slightly greater, depending on the case. This whole procedure is conducted with a quality of high-absorbed attention to the sensations occurring in the tip of the finger at the point of contact.
...LTMT has less to do with the activity of the practitioner than with the tissue response of the subject. The practitioner follows more than directs and therapeutic contact is more like palpation than pushing or thrusting.

The mental attitude of the practitioner is crucial. The challenge in LTMT is that, although it is a direct technique, the practitioner must act, and think, almost as though it were not.

Because the bone is moved in the direction of the barrier, the temptation is to push and thrust, when what is really necessary is to let the sensing fingertip lightly touch the edge of the bone as though it were a delicate leaf floating in a still pool, following its motion wherever it drifts, influencing its direction as little as possible.

To let this happen, the practitioner's attention is absorbed in the sensations of the fingertip, silently aware, with as little thought and will as possible.

Dressler mentions that he used to visualize energy emanating from his finger and the bones moving into position, but that he no longer does so. During treatment, warmth or tingling may be felt by the practitioner, while the patient may feel localized heat, tingling, pulsing or 'needlelike pain' in the joint, while relaxing deeply and even falling asleep. The bone being manipulated may spontaneously wiggle slightly, and the practitioner may feel as though it is floating in warm oil. The bone moves thus until it is gradually and gently returned to its correct position. Dressler feels that LTMT activates the patient's own healing abilities.

Dressler solicited subjects for a clinical study of his technique through a newspaper ad for "neckpain/backpain wanted". He offered free professional assessment in return for their participation in the study. All 27 subjects had chronic neck and back pain which had been either untreated or had been unresponsive to (unspecified) treatments.

A physiotherapist and chiropractor assessed "each cervical restriction of flexion or extension found between C2–C7 in every subject before and after the author examined the subject". The assessors did not know which subjects were treated by Dressler and which were in the control group. Assessments for the study were based on motion testing and palpation of the cervical spine. Criteria for improvement are not mentioned. Treatment was given during Dressler's palpation, without the subjects' knowledge.

Of the 16 treated, 14 were improved. Of the 11 controls, only 4 showed improvement (p < 0.01).

Discussion

A. Here is a significant study of healing under a different name and discipline. LTMT appears likely to help with back and neck pain. DRESSLER's clinical observations parallel those of JOHN UPLEDGER, a craniosacral osteopath, discussed in chapter II - 2.

B. Patients with both back and neck pain were included but the numbers of each allocated to treatment and control groups are not mentioned, nor is there mention of checks to see that both groups were comparable in severity of symptoms to start with. Criteria for assessment of symptoms and of improvement are not described. It is therefore unclear precisely what benefits were produced by LTMT and how valid the study might be.

T.C. Meehan – An Abstract of the Effect of Therapeutic Touch on the Experience of Acute Pain in Post-Operative Patients *(Unpublished doctoral dissertation, New York University 1985)*

MEEHAN used a pretest-posttest parallel control group design. When the 108 patients requested pain relief at least three hours after receiving pain control medication, they were randomly assigned to therapeutic touch treatment group, a single blind placebo control group receiving mimic treatment, and a control group receiving standard treatment. Pain intensity was measured prior to and one hour following treatment, using a Visual Analogue Scale... Patients treated with therapeutic touch reported statistically non-significant decreases in pain intensity compared with the mimic control group. The standard treatment control group reported significantly greater decreases than the therapeutic touch treatment group.

Discussion

A. Healing produced less pain reduction than standard postoperative pain medication. Since surveys show that pain more than any other symptom responds to healing, this study certainly warrants replication.

B. This summary is too brief for adequate evaluation. LIONBERGER adds:

Alterations to the design might produce additional information. A comparison between the standard treatment control group used in the study, and an experimental group receiving standard treatment plus therapeutic touch would seem appropriate, since the technique is advocated as an adjunct to conventional treatment, not a substitute for it.

Joyce Goodrich – Psychic Healing: A Pilot Study *(Doctoral dissertation, Graduate School, Yellow Springs, Ohio, 1974)*

This study considers the following:
(1) What do patients feel upon receiving distant healing treatments;
(2) Can independent judges identify from healees' subjective reports when a distant healing treatment has occurred.

JOYCE GOODRICH teaches the LeShan methods of healing. She has devoted her career to healing research. Her dissertation reviews the literature and extracts the following essentials on common denominators for healers in the healing process:[26]

1. Total concentration during the healing process.
2. Authentic sense of loving and caring about the healee.
3. 'Being one with the healee in their mind's eye' during the healing.

Even when all of these conditions are met, healing effects are not assured. However, if they are not met, healing effects are unlikely.

Goodrich distinguishes between *Type 1* and *Type 2* forms of healing (per LeShan 1974).

In *Type 1* healing, the healer goes into an altered state of consciousness in which he views himself and the healee as one entity. There is no attempt to 'do anything' to the healee (in Harry Edwards' words, "All sense of 'performance' should be abandoned"), but simply to meet him, to be one with him, to unite with him.
... Type 1 healing is organismic. Its results can be psychological, somatic or a mixture of both. Sometimes the effects appear to be transpersonal or spiritual. Neither the healer nor healee seems to need to, nor seems able to direct it to do a certain thing at a particular time. It can be facilitated in general but not manipulated easily, if at all. The healee's organism appears to select how and where the experience will be used in response to its own deep wisdom and need.
Type 2: The laying on of hands. It does not necessarily require entering the clairvoyant reality and may involve an energy.

Goodrich carried out study involving 12 people with physical problems who were unsophisticated in theories about healing. Change in physical condition was not a focus of the study. "The only indications of change in their conditions came from subjective evaluations." Six healers trained by LeShan were used.

A series of Type 1 healings was scheduled for each of the 12. Two healings were 'present' (healer and healee in the same room) and eight were distant (healer and healee separated by unspecified distances, all presumably in their own homes.) A few healings were conducted over greater distances. Healers and healees were told that healings would be done per schedules provided by Goodrich and were led to believe that all distant healings were scheduled synchronously. *Unbeknown to them, half of the distant healings were scheduled at least an hour after the participants expected them.*

Sensations reported by healees included relaxation, drowsiness, heaviness, decreased anxiety, increased energy and peacefulness. Sensations reported by healers included a more intense awareness of self and feelings of peacefulness.

Three judges were given healers' and healees' self-rating forms and were asked to assess whether they thought healings were synchronous or non-synchronous. Results were significant ($p < 0.005$). Goodrich, disclaiming recall for coding of data, also rated the forms and achieved significant results.

An interesting finding was that *accuracy in judging whether distant healings were synchronous or non-synchronous methodically and consistently increased with the length of time between distant healings and healings in which both healer and patient were present.* (See Table I-21.)

Table I - 21.
Judges' assessments in Goodrich healing experiment

Healings in chronological sequence	Three judges' evaluations in percentages	
	Right	Wrong
1. present - synchronous	98%	2%
2. distant - synchronous	45	55
3. distant - synchronous	55	45
4. distant - non-synchronous	70	30
5. distant - non-synchronous	87	13
6. present - synchronous	96	4
7. distant - non-synchronous	29	71
8. distant - non-synchronous	59	41
9. distant - synchronous	78	22
10. distant - synchronous	75	25

GOODRICH suggests that the most obvious explanation for this results is that meetings between healers and healees provided a stimulus for more distortive experience, although the verbal interaction between healers and healees was limited and between Goodrich and healees only slightly less limited.

Discussion

A. This study shows that healees can identify subjective sensations during distant healings with a high degree of accuracy.

One must keep in mind that physical changes were not the subject of this study. Though healees experienced subjective sensations during distant healings, this is not meant to be proof that healing is effective.

The finding that identifications of healing sensations were progressively more accurate the further away in time the healer/healee pairs were from the sessions in which they had been in each others' presence is a puzzle. Several speculative extrapolations from this data are suggested. First, perhaps the evidence points to separate, mutually interfering modalities of perception in sensory and healing realities. Attention to sensory cues (or the memories of such) may interfere with awareness of healing-experience sensations. This phenomenon could be associated with separate realities or factors as yet unknown. Second, attending to healing cues may require training in focusing on internal physical, mental and emotional states which are not common experiences in the conscious lives of the healees. This may be similar to learning about the internal changes that occur during biofeedback. The poor performance initially may derive from attention to the wrong cues, based on everyday sensory experience.

Only a few examples of the results of the healings are mentioned, as it is impossible to assess the significance of reported changes in single cases. For example, was the disappearance of a patch of psoriasis or an improvement in a particular instance of pain a result of healing? Suggestion? Chance variations in the underlying physical and/or emotional problems? The sensations seemed clearest in the areas of tension/anxiety; much less clear in areas of physical changes.[27]

B. This is an excellent study. Goodrich provides abundant raw data to permit the reader to make his own evaluation of her study and conclusions, as well as to appreciate qualitative aspects of the healer/healee interactions.

The inclusion of Goodrich's judging data in the grouped statistical analysis seems questionable. She had some awareness of the assignments of codes to data and was therefore not completely 'blind' in making evaluations. Significant results were obtained independent of her input, however.

Shirley Winston – Research in Psychic Healing: A Multivariate Experiment *(Unpublished doctoral dissertation, Union Graduate School 1975)*

Following up on the Goodrich study, this study examined the question: "Is psychic healing based on a personal relationship between healer and healee or is the healing relationship of a non-personal or transpersonal nature?"

Five hypotheses were examined:

1. Psychic healing is most effective when there is a high level of personal contact and communication between healer and healee.
2. Psychic healing is most effective when there is a very low level of personal contact and communication between healer and healee.
3. Psychic healing is most effective when there is a moderate level of personal contact and communication.
4. Personal contact and communication have no effect on psychic healing.
5. Some healers do their best healing when there is a high level of personal contact and communication, and others do better with low or moderate levels.

Four LeShan healers treated 16 healees.

Each healee kept records for a week before the healings were begun. In the first week of the experiment proper, each healee received three healings from one of our four healers, following one of our four experimental conditions. In the second week, no healings were done, but the healees continued to keep records. In the third week, each healee received three healings from a different one of our healers, under a different one of our conditions. In the fourth week, no healings were done. This cycle was repeated two more times, until each healee had experienced each healer and each condition, followed by a week with no healing being done.

The four conditions were as follows:

Condition A: Healer and healee meet, converse, get to know each other, then healing done in the presence of healee, with feedback afterwards. Next two healings at a distance.
Condition B: Healer and healee meet, healing is done in presence of healee, but there is no conversation or 'getting to know each other'. Next two healings at a distance.
Condition C: Healer receives a letter in healee's handwriting and a photo of healee. Three healings at a distance.
Condition D: Healer receives a lock of healee's hair. Three healings at a distance.

The results show a trend toward more effective psychic healing when interpersonal information and communication are lower, but miss statistical certainty. Other factors, such as the presence or distance of healer and healee, and the level of tension of the healer, seem to play a part, and may have reduced the statistical effect of the variables under investigation.

Discussion

A. It is impossible to say whether the null results are due to lack of actual differences between the study conditions or to other factors, such as limited numbers of subjects.
B. As no statistically significant results were obtained we cannot draw any conclusions from it. The author presents many unsupported speculations which I have not included here.

The largest series of studies of healing for human clinical problems focuses on anxiety, as treated by TT.[28]

Patricia Heidt – Effect of Therapeutic Touch on Anxiety Level of Hospitalized Patients (*Ph.D. dissertation, New York University 1979;[29] Nursing Research 1981*)

Journal Abstract:

Effect of therapeutic touch on the anxiety of 90 volunteer male and female subjects between the ages of 21 and 65, hospitalized in a cardiovascular unit of a large medical center in New York City, was examined. The dependent variable, state anxiety, was defined as a transitory emotional state of the individual at a particular point and was measured by the Self-Evaluation Questionaire x-1, developed by Spielberger, Gorsuch, and Lushene. Subjects were administered this tool pre- and postintervention. Three matched intervention groups were formed: Each subject received an individual five-minute period of intervention by therapeutic touch, casual touch, or no touch. Subjects who received

intervention by therapeutic touch experienced a highly significant (p < 0.001) reduction in state anxiety, according to a comparison of pre-posttest means on A-state anxiety... Subjects who received intervention by therapeutic touch had a significantly (p < 0.01) greater reduction in posttest anxiety scores than subjects who received intervention by casual or no touch.

Discussion

A. We have here clear evidence for a significant reduction of anxiety with healing.
B. Although significant results were obtained, it is hard to judge whether they were attributable entirely to TT or whether suggestion may have played some part in this study, since no blinds were employed in the evaluation phase. The person administering the anxiety tests was fully aware of who had TT and who did not. However, we should also consider that the test instrument is self-administered by the subject and tester influence may presumably be minimal.

Subjects matched for pre-test scores were assigned to each of the three groups, but no randomization procedures are mentioned.

Janet Quinn – An Investigation of the Effect of Therapeutic Touch Without Physical Contact on State Anxiety of Hospitalized Cardiovascular Patients (*Doctoral dissertation, New York University 1982*)

JANET QUINN summarizes her study:

...this research was designed to test the theorem that Therapeutic Touch without physical contact would have the same effect as Therapeutic Touch with physical contact. This theorem was derived from the broader conceptual system developed by Rogers (1970), which suggests that the effects of Therapeutic Touch are outcomes of an energy exchange between two human energy fields. Since the effects of Therapeutic Touch with physical contact on state anxiety is known, state anxiety was utilized as a measure of the efficacy of Therapeutic Touch without physical contact.

A sample of 60 male and female subjects, between the ages of 36 and 81, hospitalized on a cardiovascular unit of a metropolitan medical center, were randomly assigned to the Experiental group, receiving Non-contact Therapeutic Touch, or the Control group receiving Non-contact. Each subject completed the A-State Self Evaluation Questionnaire before and after the assigned intervention. It was hypothesized that subjects receiving Non-contact Therapeutic Touch would have a greater decrease in posttest state anxiety. scores than subjects receiving the control intervention of Non-contact. This hypothesis was supported at the 0.0005 level of significance.

In addition to the main hypothesis, two ancillary research questions were explored. Analysis of the data relative to the first question indicated that there was no difference among the effects of subjects' state anxiety obtained by four different nurses administering Non-contact Therapeutic Touch. Analysis of the data relative to the second question indicated that there was no relationship among the subjects' sex, ethnicity, religion, medical diagnosis, number of days in the hospital, number of previous hospitalizations, presence or absence of surgery, number of days after surgery, position during treatment and subjects' response to treatment by Non-contact Therapeutic Touch. There was a low correlation between subjects' age and response to Non-contact Therapeutic Touch.

Quinn defined TT in her study in the following way:

In treating subjects with Non-contact Therapeutic Touch the nurse:
1. Centers herself in an act of self-relatedness and becomes aware of herself as an open system of energies in constant flux.
2. Makes the intention mentally to therapeutically assist the subject.
3. Moves her hands over the body of the subject from head to feet, attuning to the condition of the subject by becoming aware of changes in sensory cues in her hands.
4. Redirects areas of accumulated tension in the subject's body by movement of the hands.
5. Concentrates her attention on the specific direction of these energies, using her hands as focal points.
6. Directs energy to the subject by placing her hands four to six inches from the subject's body in the area of the solar plexus (just below the waist) and leaves them in this area for approximately 120 seconds.

Total time for this intervention is five minutes. This intervention is the same as that used by Heidt (1979), with the exception of step 6, which has been changed from contact mode of treatment to non-contact mode, with length of treatment increased from 90 seconds to 120 seconds.

The C group was treated identically in all outward appearances. However, in the C treatments the nurse did mental arithmetic while going through the outward motions of a TT treatment. Nurses who administered the C treatment had no experience in TT. Checks were made with observers naive to TT and they could not distinguish whether E or C treatments were being given.

> In addition to a discussion of the findings of this study, implications for nursing practice and future research were explored. The findings of this study indicate that physical contact during Therapeutic Touch is not an important variable in terms of the effect of Therapeutic Touch. While this finding has been interpreted as supportive of the theory that an energy exchange is the means by which Therapeutic Touch has effects, it is recognized to be only a beginning step towards the construction and validation of a comprehensive theory which can describe, explain and predict about the phenomenon of Therapeutic Touch.

Quinn notes that in her study the nurses administered TT between 8 and 9 p.m., while in Heidt's study treatment was given between 11 a.m. and 12 noon.

Discussion
A. This study demonstrates the close similarity in results from contact and non-contact laying-on-of-hands treatments for state anxiety. As Quinn notes, this may be a benefit to patients who need quick relief from anxiety and are unable to take drugs. An energy interaction in healing is suggested.
B. This is an excellent study, carefully

planned and executed. Though differences in medication variables were not considered between groups, in this and the previous study of Heidt, initial anxiety levels were comparable. The medication differences appear unlikely to contribute to a change in anxiety over a few minutes' interval, but one cannot be certain of this.

Janet F. Quinn– Therapeutic touch as energy exchange: Replication and extension (Nursing Science Quarterly 1989)

QUINN again tested the effects of TT in reducing postoperative anxiety after open heart surgery, *with the elimination of eye and facial contact,* to see whether these were necessary to the reduction of anxiety. She gave the real and mimic TT (MTT) treatments from beside patient, so that no eye contact was made during healings. Independent observers, naive to TT, could not distinguish between the two treatments. A third group was included which received no treatment (NT). No significant demographic differences were found between the groups of randomly assigned subjects.

153 patients were studied. Anxiety was assessed by self-evaluation, pulse rate and systolic blood pressure. No significant differences were found between the groups, though the greatest differences were noted in the TT group and the next greatest differences in the MTT group.

A *post-hoc* finding of significantly lower diastolic blood pressure in the TT group is discussed above.

Another *post-hoc* finding was that 114 patients (76%) were receiving cardiovascular medication, with 108 (72%) receiving calcium channel blockers or beta-adrenergic blocking agents, or both. These were given to stabilize pulse and blood pressure and would have limited the response ranges of both. Beta-blockers may also decrease anxiety.

Quinn notes that it was difficult for her to ensure that she would not be healing during the MTT treatments, as the healing rituals are so habitually associated with giving healing that this might automatically have occured to some degree despite her intentions and efforts to preclude it. She found the limitation of 5 minutes for TT restrictive and felt this often did not leave a feeling that a full treatment had been given. Though the study was designed to explore whether elimination of eye and facial contact would influence the healee, the lack of feedback to the healer was also found to be a factor.

Discussion

A. Limiting healing in research to *standard time doses* does not appear consonant with clinical experience, though in several TT studies thus limited there were still positive results (e.g. HEIDT; KELLER; QUINN 1984). In one study the same healer was able to give TT and MTT treatments and obtained significant results.

The finding of lower diastolic blood pressure is of interest and bears replication. Lombardi reports that healees' iliac pulses may become impalpable during phases of her healings (witnessed by myself), suggesting transient marked reductions in blood pressure.

It is unfortunate that in setting up the study with blinds to avoid Type I errors, Quinn was also blinded to the fact of the patients being on medications which may have seriously limited the responses on the study measures. **B.** Again Quinn presents a well done and meticulously reported study.

Cecilia Kinsel Ferguson – Subjective Experience of Therapeutic Touch Survey (SETTS): Psychometric Examination of an Instrument *(Doctoral dissertation, University of Texas at Austin 1986)*

CECILIA FERGUSON assessed the internal consistency, reliability and validity of content, construct and prediction of the Subjective Experience of TT Survey (SETTS). This is a questionnaire for differentiating between experienced and inexperienced practitioners of TT. It was developed by DOLORES KRIEGER with the help of *JUDITH WILCOX*, a meditation expert, from her meditative experience and from interviews with TT practitioners. It contains 68 items tabulating the frequency with which a healer feels the following:

1. physical sensations attributed to a flow of energy through the body (e.g. heat, cold, and electricity in hands);
2. emotional changes (e.g. enhancement in connectedness with the patient);
3. alterations in mentation (e.g, focus of attention directed inward); and
4. an altered states of consciousness (e.g. altered sense of time, enhanced intuition).

Ferguson administered the SETTS to 100 nurses who practice TT (50 experienced and 50 inexperienced) and to 100 nurses who were unfamiliar with TT. With the latter she arranged for 50 to "read a brief description of the actions the practitioner of therapeutic touch performed. They were then asked to

Fig. I-8. Healees regularly sigh, breathe deeply and relax as healing is given. Children repond very readily (not knowing so many reasons not to). Photograph by Tony Sleep

complete the SETTS and the ACL while imagining that they were practitioners of therapeutic touch." Nurses in the last group of 50 answered questions modified from the SETTS to relate to their experiences in their ordinary treatment of patients. Examination of these groups revealed that the two TT level nurses did not differ in demographic variables but that the non-TT nurses were younger, less experienced and less educated to a significant degree (all at $p < 0.0001$) than the TT nurses.

FERGUSON also administered the Adjective Check List (ACL) to the nurses. This is used to evaluate a person's description of himself. It includes 37 scales grouped into five sections: modus operandi (e.g. numbers of favorable and unfavorable items checked); need (e.g. achievement, dominance, nurturance); topical (e.g. counseling readiness, self-control, leadership, masculinity/femininity); transactional analysis factors (e.g. ego states of parent, adult and child); and 'origence-intellectence' (creativity and intelligence). Special attention was focused on subscales relating to communality, change, nurturance and creative personality as these seemed relevant to Krieger's assessment of characteristics related to success in TT.

TT nurses were asked to administer (to any patient of their choosing) the Self-Evaluation Questionnaire for state anxiety before and after a healing and an Effectiveness of Therapeutic Touch Scale (ETTS) after a healing. The ETTS asks healees to choose a number between 0, representing not at all helpful, and 100, representing extremely helpful, to characterize their response to the TT treatment.

Ferguson found high internal consistency and reliability with the SETTS and, on content analysis, she discovered that more than one factor contributed to the results. The SETTS significantly differentiated the experienced practitioners from the other three groups combined and inexperienced from non-practitioners of TT (both at $p < 0.01$). Experienced TT nurses scored higher than the other three groups combined on the nurturance and creative personality subscales of the ACL. Healees showed significantly decreased anxiety scores (experienced nurses $p < 0.0001$; inexperienced nurses $p < 0.001$). The differences between the scores of the two groups were also significant for the anxiety and the ETTS measures $p < 0.001$ each).

Discussion

A. The decrease in anxiety with TT is again impressive. The significant difference in reduction of anxiety between those treated by experienced and inexperienced nurses supports the contention that healing treatment can be learned. The positive self-evaluations of the patients suggest that the degree of experience with TT makes a difference in the response to the treatment. It is unfortunate that no mention is made of types of problems treated or qualitative patient criteria for improvement.

B. Well designed and run study, demonstrating a healing effect on anxiety. Because there were highly significant demographic differences between the practitioners and non-practitioners of TT it is impossible to draw conclusions regarding the SETTS or ACL tests with any certainty. It is quite possible that the observed differences between nurses relate to the greater age, experience and education of the TT nurses than to their practice of TT. A further possibility is that experienced nurses may be better at selecting patients who will relax with TT.

Rosalie Berner Fedoruk – Transfer of the Relaxation Response: Therapeutic Touch as a Method for Reduction of Stress in Premature Neonates *(Doctoral dissertation, University of Maryland 1984)*

ROSALIE BERNER FEDORUK studied the effects of non-contact TT.

Seventeen premature infants in intermediate and intensive care were studied. Such babies are easily agitated by routine handling because of the immaturity of their nervous systems. The effects of TT in alleviating the stress of having their vital signs (e.g. blood pressure, temperature) taken during routine nursing care was studied. Stress was measured in two ways: behaviorally by the Assessment of Premature Infant Behavior (APIB) scale; and physiologically by the recording of transcutaneous oxygen pressure ($tcPO_2$). The $tcPO_2$ is thought to reflect stress. If an infant breathes irregularly or if his circulatory system is disturbed when agitated, it should have less oxygen in its blood. An increase in $tcPO_2$ was believed likely since TT has been shown to decrease stress and since Krieger demonstrated an increase in hemoglobin with TT.

Two types of controls were used: (1) Mock TT (MTT), in which a nurse untrained in TT mimicked the motions of TT while calculating simple arithmetic backwards out loud; and (2) no TT (NTT).

Duration of TT averaged 25 minutes; for MTT and NTT, 23 minutes. Infants served as their own controls, undergoing observations before, during and in the 10 minutes following routine vital sign measurements. Two observations were taken in each condition. It is unclear from the report whether blinds were used in the APIB measurements, although blinds were used in $tcPO_2$ measurements. (Fedoruk clarified in personal communication: "Blinds were not used in APIB measurements because I did the observations and I can tell even when a TT practitioner is working and when she isn't and everyone in the NICU knew who did TT and who didn't.")

Results indicated a significant *decrease* in stress with TT, per measurement on the APIB compared with baseline ($p < 0.05$). A suggestive *increase* in stress on the APIB was noted for the MTT condition, possibly related to the stimulus of the nurse counting out loud, to her distress in doing this exercise, or to other, unknown factors. No significant differences were noted on any of the tcPO2 measures.

Discussion

A. It is nice to see healing effective for anxiety in premature infants, for whom tranquilizing medication would not be prescribed.

B. This work appears to have been carefully done, with the exception that blinds were not used for APIB measurements. This leaves the possibility that the person making these clinical assessments might have biased the results in the anticipated direction. FEDORUK adds in personal communication:

> One factor that mitigates this criticism is that the MTT was expected to duplicate NTT and...that MTT stressed the infants was only discovered during the statistical analysis of the data. The likelihood of getting the results that MTT stressed infants as much as TT relaxed them while NTT is exactly in the middle is very slight.

I feel this still leaves the criticism that the APIB observer might have unconsciously biased the results in the expected direction of TT improvement.

J. W. Collins – The Effect of Non-Contact Therapeutic Touch on the Relaxation Response (*Master's thesis, Vanderbilt University, Nashville 1983*)

FERGUSON quotes COLLINS' M.A.thesis in her Summary (see also pages 235; 237):

COLLINS studied the physiological effects of therapeutic touch on normal adults. Dependent variables measured by Collins were peripheral skin temperature, electromyography, pulse, respiration, galvanic skin response amplitude, and the relaxation assessment scale (developed by Collins for this study). Each subject (total of 24) was exposed to both therapeutic touch and to the control treatment which was a mimicked therapeutic touch procedure. The order of the treatment was randomized double-blind.

The therapeutic touch treatment included the steps described by Krieger (1979) and lasted for seven minutes. During the sham therapeutic touch procedure, the '-healer' subtracted silently by sevens from 500. The hands of the healer were placed with the fourth and fifth fingers touching the palm of the hand and the second and third fingers touching the first finger of the hand. The particular hand position was used to attempt to decrease the electrodynamic effect during the control procedure. The healer was told before the control procedure began to silently affirm that the subject will not be affected. The sham procedure was developed to examine the effects of the centering step used in therapeutic touch as well as to attempt to control for placebo effect.

The experimental group showed a tendency toward relaxation from baseline with EMG, temperature, pulse, and GSR amplitude achieving significance above the 0.05 level of confidence. However, the control group also showed a tendency toward relaxation. Therefore, there were no significant differences between the experimental group and the control group for change scores on the six criterion variables.

Collins explained the lack of significance by reference to the effect of suggestion. Subjects knew the title of the study from signing the consent form. Also, therapeutic touch appeared to work best if the subjects reported themselves as tired and/or anxious; whereas the control procedure seemed to work best when the subject was alert...

Discussion
A. I have not seen the original of this dissertation. It seems that TT in normal people cannot be expected to produce a greater effect than placebo.
B. It may be that in mild anxiety any attention can reduce anxiety.

Jan Gulak – Lowering the anxiety levels in persons undergoing bioenergotherapy (*Psychotronika 1985*)

JAN GULAK, a bioenergotherapist, studied the anxiety levels of his patients before and after his 15-minute treatments. His measure of anxiety was the *questionnaire of Spielberger and Taylor*, administered 14 days prior to and 21 days after his treatment of 76 people (56 females and 17 males). Various statistical analyses showed the results to be significant ($p < 0.01$ and $p < 0.001$). Accompanying the decrease in anxiety were cessation of migraines and sleeplessness, improvement of circulatory insufficiency, and relief of digestive and reproductive organ pains.

Discussion
A. The results appear impressive.
B. As neither blinds nor randomization are mentioned, the results of this study may represent experimenter or placebo effects.

Gretchen Lay Randolph – The Differences in Physiological Response of Female College Students Exposed to Stressful Stimulus, When Simultaneously Treated by Either Therapeutic Touch or Casual Touch *(Doctoral dissertation, New York University 1974)*

G.L. RANDOLPH's dissertation is summarized by J.F. QUINN in her own Ph.D. thesis (1982):

Randolph [*studied*] the physiologic responses of female college students to a stressful stimulus while being treated with Therapeutic Touch. Reasoning that Therapeutic Touch is a 'healing meditation' (Peper and Ancoli, 1976), which produces a relaxation response in the client, and that, further, persons exhibiting the relaxation response were also less reactive to stressful stimuli, she hypothesized that "when subjected to stressful stimuli, the physiological response of persons treated with Casual Touch will exceed the physiological response of persons treated with Therapeutic Touch".

Randolph utilized a film entitled *Subincision* which has been validated as a stress-producing stimulus. Two groups of 30 female college students (N-60) viewed the film while being monitored simultaneously for skin conductance level, muscle tension and skin temperature. One group received Therapeutic Touch while watching the film. Therapeutic Touch was operationally defined as follows:

"The practitioner made the intention mentally to therapeutically assist the subject. She then concentrated her attention on the subject, using her hands as focal points. Energy was then directed to the subject by placing hands on the lower abdomen and back, leaving them in this area for thirteen minutes."

The second group received Casual Touch while watching the film. Casual Touch consisted of the nurse imitating the hand position of the Therapeutic Touch technique, but without benefit of any knowledge or training in Therapeutic Touch.

Analysis of the data revealed no significant difference between groups on any of the three indices of physiologic stress response.

Randolph offers several possible reasons for the failure of her hypotheses to be supported. One should note that a substantial deviation in the administration of Therapeutic Touch occurred. The treatment was given without benefit of an assessment, that is, without attuning to the patient prior to actual treatment. Moreover, Randolph utilized healthy college students as her subjects. Since the goal of Therapeutic Touch is to assist the subject towards optimum wellness, one would expect to see very little change in a subject who is already quite well when receiving Therapeutic Touch.

Discussion

A. The above summary speaks for itself. Most healers believe that healing works primarily on those who are truly in need of it. I think that this is the most important limiting factor in the study. Another possibility is that the healer in this study migh not be as potent as healers in other studies which demonstrated significant findings.

B. In mild anxiety it may be that healing is no more effective than suggestion.

Brenda Sue Parkes – Therapeutic Touch as an Intervention to Reduce Anxiety in Elderly Hospitalized Patients *(Doctoral dissertation, University of Texas at Austin 1985)*

BRENDA SUE PARKES studied the effects of TT on the anxiety of 60 hospitalized patients aged 65–93. Parkes assumed that elderly patients would be anxious since they were hospitalized. Patients were randomly assigned to three groups. There were no differences between groups in mean age, sex, religion, numbers of previous admissions, medical/surgical diagnosis and practice of meditation. Patients with 43 different diagnoses were included. Group 1 received 5 minutes of TT; Group 2 had mock TT; and Group 3 had a nurse hold her closed hands over the shoulder of the subject 'with no intent to transfer energy'.

The measure of state anxiety was a pencil and paper questionnaire, the Y-2 form of *Spielberger*. There were no differences between groups in the pre- to post-treatment anxiety test scores. In fact, all three groups evidenced a slight increase in anxiety.

Parkes notes: "The mean pretest scores were very close to the mean scores of what Spielberger termed the normal means for this questionnaire." She speculates that elderly patients may actually experience reduction of anxiety because they are in hospital.

Discussion This study is an embarrassment. It seems useless to study the effects of healing on anxiety when no significant anxiety is present.

Barbara Schutze – Group counseling, with and without the addition of intercessory prayer, as a factor in self-esteem *(Proceedings of the 4th International Conference on Psychotronic Research)*

BARBARA SCHUTZE addressed the question: "Does group counseling with the addition of intercessory prayer for psychological (inner) healing change self-esteem more than counseling without the intercessory prayer condition?"

The subjects were 37 young adults in a suburban youth organization. They were given a Self-Esteem Inventory pre-test followed by five consecutive weeks of counseling in small groups. Each group had two facilitators. The Self-Esteem Inventory was used as the post-treatment measure of change.

The experimental group (10 subjects) was randomly selected from among the participants of the small group counseling sessions and randomly assigned, one per facilitator, for intercessory prayer for psychological (inner) healing. Aside from the experimental condition, which was kept secret until after completion of the study, the participants in the study were treated identically. Only the researcher knew the names of the experimental group until after the

Table I - 22. Healing effects on subjective sensations

Subject of healing	Researchers	T/N/D*	Duration	Healers	Results	Significance
Pain Tension headaches	Keller & Bzdek	N	?	?	Tension headaches decreaed Immediately following TT 4 hours following TT	 p< .005 .005 < p < .01
Neck / Back	Dressler	T/N	?	Dressler	14 / 16 E vs 4 / 11 C 'improved'	p<.01
Postoperative	Meehan	?	?	?	TT ineffective Standard treatment (non healing)	NS Significant
Healee sensations	Goodrich	D		6 Le Shan	Synchronous vs non-synchronous healings	 p< .005
Personal relationship	Winston	T & D	5 mins	4 Le Shan	16 healees rotated through pat- terns of familiarity with healers	 NS**
Anxiety (state)	Heidt	T	5 mins	TT healer	Cardiac ICU patients: 30 pre- vs post-TT 30 TT vs 30 casual touch 30 TT vs 30 no touch	 p< .001 p< .01 p< .01
	Quinn	N	5 mins	4 TT healers	Cardiac ICU patients: 30 TT vs 30 mock TT	 p< .0005
	Ferguson	T	?	50 & 50 TT healers	Healees pre- vs post-healing: Experienced healers Inexperienced healers Experienced vs inexperienced healers	 p< .0001 p< .001 p< .001
	Fedoruk	N	25 mins	TT healers	17 premature infants, pre- vs post-stress + TT Physiological measure Mock TT (suggestive increase)	 p< .05 NS NS
	Collins	T	7 mins	TT healer	24 TT and mock TT in normal people	 NS
	Gulak	?	15 mins	Gulak	76 healees improved	.001<p< .01
	Randolph	T	13 mins	TT healer	30 college students stressed with movie: GSR, muscle tension, skin temperature	 NS
	Parkes	N	5 mins	TT healer	20 hospitalized patients, age 65 - 93, 43 illnesses: TT and mock TT both *increased* anxiety	 NS
Self esteem	Schutze	D	?	Prayer	10 healing vs 27 control	p< .05

* T/N/D: Touch/Near/Distant   **NS: Non-Significant

posttest and the facilitators were required to keep silence as to the name of the person assigned to them. No member of the experimental group participated in the small group counseling session facilitated by the individual assigned to pray for them.

Statistical analysis demonstrated significantly greater improvement in the subjects who had intercessory prayer ($p < 0.05$).

Discussion
A. Intercessory prayer (presumably a form of distant healing) was apparently helpful in enhancing self esteem.
B. This report is too brief to permit proper assessment of procedures such as methods of randomization and firmness of blinds. Data are not presented to support the reported results.

The studies on anxiety and self-esteem are summarized in Table I-22 (see page 242).

Two studies of healing for inadequately described problems remain.

C.R.B. Joyce and R.M.C. Welldon – The objective efficacy of prayer: A double-blind clinical trial (Journal of Chronic Diseases 1965)

Authors' Summary:

One of a *[matched]* pair of patients seen by a psychiatrist or a specialist in physical medicine was allocated to a group 'treated' by intercessory prayer, the other to 'control'. Neither the patient, the physician nor the participating prayer groups knew to which group each patient belonged. The patients were unaware that a trial was in progress and all the other individual medication and physical treatment prescribed by the consultant was re-evaluated by the same physician 8–18 months later. *[Clinical criteria used in evaluations are not specified.]* The first six valid and definite results available all showed an advantage to the 'treated' group. Five of the next six showed an advantage to the 'control' group. These results may be due solely to chance, but the possible involvement of other factors is discussed. The attitudes of possible participants in such studies are important, and some implications of this for future work are also discussed.

Patients are described as suffering from "chronic stationary or progressively deteriorating disease"; either "psychiatric or joint disease such as rheumatoid arthritis". Although the patients were allegedly matched, criteria for matching are not given. Neither specific psychiatric diseases, specific joint diseases, nor even numbers of patients in each of the two gross categories included in the study are mentioned.

Discussion
A. Combining patients with very different chronic illnesses in the same study seems questionable, even when one matches them in some way.
B. This is a poor study despite a basically good underlying strategy of matching patients. The following problems invalidate this study from serious consideration:
1. Clinical criteria used in evaluations are not specified.
How were healees evaluated as improved?
2. How can conclusions be drawn from such a small sample?

3. What sort of prayers were offered? When? How often?

Julio C. di Liscia – Psychic healing: An attempted investigation *(Psi Comunicacion 1977; Parapsychology Abstracts International 1984)*

Journal Abstract:

An experimental test of psychic healing at a distance is reported. Jaime Press, a well-known healer in Argentina, was the subject ... A physician selected two patients with similar medical conditions and gave the experimenters a sheet of paper on which were written the names and ages of the patients only. One of the patients was selected later by the experimenters, without the doctor's knowledge, as the experimental target. The healer was informed of the name of the person to be healed. Meanwhile, the physician continued medical treatment of the patients with no knowledge of the previous selection. The names of the selected patients were mailed to a third person and were unopened until the research was finished. It was planned to include 100 patients in the study, but the healer could not continue the work due to legal problems concerning his healing activity. A total of 58 patients was available for statistical analyses. Chi-square analyses of control and experimental groups were made in relation to improvement, worsening, and no change categories, but there were no significant differences.

Discussion

A. Though my high school Spanish is somewhat rusty, my reading of the original report suggests the author is biased against healers, in that he labels their overstatements about their prowess as 'megalomania'.

B. Unfortunately, the original article does not describe the conditions treated or criteria for inclusion in the 'improved', 'unchanged' or 'worse' categories. Evaluation of this report is therefore impossible.

This concludes the studies controlled I have been able to locate on healing.[30]

Clairsentient Diagnosis

Clairsentient diagnosis promises to be an important adjunct in medical evaluations. Unfortunately, little has been done to evaluate this aspect of psi healing. Few physicians are willing to risk criticism by their colleagues for collaborating with psychics and healers.

Karel Mison – Statistical processing of diagnostics done by subject and by physician *(Proceedings of the 6th International Conference on Psychotronics Research 1968)*

KAREL MISON, of Prague, presents a brief note on 2,005 diagnoses each made by a physician (P) and by a 'biodiagnostician' (identified as 'subject' or S). Six P and eight S participated. Data were gathered from six different centers on diseases. Distant diagnoses of 205 cases are not given individually, as they demonstrated an overall congruence of only 28.67%. The Table I-23 shows which P worked with which S and the following data:

1. Number of processed dyads (x);
2. Number of congruent diagnoses; and
3. Percentage of congruency.

Data were also gathered for instances where either P or S made a diagnosis and the other did not, but these are not presented.

Discussion

A. This study is a good beginning, indicating that in some instances clairsentient diagnosticians can achieve as high as 85% congruence with medical diagnosticians. This study suggests that in some cases a clairsentient diagnostician might work well with a physician. As this is a quick, safe, and inexpensive method for diagnosis it seems well worth further study.

It would be interesting to know whether any particular characteristics differentiated the P and S as individuals and/or as pairs who were more often congruent or incongruent.

Medical diagnosis is far from a perfect science. This percent of congruence is probably as good as diverse medical diagnosticians might achieve in many instances.
B. The report does not tell us whether the various diagnoses were validated by laboratory data. No controls or statistical analyses are presented.

For detailed figures of Karel Mison's diagnosis experiments see Table I-23, on page 246.

*Table I - 23. Mison's diagnosis experiment**

		S I	SII	S III	S IV	S V	S VI	S VII	S VIII	Totals
PA	a							125		125
	b							56		56
	c							44.80%		44.80%
PB**	a		256		45	34	117		74	586
	b		171		25	24	61		63	399
	c		66.80%		55.56%	70.59%	65.53%		85.14%	68.09%
PC	a	140								140
	b	78								78
	c	55.71%								55.71%
PD	a							157		157
	b							84		84
	c							53.50%		53.50%
PE	a		70		189	229	52		140	680
	b		34		97	123	35		102	381
	c		48.57%		51.32%	53.71%	48.08%		72.85%	56.03%
PF	a			112						112
	b			61						61
	c			54.56%						54.56%
Totals	a	140	326	112	234	263	229	282	214	1800
Totals	b	78	205	61	122	147	141	140	165	1059
Avg.	%	55.71%	62.88%	54.46%	52.14%	64.19%	61.57%	49.65%	77.10%	58.83%

(a) Number of processed dyads

(b) Number of congruent diagnoses

(c) Percentage of congruency

*Data were also gathered for instances where either P or S made a diagnosis and the other did not, but these are not presented.

**Errors in the original of this table for PB are corrected from a second table which gave the inverse figures for *in* congruent diagnoses.

Robert Brier, Barry Savits and Gertrude Schmeidler – Experimental tests of Silva Mind Control graduates (in: W.G.Roll, R.L.Morris, and J.D. Morris (Eds.) – *Research in Parapsychology 1973)*

The researchers note:

The Silva Mind Control organization advertises that it enables its graduates to develop E.S.P. Many graduates who seem intelligent and sincere claim they can diagnose ailments clairvoyantly, given some minimum information about an individual.

BRIER ET AL. performed two experiments in which a surgeon selected 25 cases and "identified each by first name and initial of last name, age and sex and divided them into five groups so that there was minimal overlap of symptoms among the five members of a given group". Five enthusiastic mind-control graduates each received one group of data and made their clairsentient diagnoses. No significant results were found.

A slight tendency was noted for more positive results in more recent graduates of the Mind Control program. A second experiment was therefore run with subjects tested on the day after graduation from training. Although the overall results were not significant this was misleading. "Two of the subjects were children, aged 10 and 12, and their readings were meager and uninformative." One subject's results taken alone were significant ($p < 0.05$) and "If the scores of the three older subjects had been examined separately, they would have been significant." Another graduate of the same course volunteered to be tested and also achieved significant results ($p < 0.05$).

The researchers are unenthusiastic about their results. They note:

> Our data still hold open the possibility that immediately after they have completed the Mind Control course, clairvoyant diagnostic ability may be strong in some individuals. If this possibility is confirmed, it might be considered a not unexpected outcome of a training method which combines meditative and hypnoidal techniques with strong positive suggestion and high group morale.

Discussion

A. The second experiment suggests that some positive results are obtained with this training, assuming that the subjects did not have clairsentient abilities prior to taking the course.

B. It would appear reasonable to request more careful research be done on more subjects before reaching any firm conclusions.

GERTRUDE SCHMEIDLER, in personal communication, added that her impression was that the Silva graduates attended very closely to verbal and nonverbal cues which led them towards diagnoses that were known to the experimenters and that little if any psi was likely to have been involved.

Alan Vaughan – Investigation of Silva Mind Control claims (Research in Parapsychology 1973)

VAUGHAN notes:

> ... a nurse... who had completed the Mind Control course and had received her diploma... asked me to arrange for an objective test of her and her fellow graduates' distant clairvoyant diagnosing ability. Accordingly, with cooperation from a physician, I sent her the first names, last initials, sex, age, and city of residence of five patients whose conditions were unknown to me. The nurse and 20 other Mind Control graduates attempted to make clairvoyant diagnoses for these and returned them to me.
>
> To evaluate the readings quantitatively, I selected two patients of the same sex and comparable ages, put their 21 readings each (total of 42) on coded cards, randomized them by flipping a coin, and sent them to the physician for judging, asking him to guess which of the two patients was being described by the diagnosis. Chance would give 21 'hits'. The physician's judgings gave 16

'hits'. In addition, he indicated on the cards any apparently correct diagnostic statements that guided him in his choice. Only one card bore a correct diagnostic statement... I then sent the physician the remaining 63 readings (for three patients by 21 students) and asked him to report to me any additionally correct statements. He found no other striking correspondence to his patients' conditions. These findings would seem to put in doubt the claims of Silva Mind Control.

Discussion

A. Before dismissing totally the claims of the Silva methods, one would want more substantial studies. Details of specific known and intuitive diagnoses should be presented for comparison. The doctor may have been unduly critical in his assessments.

B. The author's conclusions seem warranted.

My personal impression is that the claims of Silva Mind Control are greatly inflated, based on my attendance at a course, personal contact with a number of graduates and experience with many healers. Few of the better healers and fewer of the average ones are good at distant diagnosis so I would hardly expect the inexperienced, with just a few hours' lessons, to have even modest success.

C. Norman Shealy – Clairvoyant diagnosis (*Energy Medicine Around the World 1988*)

C. Norman Shealy – The role of psychics in medical diagnosis (in: Rick Carlson [Ed.] – Frontiers of Science and Medicine)[31]

DR. SHEALY, past president of the *American*

Holistic Medical Association, is a physician who has spent many years exploring ways of helping people cope with chronic pain. He performed three studies of diagnosis:

1. In a pilot study, Shealy selected 17 patients for 8 psychics, including *HENRY RUCKER*, to diagnose.

Each patient was brought into a room for about 10 minutes. The patient was then escorted out of the room and each of the sensitives was asked a variety of questions concerning the patient's personality and physical condition. We then pooled the results: only when a clear majority of the sensitives agreed on a given diagnosis was it considered the proper answer... we found this group to be 98% accurate in making personality diagnoses and 80% accurate in diagnosing physical conditions. For instance, they clearly distinguished between three totally separate cases of paraplegia – paralysis from the waist down – one traumatic, one infectious, and one degenerative in nature.

2. In a more formal study, Shealy diagnosed a series of patients by his own physical examination and administration of the Minnesota Multiphasic Personality Inventory. A photograph was taken of each patient, and his name and birth date written on the back. Handwriting samples and palm prints were obtained. Six clairvoyants were given the photographs, names and birth dates; a numerologist was given just the names and birth dates; a graphologist was given the handwriting sample; and the chirologist had the palm prints. No other contact with patients was allowed. A professor of psychology, who made no claim to psychic ability, also guessed the answers on the basis of the photographs. Two major questions were asked: "Where is the difficulty or pain?" and "What is the major and primary cause of the patient's illness?" Each diagnostician had a questionnaire to fill out.

> We had complete data on some 78 patients and at least one or more clairvoyant diagnoses carried out on almost 200. Two of the clairvoyants were 75% accurate and a third was 70% accurate in locating the site of pain. (Numerology was 60% accurate, astrology 35%, and palmistry and graphology 24% – the same as chance.) In determining the cause of the pain, the clairvoyants ranged from 65% accuracy down to 30%. Here, there was only a 10% probability of obtaining the correct diagnosis by chance.

The psychologist did not exceed chance levels with his guesses.

3. Dr. Robert Leichtman, an internist who is a gifted clairsentient diagnostician, was given photographs, names and birth dates of patients (numbers not specified). He was 96% accurate in descriptions of patients' personalities.

4. C.N. Shealy visited about 75 psychics or clairvoyants, finding six of them 70–75 percent accurate with physical diagnoses and 96% accurate with psychological diagnoses.

5. In informal testing, Shealy gave *Caroline Myss*, a gifted clairsentient diagnostician, only the names and birth dates of 50 patients. He found her to be 93% congruent with his own diagnoses. Shealy lists the pairs of clinical diagnoses.

Discussion

A. Shealy's daring in performing and reporting such research in the face of the skepticism and criticisms of the medical profession are commendable. He appears to have devoted considerable efforts to performing these studies. His results support a belief that clairsentient diagnosis may be a most useful adjunct to conventional diagnostic techniques, especially with concensus of multiple psychic diagnosticians.

Further study might clarify whether the successful intuitive diagnoses are achieved via clairsentience or via telepathy with the medical diagnostician. Doctors often achieve no better than 70–80% consensus in diagnosis with each other. The high rates of success of Myss with Shealy suggest that she might have been reading his mind.

B. Shealy does not give sufficient details in studies 1 – 4 to permit independent evaluation of his results, nor was statistical significance analyzed. In (2) it is not clear whether there were three more clairvoyants whose guesses were poorer and excluded from the report or whether some of the other intuitive diagnosticians were included in the six mentioned. Even (5) does not specify how patients were selected. There is the possibility that Shealy may have chosen better or clearer cases and that the results are biased by Shealy's intuitive selection of cases.

Nils Jacobson and Nils Wiklund – Investigation of claims of diagnosing by means of ESP (*Research in Parapsychology 1975*)

The Swedish *Mind Dynamic* method claims that its practitioners learn to diagnose illness at a distance when they are given only the patients' names and addresses. The researchers investigated the diagnostic abilities of a teacher of this method, *Mr. B. A.*

Experiment 1: One of the experimenters, N.W., gathered information on 10 sick male persons. Two lists were prepared, each randomized independently. "One contained the names and towns of residence (but not street addresses), and the other contained correct diagnoses…" Both lists, each in a sealed envelope, were given to the other experimenter, N.J., who conducted the study thereafter. N.J. did not know which name corresponded to which diagnosis. Mr. B.A. gave verbal diagnoses for each of the named persons, and then also matched the diagnoses from the list with the named persons.

Experiment 2: The above was repeated with female patients. In addition, N.J. knew the correct matching of names and diagnoses. He did not reveal to Mr. B.A. that he knew them. N. J. made every possible effort not to give out any cues. In actuality, the names and diagnoses were invented by

Table I - 24. Clairvoyant diagnosis

Researchers	Diagnostician	Results	Significance
Mison	Biodiagnosticians 8	45-85% congruence with physicians' diagnoses (mean 59%)	?
Brier, et al.	Silva Mind Control 5	1. 5 diagnoses each 2. One of the five	NS* p < .05
Vaughan	Silva Mind Control 5	5 patients each diagnosed by the 21 SMC graduates	NS

Shealy	1. 8 psychics, including Rucker	17 patients, pooled diagnoses:
		  Personality 98% accurate
		  Physical problems 80% accurate
			
			?
			?

	2. 6 clairvoyants, 1 ea. graphologist, numerologist, chirologist and psychologist	278 patients:
		Site of pain -
		  2 clairvoyants 75% accurate
		  1 clairvoyant 70% accurate
		  numerologist 60% accurate
		  astrologer 35% accurate
		  chirologist, graphologist 24%
		Cause of pain -
		  clairvoyants 30-65% accurate
			
			?
			?
			?
			?
			Chance
			
			?

	3. Leichtman	Patients' personalities 96% accurate	?
	4. 6 of 75 psychics or clairvoyants	Physical diagnoses 70-75% accurate Psychological diagnoses 96% accurate	? ?
	5. Myss	50 patients, psychological and physical diagnoses 93% accurate	 ?
Jacobson & Wicklund	Mind Dynamic	10 names, 10 diagnoses	NS

*Non-Significant

N.W. This subterfuge was unknown to N.J. at the time of the experiment.

A check was run on Mr. B.A. by asking him whether he knew personally any of the 10 real people listed in *Experiment 1,* along with 4 people whom he presumably knew. He admitted only to knowing one of these four.

> As he had in *Experiment 1*. Mr. B.A. expressed some disappointment that he did not reach his usual level of contact with the target persons. He showed distress and on two occasions asked for a rest. After three hours only seven target persons had been worked through. The work was terminated at this point, as seven trials was a suitable number for the intended statistical procedure... seven descriptions were matched with 10 different diagnoses...

In both experiments there were no correct diagnoses, which could occur purely by chance.

Mr. B.A. was highly motivated during the experiment. He complained that he usually knew the address of the patient and that the patient or someone who knew the patient was usually present when he made his diagnosis.

Discussion

A. The imposition of restrictive and misleading laboratory conditions on a clairsentient diagnostician appears to be poor practice, muddying the experimental waters. It may be that he is able to make correct diagnoses under the conditions with which he is familiar and comfortable.

The distress of the subject in the second experiment suggests he was aware (unconsciously?) of irregularities in the procedures. **B.** The first experimental design is simple but the number of trials is too small for assessment with great confidence of the issues addressed.

See Table I-24 (on page 250) for a summary of the clairsentient diagnosis studies.[32]

Summary

About two thirds of the controlled trials demonstrate positive effects of healing. Though many studies are flawed in minor aspects, and some in major ways, there still remain a convincing number of excellent studies with significant results.

Healing is certainly more than a placebo, unless enzymes, yeasts, bacteria, plants and mice are subject to suggestion, and the best efforts of numerous researchers did not provide for adequate experimental controls.

The implications of these studies are far-reaching. Psi healing appears to be a therapeutic modality with vast potentials for enhancing health care. In the UK, The Netherlands, Russia and Eastern Europe this is being integrated into conventional medical settings. Elsewhere, people are seeking it out on their own.

If healing were a drug I believe it would be accepted as effective on the basis of the evidence.

CHAPTER I - 5

Uncontrolled Studies

The reticence of medical orthodoxy to accept every healing claim which surfaces or which attracts the public eye has been and should continue to be a public protection. On the other hand, the role of public protector all too easily can be an armour for the protection of limited self-interest and a professional insulation inimical to the public good. Although the contributions of medical science well may be considered with gratitude—one of the blessings of mankind, there also may be useful contributions outside the medical mainstream. At what point should the individual be permitted freedom of choice in the regulation of his/her own health and healing practices? At what point does the medical profession's 'right' to arbitrate these matters cease? These are weighty questions calling to be answered. It seems clear that these matters cannot usefully be reconciled without recourse to an informed public and a healing profession educated beyond the confines of its own orthodoxy.

Jeanne Pontius Rindge

This chapter is a varied feast, including items primarily of historical interest, such as Galton's study of whether monarchs for whom prayers are offered live longer, reports by healers themselves, and more direct attempts with varying degrees of rigor to tease out what healing involves. It is difficult to know in some cases which findings may be legitimate effects of healing and which are chance occurrences, placebo effects or spontaneous waxings and wanings of chronic illness. The reader will have to decide which might come closer to Type I and which closer to Type II error.[1]

These items add descriptive clues which may contribute to our understanding of healing. Selection was made on the basis of unique observations, particular patient populations, special methods of healing and originality of opinions. Articles based on clinical observations, especially those with more objective perspectives, were given preference over articles advocating more narrow belief systems concerning healing.[2]

Franz Anton Mesmer – Mesmerism: A Translation of the Original Medical and Scientific Writings of F. A. Mesmer (Translated by G.J. Bloch)

FRANZ ANTON MESMER (1734-1815) was one of the earliest scientists to study healing. He developed methods he labeled 'animal magnetism', in which he made 'passes' (hand movements) around the bodies of his patients, inducing hypnotic trances and relieving a wide spectrum of symptoms. In deep trance, mesmerized patients were able to diagnose themselves with apparent accuracy (DINGWALL). Mesmerists were also able to hypnotize subjects telepathically from a distance.

Far ahead of his contemporaries, he explored realms which they found too dissonant with their materialistic theories. At the time he lived, there were neither sufficient understanding of psychological mechanisms nor explanatory theories which could coherently account for these phenomena. It is not surprising his methods were questioned, criticized and even condemned in some quarters.

Mesmer's theories were mechanistic, limited by conceptualizations of a world not yet aware of today's theories of psychology and physics. He states:

> ... everything is explicable by the mechanical laws of Nature, and ... all effects relate to modifications of 'matter' and of 'movement.'

He believed that his approaches would eventually explain these difficult problems:

1. How is a sleeping man able to consider and foresee his own illnesses, as well as the illnesses of others?
2. Without any instruction whatsoever, how is he able to prescribe the most accurate means of cure?
3. How can he see the most distant objects and have presentiments of events?
4. How is a man able to receive an impression from a will other than his own?
5. Why is a man not always endowed with these faculties?

Discussion   With knowledge of psi, hypnosis and healing one can appreciate Mesmer's perspicacity. Though many of his cures were probably due to relief of conversion (hysterical) symptoms,[3] his work seems to have included healing as well. He did not know to differentiate between these nor between aspects of hypnosis and psi. This is not to say that making clinical and scientific distinctions on the basis of modern knowledge is necessarily the correct or best way to do it. We can only observe that there are definite similarities between Mesmer's approaches and modern studies of healing.

Modern hypnosis uses brief inductions, usually without passes of the hypnotist's hands around the body. In Mesmer's days, passes would be made for many hours, achieving profoundly deep ('plenary') states (DINGWALL) in which psi effects were demonstrated. The extensive hand passes around the body practiced by the Mesmerists strongly resemble laying-on-of-hands healing, and the telepathic influences of hypnotists over their subjects appear to overlap with absent healing. The latter may indicate that healers (and probably other health care personnel and clergy) can sometimes introduce suggestions telepathically to their healees.

surveyed lived one to two years longer than lawyers or members of the medical profession, when *eminent* members of these other professions are compared the results are reversed. Other factors, such as residence of the majority of clergy in rural versus most other professionals in urban settings, introduce variables which render such comparisons questionable. One would also think the longevity of royalty must be influenced by more critical variables than prayer. (PEARSON)

Discussion   Galton's summary highlights the limitations of this report. Nevertheless, as the first recorded effort to establish the effects of healing scientifically, it is a historical gem .

Table I - 25. Mean age of various classes of males living beyond 30, 1758 - 1843 (Deaths by accident or violence are excluded)

F. Galton – Statistical Studies Into the Efficacy of Prayer *(Fortnightly Review 1872; reprinted in: Archives of Internal Medicine 1970)*

GALTON reasoned that if prayer were efficacious, then clergymen who pray frequently or monarchs for whom people pray frequently should live longer. "There is a memoir by Dr. Guy[4] ... in which he compares the mean age of sovereigns with that of other classes of persons." DR. GUY's results are presented in Table I-25.

As Galton himself notes, no clear conclusions can be drawn from this line of approach. Although the clergymen

	Number	Average age	Eminent men
Members of Royal houses	97	64.040	
Clergy	945	69.409	66.42
Lawyers	294	68.104	66.51
Medical Profession	244	67.301	67.07
English aristocracy	1179	67.310	
Gentry	1632	70.220	
Trade and commerce	513	68.740	
Officers in the Royal Navy	366	68.400	
English literature and science	395	67.505	65.22
Officers of the Army	569	67.070	64.74
Fine arts	239	65.960	

D. J. West – Eleven Lourdes Miracles *(Helix Press 1957)*

Visits to shrines such as Lourdes are alleged to cure many diseases. D. J. WEST, a physician, critically discusses a number of cases that had been declared 'miracles' by the church after extensive medical and ecclesiastical reviews.

The Story of Lourdes

In 1858 a peasant girl named BERNADETTE SOUBIROUS was gathering wood by the River Gave, at the base of a cliff known as Massabieille. A vision of the Virgin Mary appeared to her, standing at a split in the rock. Miraculous cures were alleged to have occurred at this spot within a few weeks of the first appearance of the Virgin. This became the healing grotto, where people with all varieties of illnesses come from all over the world to ask the Virgin for a cure. Thousands bathe daily in the waters of the grotto. Conservatively estimated, 15,000 to 20,000 sick and a further two to three million religious pilgrims visited Lourdes in 1948-1949, and the numbers have grown since then.

Because a few of the people coming to Lourdes have had miraculously rapid cures of intractable, serious illnesses, much interest has been stirred in religious and medical circles. A local medical board, staffed by volunteers and supported by donations from private (non-clerical) sources, has reviewed cases of cures since 1885. An independent body, *The International Medical Commission*, has been reviewing these cases since 1947. The *IMC,* sitting deliberately in Paris (removed from the emotional atmosphere of Lourdes), goes over medical records of patients' evaluations from before and after their cures to decide whether each exceeds the normal expectation for recuperation from that particular illness. The church then performs its own, independent evaluation before deciding whether a cure is miraculous.

Here is how the Lourdes cases are evaluated: When an unusual recovery is noted, the patient is examined by members of the local medical bureau. Medical documents of the patient are scrutinized, along with the testimonies of the patient and of those accompanying him and of those witnessing his cure. One of the physicians of the Medical Bureau is designated as the case reporter to gather all available information for the full Bureau. Visiting physicians are also invited to participate in the discussion of such cases. If there is agreement that the case is sufficiently unusual a physician near the patient's home is assigned to seek further testimony and to follow the case during the next year. At the end of a year the patient is examined again by the Board. The physicians deliberate on whether the cure still appears inexplicable. If this is their decision they forward the dossier to the IMC, which likewise assigns a coordinator to review the case and to report to the entire IMC. If the IMC then considers the case inexplicable by ordinary laws of nature, the dossier is submitted to the Archbishop of the diocese of the healed person. He designates a *Canonical Commission* to review the case afresh. They take separate testimony from the witnesses and express their opinions on whether the case can be considered miraculous by the Church's standards. It is only on the favorable recommendation of the Canonical Commission that the Archbishop may pronounce the cure attributable to the miraculous intervention of the Virgin Mary.

West's Analysis

West presents a thorough and critical analysis of 11 cases and a more sketchy overview of another 87 reports. He is clearly a disbeliever in the phenomena as miracles. He states:

> The present study is concerned solely with the evidence relating to remarkable or unexplained cures, the aim being to keep as far as possible to factual matters and to limit discussion to consideration of the plausibility or otherwise of various natural interpretations. The fact that these particular cures are believed to have religious significance is irrelevant to the purpose of the study. A critical survey of the factual evidence would be equally valid whether the cures were brought about by a new drug or by the intervention of the Virgin Mary.

West points out that in most of the 11 cases there were possible diagnoses which were not seriously entertained by the Board or the Commission (including malingering) and in some cases diagnoses such as 'tuberculosis' are not supported beyond reasonable doubt by laboratory data. The declarations of miraculous cures rely heavily on clinical impressions and a variety of testimonies which could conceivably be erroneous.

West concludes:

> The rarity of the cures, and the incompleteness of the medical information on most of the cases put forward as miracles, makes any kind of appraisal exceedingly difficult. As far as it goes, and taking the dossiers at their face value, the evidence for anything 'miraculous' in the popular sense of the expression is extremely meagre. Self-evidently impossible cures, involving something like the regeneration of a lost eye or limb, are not in question because they are never claimed. The great majority of the cures concern potentially

recoverable conditions and are remarkable only in the speed and manner in which they are said to have taken place. In no case is a sudden structural change confirmed by the objective evidence of X-rays taken just before and just after the event.

In his lighter survey of cases, West grudgingly notes that there are chronic suppurating wounds which closed very rapidly and completely at Lourdes.[5]

Discussion   WEST is the most rigorous of the reviewers of Lourdes healings. His cautious tone underscores a careful scrutiny of the reported cures. This is an excellent review, with details of methods of inquiry and criteria for inclusion or exclusion of cases as miraculous cures. The review is weak in that it is a retrospective survey by West of work performed by other physicians and other evaluators. It is also clearly biased against the possibility of the truly miraculous which might occur among these cures.

It is impressive that positive findings remain after the many siftings of the evidence. Although X-ray evidence of instantaneous body cures is not observed among the Lourdes cases considered in the review, there are witnessed reports from apparently reliable sources testifying to instantaneous total healings of chronic fleshy suppurating wounds. These are impossible to account for in any conventional way. They appear to constitute recoveries from infections of chronic nature and acceleration of the rate of wound healing when these have resisted all conventional treatments. We are left yet again to postulate new ways of understanding what is possible in the healing of the human body.

Douglas Dean reports that analyses of water from Lourdes and from several other holy springs and places regarded as geological *power points* demonstrate altered infrared spectrometry readings which are characteristic of water treated by healers (1989). This was true of some but not all samples from Lourdes. Dean clarified that this was dependent on whether the samples were taken from the grotto spring itself or from other locations.[6]

Inge Strauch – Medical Aspects of 'Mental' Healing (International Journal of Parapsychology 1963)[7]

Inge Strauch explains that her "... paper is based on a joint study undertaken in Germany by the Institute for Border Areas of Psychology and Mental Hygiene and the Medical Polyclinic, both affiliated with the University of Freiburg i. Br." Patients in a rural setting treated by Kurt Trampler, a 'mental healer,' were studied before and after his treatments. Characteristics of the patients are described in some detail. Categories of illnesses treated are mentioned, but not specific diagnoses or numbers of patients in each category.

It proved possible to evaluate the extent of objective changes in 247 patients. Where changes in condition corresponded to the expected course of a patient's disease, the doctors (H. Enke and J. Marx) listed these as in the 'objectively no change' group. (See table I-26 on the top right of the page.)

Table I - 26.
Objective changes, all patients

Objective changes	%	absolute
Improvement	9	22
Temporary improvement	2	4
No change	75	187
Deterioration	14	34
Totals	**100**	**247**

Within the major disease groups, most of the objective improvements (15%) occurred in diseases of the digestive tract. The next table [Table I-27, below] shows the objective changes with the more organic or functional aspects of a disease.

Evidently the prospects for objective improvement are much greater in the predominantly functional diseases. Furthermore, improvement was closely related to the gravity of the disease; the graver the condition, the fewer improvements there were ...

The statements of the patients themselves in regard to their subjective feelings show great deviation from the results of the objective checks. All those who were objectively improved also stated that they felt better. But the group of those who showed no objective change by no means

Table I - 27.
Objective changes, organic compared to functional illness

Objective changes	Predominantly organic	Predominantly functional	
Improvement / temporary improvement	46%	54%	(=100%)
No change	62%	38%	(=100%)
Deterioration	84%	16%	(=100%)

regarded their condition as unchanged: 61% of these patients thought that it had improved during the time of the investigation. And of those whose condition had objectively worsened, 50% nevertheless declared that they were considerably better, at least temporarily.

This obvious discrepancy between the changes determined by clinical methods and the patients own statements fits in with our general impression that Trampler's influence produced in the main subjective changes – which, however, can be of great importance to the patient... In the course of the study at Freiburg the doctors came to the conclusion that Dr. Trampler had not, during the period of the investigation, exerted influence prejudicial to the health of any patient he treated.

Characteristics of responders vs. non-responders are listed, per profiles on Zulliger's Z-test and Pfister-Heiss Color Pyramid test. Graphological analysis of handwriting was also obtained.

The positive group... had on the whole a lower level of intelligence and a markedly low critical capacity. Although predominantly affectively impressionable, it was less so than the negative group, was also less imaginative, possessed of extremely feeble self-confidence, and less tense...

Discussion   This is one of the few published clinical studies, providing information obtained by the same group of researchers on a large number of patients before and after healing. Descriptions of methods and general criteria for evaluations are reasonably presented. More detailed reports on the types of problems treated/improved would have helped.

Because no control groups of untreated patients were used for comparison with those receiving healing, an objective observer is left, at the best, with the choice of accepting the opinions of researchers he does not know and cannot evaluate or of suspending judgment or of expressing severe doubts at the worst.

Of help are the observations on types of patients likely to benefit from healing. The larger number of objective improvements where a functional (psychosomatic) component was present implies that suggestion may be a major component in the response to healing. This is further supported by the better response in less intellectual and analytical personality types, whom I would expect to be more receptive to suggestion.

The functional illnesses may also be more susceptible to healing because they involve neuronal and/or hormonal influences; or may involve the immune system; may be related to smooth muscle tension (in gut, bronchioles, blood vessels) and are therefore subject to mental control as shown in biofeedback. Self- healings may be occurring via telepathic suggestion.

The fact that people who are less tense responded better is hard to reconcile with the above alternatives. If anything, one would expect *more* response from suggestion in patients who were more anxious. These would have more pressing needs for relief and more room for improvement on a parameter which is notoriously responsive to suggestion. This discrepancy hints at the possibility that something other than suggestion may be occurring. Many healers say a relaxed state in healees contributes to a positive response.

Many patients reported subjective relief of symptoms even when no objective changes were measurable. Even if this is only due to suggestion, it appears to be a very worthwhile addition to the management of dis-ease associated with disease. Surveys of healees, considered near the end of this chapter, almost uniformly repeat this finding.

Zofia Mialkowska – Statistical assessment of Dr. Jerzy Rejmer's biotherapeutical activity at an IZIS clinic in Warsaw *(Proceedings of the Sixth International Conference on Psychotronic Research, 1986)*

ZOFIA MIALKOWSKA, a psychologist, reviews the 'biotherapy' work of DR. JERZY REJMER in a Polish clinic between 1982 and 1985. He saw 2,820 people (1,913 women and 907 men). Many people had more than one problem and 3,837 clinical complaints (2,699 by women; 1,138 by men) were tabulated. Results of Dr. Rejmer's treatments are mentioned for only 1,684 of the 3,837 problems (43.89%) since many healees had only one treatment and no follow-up data are available. Many of the cases had been unresponsive to conventional therapies. In 293 instances (7.64%), hospital testimony to this effect was obtained.

Dr. Rejmer treated each person by giving healing to the local body region requiring help (3,090, or 85% of problems). Alternatively, "when the organism was remarkably weakened with a generalized character of complaint, he used a generally strengthening technique". Biotherapy was clearly used in a complementary (rather than alternative) manner, with attending physicians and specialists consulted in 917 cases (27.26%). In 83.25% of cases patients reported improvement in well-being. In 52.67%, "the effects of Dr. Rejmer's procedures were confirmed by the appropriate analytical and medical examinations".

The greatest objective changes were noted in nervous (especially epilepsy) and urinary systems; the lowest in the digestive system. "The improvement ... was most

Table I - 28. Effectiveness of J. Rejmer's Biotherapeutic Actions*

System	Number of cases	Sense of well-being	Medical data	No change
Digestive	593	507 85.50%	252 42.50%	37 6.24%
Respiratory	276	204 73.91%	143 51.81%	14 5.07%
Nerves and sense organs	226	155 68.58%	151 66.81%	16 7.08%
Circulatory	196	184 93.88%	118 60.20%	4 2.04%
Genital	177	167 94.35%	89 50.28%	4 2.26%
Urinary	132	105 79.55%	84 63.64%	2 1.15%
Endocrinal	84	80 95.24%	50 59.52%	1 1.19%
Total	1684	1402	887	78
Average %		83.25%	52.67%	4.63%

*This table is slightly modified from the original source to improve its clarity.

distinctly marked with reference to the endo-crinal, the genital and circulatory systems, and least marked with reference to the respiratory system." (See Table I-28.) Pain responded extremely well, especially for headaches and arthritis. Only 4.63% of all cases demonstrated no change. Some (especially with genital, urinary or endocrinal problems) reported pain during or immediately following treatments, but after a short while felt marked and lasting improvement. In all cases where follow-ups are available – up to two years post-treatment – the results have been permanent.

Discussion   Again, we have a tantalizing report indicating healing can be helpful in some ways with some illnesses. But again we lack details of diagnosis, criteria for improvement and control groups against which to judge the results.

The occasional occurrence of pain early in the course of healings has been reported by several healers and may be a clue to how healing works. It generally bodes well when this happens.

Gordon Turner – What power is transmitted in treatment? *(Two Worlds, July 1969)*[8]

GORDON TURNER was a remarkably gifted, natural healer from Britain. He returned to university studies in order to understand better the 'whys and wherefores' of his healing. He is among the few healers who carefully observed and documented their results.

1. A survey involving 954 direct contact healing treatments on 353 people by 23 healers showed subjective sensations in touch healings: heat (mild to 'burning'); leaving of a red weal for several minutes; tingling;

prickling like electricity; and coldness. Less specific sensations were also recorded, such as "saw colors mentally" (46/73 saw blue; 11 red). Only a few had emotional responses. Many spoke of a "sense of peace", but this was not tabulated since it was not in the category of physical sensations being surveyed. (See Table I-29.)

The majority of those who felt Nothing were suffering from mental illness. Of the 76 patients, 49 had various neuroses. Whilst it was apparent that a high percentage of those who responded immediately to healing had some intense sensation during the treatment; those who had no sensation were often equally responsive.

There was some evidence for believing that the frequency with which a patient attends healing diminishes his responsiveness to physical sensation during treatment.

Patients receiving healing consecutively from different healers tended to experience the same sensations, though with varying intensity. Individual healers often produced a wide range of sensations. Only three healers had the same sensations as their patients. Those sensations associated with cures were examined separately. (See Table I-30.)

2. Photographic plates between healers' hands and healees' bodies showed evidence of healing energy transfer. Film exposures were produced only with sick plants and persons in need of treatment, not with healthy ones.

In all we repeated this experiment 93 times, producing 57 marked plates... The 'radiation' patterns on the film were very similar to those produced if it was

Table I - 29. Contact healing responses

	Heat	Cold	Intense cold	Intense heat	Elec-trical	Miscel-laneous	Nothing	Totals
Patients:	163	39	17	5	47	11	76	353
Treatments	432	77	36	9	71	21	308	954
Percentage	45.3%	8.0%	3.7%	0.9%	7.4%	2.2%	32.3%	100%

Table I - 30. Sensations associated with cures

	Heat	Cold	Intense cold	Intense heat	Elec-trical	Miscel-laneous	Nothing	Totals
Patients	4	3	9	4	13	5	1	39
Treatments	7	6	10	8	20	6	1	58
Percentage	12.0%	10.3%	17.2%	13.7%	34.5%	10.3%	1.7%	100%

placed close to a hot iron for 10 to 12 minutes. In some instances the palm and finger prints of the healer came out on the developed plate. It should be stressed that we were at pains to ensure that healer's hands did not come into direct contact with the screened film. It may be significant that the best 'results' were always achieved in the first 30 seconds. An indication of the extent of this 'radiation' is that 30 seconds of healing produced a similar marking to 12 minutes exposure to a hot iron.

The best results were obtained with infrared film or X-ray plates.

Gordon Turner – I treated plants, not patients *(Two Worlds, August 1969)*

3. TURNER describes why he used plants as experimental subjects.

Experiments take time. It was becoming difficult to find patients willing to put up with tedious research procedures.

Volunteers were all too easily come by, but they seldom lasted more than one or two sessions. It was ironic that we were treating several hundred people weekly, yet we were still short of patients! Another source of concern was my conviction that 'volunteer patients' were not really representative. They wanted to be helpful. Therefore if we asked them what they felt, their subconscious mind would try to supply what it imagined we wanted to hear.

Turner used cut flowers.

A typical experiment by me, among several dozen along these lines, was followed by the *Daily Sketch,* where Neville Randall reported: "He began by taking two bunches of chrysanthemums cut from the same plant at the same time. He placed them in two identical vases filled with the same amount of water and stood them together in the same amount of light.

There was just one difference. One bunch he left untouched. On the other, he placed his hands for five minutes once a day exactly as with a sick patient. He gave these flowers healing. Two weeks later the untreated flowers had wilted badly. The flowers which had treatment were still in full bloom and only just beginning to wilt. ...When he passed his hands over the flowers to give them treatment, their heads seemed to sway slightly following the movements he made."

sible to hold my hand about an inch from the flowers and sway their heads back and forth.

Controlled experiments were run to see whether the life of cut flowers could be prolonged with healing treatments.

...the flowers which received healing would stay fresh for about a third as long again as those that did not. The most outstanding result we achieved was with a sample of chrysanthemums which only started to fall 32 days after the corresponding untreated sample had completely withered. In all they stayed fresh for no less than 55 days.

4. Germination of seeds was the subject of eight controlled experiments. Measured quantities of grass seed were planted in identical boxes, provided with identical water and placed beside each other in a conservatory. Ten minutes of healing twice daily was given to the experimental box.

The treated seeds sprouted earlier than the untreated ones by at least three days.

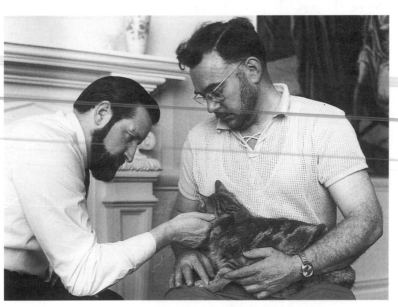

Fig. 1-9 Gordon Turner was known for healing animals.

Photograph by courtesy of Psychic News

This flower movement was a most revealing 'side effect'. For the first ten days it would be imperceptible. But after 14 or 16 days the flowers would move, just as if they were 'hungry' for the healing... it was pos-

5. Two healers 'treated' the potting mixture and seed (separately) for 30 minutes before planting. No further healing was given the plants but water was 'treated' for 10 minutes before sprinkling. The treated seed gave shoots 10 days before the un-treated seed.

6. Only the water was treated for 10 minutes and shoots appeared six days ahead of the control sample. Turner speculates:

> It may be that such old-fashioned rituals as 'blessing crops' have considerable substance in fact. Simple prayer might prove to be far more efficacious than fertilizers and a great many expensive and dangerous chemicals.

Gordon Turner – I experiment in absent treatment *(Two Worlds, September 1969)*

8. Out of 458 patients queried regarding absent healing 197 responded, receiving collectively 1,379 treatments. They gave the impression that fewer and less intense sensations were felt. Eighty-three reported color sensations (59 blue or violet; 7 red);

Table I - 31. Absent healing responses

	Heat	Cold	Electrical	Touch	Movement	Nothing	Totals
Patients	41	16	9	27	13	91	197
Treatments	181	71	35	112	42	937	1379
Percentage	13.1%	5.1%	2.5%	8.1%	3.0%	67.9%	100%

7. Healing was studied as a *preventive.*

> A farmer who wrote to ask us to put his herd of thoroughbred Friesian cows on absent healing in the hope that they might avoid infection during an outbreak of foot-and-mouth disease, reported that not only had they remained disease free, but their milk yield had increased by as much as 8% over a period of 12 weeks!

For six months prior to confinement 19 pregnant women received healing.

> In every instance they had a comparatively easy delivery – and this despite the fact that complications were expected in 9 instances... it could be of some significance that 13 of these mothers regularly kept in touch with us for a period of 4 years and not one of the babies contracted any infantile illness.

19 saw spirit forms. Almost all reported, they "were conscious of healing at quite different times to the evening intercession". Aspects of this experiment were puzzling. As Table I-31 indicates,

> ... 106 people refer to sensations over 442 absent healing sessions. An additional 91 people felt nothing and 937 sessions produced no reaction. Thus even those who 'felt' the healing did not do so on every occasion.

The 'sensory' phenomena could be expected to be fairly evenly distributed throughout the week. The experiment covered a week from Thursday to Wednesday and reactions each day varied considerably, as shown in Table I-32.

Table I - 32. Daily reactions to absent healing

Thur	Fri	Sat	Sun	Mo	Tues	Wed	Totals:
38	97	85	82	7	25	98	**442**

If these figures are of any significance, then it would appear that the 'conditions' on some evenings were far more conducive to physical reactions than on others. Ruling out any 'esoteric' significance to particular days of the week, it might be reasonable to assume that our absent healing 'network' was less effective on certain days.

What governed the variable factor? The possibilities are limitless. The attunement of the healers? The receptivity of the patients? Even the psychic link between the worlds may have influenced the results.

I attach considerable importance to the fact that there were thunderstorms around London on both Monday and Tuesday nights. Admittedly the patients were scattered over a far wider area. But in this instance our 'transmitting station' might have been affected.

9. A study was conducted on absent healing for healees who were showing no physical improvement.

We decided ... to ask for the cooperation of a small number of patients who had been receiving absent healing for a considerable time without noticing any physical betterment.

The object of this experiment was to determine whether it was possible to improve results by telepathic aids to the link between patient and healer. Twelve of these 'stubborn' patients were asked to furnish us with photographs, from which we had slides made, to be projected on to a screen at the time of healing.

Each patient was given an individual appointment time when we would be linking with them and supplied with a photograph of a 'simple country scene'. In addition to

this we decided to use a 'tuning signal'. They were asked to read the first verse of the 23rd Psalm aloud.

At the stated time we projected the photograph of the country scene to our screen and read the first verse of the 23rd Psalm. Then we replaced the country scene with a picture of the patient. We continued the healing link for about ten minutes. Thus healers and patient were using similar aids to concentration at the same time. The number of healers involved varied from 6 to 20.

On the face of it the experiment was a success. One patient, a doctor's wife, who suffered from a depressive mental illness, was so improved that within a week she was able to discontinue all drugs. A child suffering from a spinal illness stood, for the first time for several years, during the actual experiment.

Of the other patients nine felt a measure of alleviation of their symptoms and only one remained unchanged. What was more impressive was that eight of these patients continued to report benefit from their absent healing where they had previously noticed no difference.

What had been the governing factor, an improved 'link' by the healer, or greater receptivity on the patient's part? A further experiment seemed to suggest that both had played some part. At that time we were conducting a weekly healing clinic at a North London hall.

We collected a further 12 pictures of absent healing patients. At the end of this session we gathered 16 healers and more than 100 patients into the main hall. We asked them to join in a communal absent healing concentration. Each picture was shown for three minutes with a brief description of the patient's illness.

The essential difference was that the patients were not aware of the time at which the link would be made, although they knew it would occur at some time during the week. Only two out of the 12 showed any marked improvement. Both felt the healing at the time of the intercession. There was no evidence to support the idea that any greater amount of power was generated by the large number of people involved in the intercession.

TURNER states in the first part of this four-part series:

> Absent and contact healing seemed to achieve a similar percentage of success (possibly between 55 to 70 percent). Yet there seemed to be certain people who were more responsive to one type of treatment rather than the other.

Turner mentions, for instance, that in both touch and absent healings patients with arthritic problems may note a sensation of a joint being moved or realigned. This occurs even though no pressure is applied in touch healing, and certainly none can be in distant healing. He concludes:

> Despite the fact that many people have less faith in absent healing than in contact treatment, I am convinced that it achieves just as high a ratio of success. A careful analysis of absent healing and contact healing results show just as many physical disorders yield to one as the other.

Discussion   This is a fascinating series of studies with many hints about aspects of healing. Unfortunately, little detail is provided regarding methods of healing or types of

illnesses treated and no rigorous controls were attempted.

Regarding specific experiments detailed above I note the following:

1. Healee sensations of intense heat, cold and 'electrical' during contact healing appear to be correlated with healing effects, per Tables I–29 and I–30.

2. A healing energy is suggested by this experiment, as in two similar cases: (A) WATKINS demonstrated exposure of film placed under anesthetized mice who were the subjects for healing (1979), and (B) MOSS showed patterns on photographic film were produced by OLGA WORRALL by holding film between her hands (1979). It is difficult to differentiate whether this is an effect specifically of the healing or an exposure of film produced by direct action of thought.[9]

3. Other healers have caused plants to move during healings.[10]

4.-6. With widespread pollution caused by pesticides and chemical fertilizers, potential contributions of healing have much to offer in protecting crops and enhancing growth.

7. HARRY EDWARDS is the only other healer I have found who reports a preventive clinical use of healing, summarized later in this chapter. In a loose survey, he found that absent healing appeared to lessen the incidence of influenza during an epidemic.

8. In support of TURNER's reports of sensations during distant healing we have GOODRICH's controlled experiment, reviewed in Chapter I–4. The timing of healing to coincide with healees' being in a receptive state appeared to produce more intense sensations in both these studies.

9. Whether the effectiveness of healing is influenced by healees' being in a receptive state during the sending of healing requires further study. Some healers believe healings take place irrespective of their timing or of healee synchronization with the healer. The beliefs of healers and healees may influence this factor. It may also not be an either/or situation but rather that suggestion plus healing are more effective than either alone.

Frederick W. Knowles – Some investigations into psychic healing (Journal of the American Society for Psychical Research 1954)

Frederick W. Knowles – Psychic healing in organic disease (*Journal of the American Society for Psychical Research 1956*)

Kenneth Richmond – Experiments in the Relief of Pain (*Journal of the Society for Psychical Research 1946*)[11]

FREDERICK KNOWLES learned Indian methods of psi healing and then studied medicine to better understand what he was doing. Though initially instructed in secret rituals for healing, he found with experience that these were inessential. He also demonstrated that suggestion alone was insufficient and that a period of concentration on his part was necessary in addition to suggestions in order to effect healings. *Neither alone was nearly as effective as both together* (1954).

... an important factor in psychic healing is the healer's mental concentration upon the process of recovery which he desires to promote. Whether he touches the pa-

tient and the diseased region of the body, or passes his hands over it, or breathes on it, or carries out any formality, is irrelevant. In one process I use, the healer preferably looks at, but at least visualizes the patient or the region of the body affected, and imagines the intended recovery process by a series of thoughts or meditations. In the case of a painful joint, for instance, I visualize the disappearance of any effusion, swelling, or inflammation, and form images of easy painless movements. To keep up undistracted mental effort I change the images frequently, e.g., I visualize improved blood circulation and lymphatic drainage of the region, or again I imagine that I possess an invisible analgesic substance which I mentally throw at the region, seeming to see it penetrate the painful tissues with soothing results. Such concentrated thought effort is maintained for 3–20 minutes, and repeated, if need be, a few times at intervals of a few days.

Speculating on whether suggestion rather than healing is involved, he adds:

It might be asked whether my experience with pain and relief in organic disease are not fully accounted for by the effects of suggestion, as understood today. It is probably true to say that the effects of suggestion, e.g., in osteoarthritis have not been adequately explored, but that, on the whole, clinicians are not impressed by them. More important, I have found my results to depend very largely on the amount of concentrated effort of thought that I put into the process of psychic treatment. But unless this concentration acts through a parapsychological process, it should not be suggestive to, or affect the patient. In a few whom

I treated many times, and where this treatment produced complete but only temporary relief from severe pain (e.g., in carcinomatous involvement of sensory nerves), I had the opportunity to omit this mental concentration upon occasion, behaving otherwise outwardly exactly in my usual manner during the 'treatment'. On these occasions relief did not occur. This seems the more remarkable in that these patients had been accustomed by several previous genuine treatments to obtain complete relief, and were thus conditioned to expect relief again. After such a failed 'treatment', I then applied the concentration process and relief occurred as rapidly as usual.

RICHMOND chronicled KNOWLES' treatment of 43 cases of painful conditions such as chronic osteoarthritis, rheumatism and sciatica, selected for chronicity and absence of concomitant medical treatments. Knowles was concentrated for about two minutes per patient visit, with 3–5 visits weekly per patient. He checked patients' responses between periods of concentration, asking about decreased pain and increased range of motion of joints. He allowed up to three visits in cases of no response before withdrawing from a case. Where partially successful he would give up to 12 sessions. He preferred skeptical patients.

Table I-33 (RICHMOND) shows his results.

Table I - 33. Results in patients treated by Knowles

Decreased pain	35	(13 Established freedom from pain; 12 pain decreased more than two days but not promising permanent relief)
No relief	2	
Indeterminate	6	(5 pain transiently decreased a few hours - two days)
Totals:	43	30 (13 unaccounted for in report)

Knowles concludes (1956):

Concerning the nature of the effort of mind or will that is required on the part of the physician... whatever concentration, meditation, or effort of will is used, it probably depends essentially on establishing in the physician's mind a vivid expectation of benefit to the patient. Any method that establishes such an expectation in the physician's mind may be adequate... Possibly that expectation telepathically enhances the patient's own expectation to a level sufficient to secure benefit.

The best results were in conditions such as osteoarthritis, in which definite physical lesions were observable (e.g. three complete-relief cases each were found for osteoarthritis and rheumatism). Poorer results were generally found in cases of sciatica. The authors also report pain relief in the following illnesses: neuritis, cancer, persistent postoperative pain several years after mastectomy, toothache, inoperable kidney stones, headaches, sprained ankles, tenosynovitis (inflammation of a tendon sheath), dysmenorrhea and only occasionally sciatica. Pains in monarticular arthritis (affecting only one joint), with one or a few treatments, could be eased for several years.

KNOWLES and RICHMOND report experiments to try to tease out mechanisms of healing action. Experimental pain was inflicted on volunteers by prolonged occlusion of circulation with a pressure cuff applied to the arm. Healing was not effective in such cases. Knowles did have some success in instances where only the brachial artery was experimentally occluded. The authors conclude that "...If any inference can be drawn from these experiments, it may be that Mr. Knowles' effect operates upon the vasomotor system and relieves the local congestion concerned in a painful condition." Richmond proposes alternatively that healing may decrease muscle spasm.

Discussion   Though not using formal controls, Knowles and Richmond teased out some of the relevant and important from the superstitious and useless by serial additions or deletions in procedures. The length of follow-up time is unfortunately not specified in the RICHMOND series. Though hypothesizing healer and/or healee that expectations are important, KNOWLES does not speculate further on how these expectations may bring about the physical changes of healing.

The benefits of suggestion *in addition to* healing are rarely appreciated. It is not that *either* one *or* the other is effective. *Both* are and that each may enhance the other.

Experiments with pain from obstruction of circulation are unique in healing literature. Drawing conclusions from these is difficult because of limited details, inadequate controls, lack of true need for healing, and expectations that healing could selectively decrease pain in one of two burns in the same healee.

Hans G. Engel – Energy Healing (Research report 1978)

HANS ENGEL is a physician who discovered

he had healing abilities when his wife reported relief of a severe headache after he placed his hand on her forehead to soothe her.

Engel had several experiences with self-healing. His glaucoma (elevated pressure in the eyeballs) for which he had taken eyedrops for several years, improved "along with other positive changes in my life".

Following the accidental death of one of his children and a painful divorce, he noticed enlargement of his lymph nodes. He suspected he had cancer and, in his depression, actually hoped for death. Eventually he went for a biopsy, then for removal of some of the nodes and a bone marrow biopsy. A malignant lymphoma was found, with several prestigious pathologists concurring on the diagnosis. He expected to live only a few months. For several weeks he took anticancer drugs but then stopped, saying to himself, "If I was fated to die I did not intend to interfere." He even published an article on his attitude towards his patients while he was aware he had only a few months left to live. Then "somehow my outlook on life changed and I again considered the possibility of a personal future." Several months later his lymph nodes began to shrink and he has enjoyed excellent health ever since.[12]

Engel proceeded to develop his healing abilities. He routinely experienced sensations of cold as he passed his hands over diseased portions of his patients' bodies but occasionally felt tingling or something like a "'bulge' in the air above the skin surface overlying the painful site". In 80–90% his impressions were confirmed by his patients. He found that the sensations were far more distinct in his left hand than in his right (perhaps because he was left-handed) and that any slight distraction eliminated or detracted from the sensations. In the first few months of intensive involvement with healing he was tired and quite drowsy after giving a half-dozen treatments but this cleared up and did not recur.

Once the site to be treated has been identified, a voluntary effort must be made to 'send energy' into the area. This technique cannot really be taught by the author: the reader must attempt this by trial and error. The writer concentrates in an effort to produce a state in which he feels a sensation going down his arm, into his hand and out to his fingertips. Occasionally a steady flow of energy is noted, but more commonly it occurs in waves.

Engel's hands tired easily during energy healing and he stopped every two or three minutes to clench and unclench his fists or to shake his hands vigorously. He gave treatments for as long as sensations remained, usually 2–10 minutes. Acute disorders responded more rapidly than chronic ones. With severe illnesses he stopped after a while, even though the sensations continued, but pursued treatment in subsequent visits.

Engel shares the observations on healing in 52 people with a variety of disorders, especially pain. Treatments in this series involved 1–50 or more weekly visits. Those unresponsive within four visits were dismissed from the program.

1. Engel made several notes on treatment oddities. Patients commonly felt he had touched them when he had only made passes near the body. When he included the face in his treatments there was significant flushing, usually only on the side of the face treated. Many became drowsy during or after treatments. On rare occasions pain worsened during treatments before subsiding with subsequent healings. Thermistors (sensitive electronic thermometers) attached to his hands and to healees reveal no consistent changes in temperature before, during or after healings.[13] Significant changes were also not found in measurements of skin resistance.

2. Using a Mind Mirror to record EEGs, Engel was found to have strong surges of delta rhythm during healing. Pairs of Mind Mirrors were attached to healers (*ENGEL, BRUGH JOY* and *ROSE GLADDEN*) and healees during healings. Each of the healers showed similar strong delta-wave bursts. Previous tests in England showed that Gladden produced EEG patterns in her healees that were similar to her own but none of the healers generated such effects here.

3. Healee responses to healing appeared random and unpredictable. Primary disorders might respond, while minor, secondary ones did not, and conversely. Retrospective questionnaires were sent to all subjects who had been studied, seeking demographic, social or psychiatric factors or belief systems which might correlate with the results of healing. Responses were obtained for 34 out of 52, with representative sampling of good, poor and nonresponders to treatment. Only one question produced a suggestive statistical correlation ($p < 0.0544$): "I have had some kind of experience with psi (psychic) phenomena." Persons claiming to have had psi experiences actually tended to respond less to healing than those reporting no such experiences.

4. Pain (including tic doloreux, an excruciating facial neuritis) tended to respond well, although not universally. In addition, musculoskeletal disorders such as arthritis tended to clear up. Fifty-two healees were graded by Engel and his associates on their subjective improvement on a scale of 0–4 : 7 showed no response; 8 had minimal response; 11 moderate; 13 marked improvement; and 4 total pain relief.

5. During healings, some persons reported muscle twitches. For instance, a woman treated for osteoarthritis of the hip had tingling and twitches of her large toe. This was a patient who had focalized referred pain from her hip to her buttock, thigh, back or groin which was relieved by healing. "Two patients with *tic doloreux* ... exhibited jerking of their bodies or violent twitching during treatments."
6. Engel cautions that healing should not be substituted for conventional therapy and should not be applied prior to obtaining a definitive medical diagnosis.

Discussion   ENGEL appears a well-qualified, careful observer and reporter. He is perhaps too cautious and conservative in his report. For instance, in grading improvement he gives a zero to a person with a progressive neuromuscular paralysis called amyotrophic lateral sclerosis (also called motor neuron disease, or Lou Gehrig's disease) who "claimed that he felt stronger and had greater muscular control after some treatments but showed no other significant response to his primary disorder". Had his research included greater numbers of patients and prospective rather than retrospective questionnaires, Engel might have gleaned even more information from his studies. The finding of an inverse relationship between the claim of psi experiences and positive response to healing is surprising and deserves further scrutiny.

Dolores Krieger – The Therapeutic Touch: How to Use Your Hands to Help or Heal

DOLORES KRIEGER has been a healer and has taught healing for many years. She interlaces descriptions of clinical experiences, practical instructions in developing TT skills in professionals and in relatives of patients, and comments from students and healers about their subjective sensations and inner experiences in developing as healers. This book covers Krieger's experience in teaching more than 4,000 people to heal over nine years. She feels that healers must want to heal, must be motivated to help others and be willing to introspect.

Krieger recommends TT for relaxation; alleviation and/or elimination of pain (e.g. traumatic, arthritic); accelerating natural healing processes; nausea; dyspnea; tachycardia; poor circulation in extremities and

Fig. I-10.

Cartoon by courtesy of the artist, Bill Sykes, and Healing Review

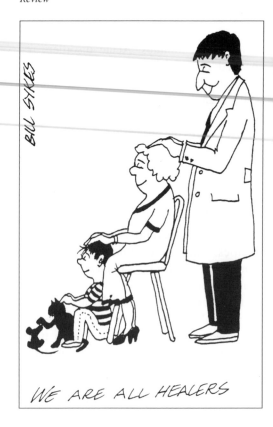

pallor; colicky pains of unexpelled flatus and constipation; physiological development of premature infants; the soothing of irritable babies; and more. She does not know of any illness where TT is totally or always ineffective.

She notes that cotton can both store and facilitate healing energy. (This observation is credited to the healer ESTEBANY.)[14]

KRIEGER finds that belief in effectiveness of healing does not affect performance, i.e. skeptics can be helped. "...However, two personality variables – denial of illness and hostility – do have a negative effect on Therapeutic Touch, perhaps because they both may translate themselves graphically to the healer and inhibit the healer's efforts."

She observes that people practising TT develop their intuition and psi abilities concomitantly with improvement in their healing skills.

Researchers studied Krieger with EEG, electro-oculogram (EOG) and electrocardiogram (ECG) during TT treatments on patients suffering from a variety of pains. Rapid synchronous beta activity was noted on EEG when Krieger was in a sitting or standing position, with eyes open or closed during TT treatments. EOG records showed slight divergence of her eyes with no movement during the treatments. Healees' EEG, EMG, GSR, temperature and heart rates were unchanged during treatment. Marked improvement was noted in the three people treated (severe neck and back pain following spinal injections of dye; migraine headaches; and disappearance of fibroid cysts in a woman's breasts).

Discussion   This book presents excellent *'how-to'* exercises for learning healing and some of the best descriptions, occasionally poetic, of inner changes accompanying the learning/development of healing.

Louis Rose – Faith Healing (1971)

LOUIS ROSE reviews healing anecdotally through ancient and modern history. He describes in detail his efforts at investigating various healers, with all the attendant problems of obtaining reliable examinations by physicians before and after the healings in cases where there was no conventional treatment to obscure the effects of healing. His major focus was on HARRY EDWARDS, the renowned English healer.

Rose summarized as follows:

In essence, then, I analysed 95 instances of purported faith cures and found that:
1. In 58 cases it was not possible to obtain medical or other records so that the claims remained unconfirmed;
2. In 22 cases, records were so much at variance with the claims that it was considered useless to continue the investigation further;
3. In 2 cases the evidence in the medical records suggested that the healer may have contributed to amelioration of an organic condition;
4. In 1 case demonstrable organic disability was relieved or cured after intervention by the healer;
5. 3 cases improved but relapsed;
6. 4 cases showed a satisfactory degree of improvement in function although re-examination and comparison of medical records revealed no change in the organic state;
7. In 4 cases there was improvement when healing was received concurrently with orthodox medical treatment;
8. One case examined before and after treatment by the healer gained no benefit and continued to deteriorate.[15]

Discussion ROSE presents an excellent clinical survey of carefully screened healing reports. Unfortunately, the screening was done retrospectively with multiple, independent evaluators, which leaves the reader uncertain regarding criteria used in evaluations. This book should be read in conjunction with any of the enthusiastic writings of Harry Edwards himself. (See examples in this chapter).

Rose raises many interesting questions. How can one obtain reliable medical evaluations when doctors are reluctant to be involved with healing and healers? Do people go to healers without checking with their physicians? If so, for which types of illnesses? A number of doctoral dissertations in sociology and public health lie waiting to be written in this field.

Item (2) points out how claims made by laypeople unfamiliar with suggestion, placebo response, or ordinary changes in disease processes can be widely divergent from assessments of physicians working daily with diseases in all stages and manifestations.

Items (3) to (7) reveal 14 cases in which some healing effect was verified by medical reports. This is a lower percentage than Strauch reports but may be due to the loss of data via items (1) and (2) and to inclusion of reports from diverse evaluators. Several healers have indicated that they consider Rose extremely skeptical about healing, so that he may have applied excessively stringent criteria in his survey. It is therefore even more impressive that he finds healings which cannot be explained by conventional medical models.

Item (8) may be a low estimate for reasons similar to those in (1) and (2).

Rose confirms common claims that there are no detrimental effects from healing. Healing either helps or is ineffective. It does not harm.

Richard A. Kirkpatrick – Witchcraft and lupus erythematosus (Journal of the American Medical Association 1981)

RICHARD KIRKPATRICK is a physician in the state of Washington. He contributes a case study of a 28-year-old Philippine-American woman who had systemic lupus erythematosus (SLE) in 1977.

This is a disease of unknown etiology, suspected to involve malfunction of the immune system. It can manifest as any combination of anemia, arthritis, vasculitis, enlargement of lymph nodes, nephritis (kidney inflammation), hepatitis (liver inflammation), rashes and other symptoms. It may improve with aspirin, other anti-inflammatory agents, anticancer drugs, steroids and other medications – most of which have toxic side effects.

The diagnosis of this woman was confirmed by laboratory tests, including high sedimentation rates, mild anemia, albumin with red and white blood cell casts in the urine, nonspecific inflammatory changes on biopsy of lymph nodes and liver, and positive antinuclear antibody and SLE clot tests. Substantial doses of prednisone (60 mg/day) reduced both her liver enlargement and the albumin in her urine; her enlarged lymph nodes returned to normal; and she felt well. The steroid medication was lowered. A month later hypothyroidism was diagnosed and levothyroxine was started.

Her disease smoldered on, however, necessitating repeated increases in her prednisone. She started to have edema (water retention), swelling and steroid-related obesity (cushingoid), with periodic irrationality. As this was presumably due to the prednisone, azathioprine (a toxic anticancer medication) was prescribed so that the steroid dose could be reduced. Her serum creatinine levels then rose, indicating kidney damage, confirmed on kidney biopsy. This showed changes typical of SLE. High doses of prednisone and cyclophosphamide (another toxic drug) were recommended.

The patient refused, choosing instead to return to her remote Philippine village.

> Much to the surprise of distraught family members and skeptical physicians, the patient returned three weeks later. She was neither cushingoid nor weak. In fact, she was 'normal.' She declined medications and refused further testing of blood or urine, as directed by the village witch doctor, who had removed the curse placed on her by a previous suitor. Twenty-three months later she gave birth to a healthy girl. During the pregnancy she had intermittent minimal albuminuria and mild anemia. Even now she insists that her lupus was cured by removal of the 'evil spirit' that had caused her original symptoms. No signs or symptoms of adrenal insufficiency or myxedema [hypothyroidism] have developed.

Kirkpatrick points out that it is unlikely the patient's SLE 'burned out'. When she discontinued medication her SLE was quite active, with protein and both white and red blood cell casts in her urine, low serum complement levels and high erythrocyte sedimentation rates. Kirkpatrick asks:

> ... by what mechanisms did the machinations of an Asian medicine man cure active lupus nephritis, change myxedema into euthyroidism, and allow precipitous withdrawal from corticosteroid treatment without symptoms of adrenal insufficiency?

Discussion Although the symptomatology of SLE is known to fluctuate, a person requiring high doses of the above medications is very unlikely to improve so abruptly, dramatically and completely and maintain that level of recovery over several years. Furthermore, discontins of steroids and of thyroid replacement therapy are stressful and usually lead to a return of symptoms.

I include this case because it is well documented. I have spoken with numerous physicians who mention cases of healings but who have not taken the trouble or have hesitated to publish them. The sharing of such reports can contribute to our understanding of the range of effectiveness of healing.

BRENDAN O'REGAN of the Institute of Noetic Sciences has collected 3,000 cases of 'spontaneous remissions' from serious illnesses. (See also EVERSON/COLE in Chapter II-1.) Many of these may be found to involve healing if the doctors will only ask about this.

Healers have pleaded with healees and doctors to document their successful healings. Too often doctors dismiss them as mistaken diagnoses, 'spontaneous remission,' or are too busy to pursue full examinations and documentation.[16]

M. Gmur and A. Tschopp – Factors determining the success of nicotine withdrawal: 12-year follow-up of 532 smokers after suggestion therapy by a faith healer (International Journal of the Addictions 1987)

GMUR/TSCHOPP studied 532 heavy smokers at the University Psychiatric Clinic in Zurich. The healer, called 'HERMANO', treated by placing his hands on the healee's head with a vibrating movement. He claimed to "put out of action... [the] cerebral nicotine addiction center, from which the smoker's repeated reaching for a cigarette was triggered".

Of the total, 40% stopped for four months; 32.5% for one year; 20% for five years; and 15.9% for 12 years. At the final check, 37.5% were not smoking.

They compared 75 discontinued smokers with 23 who resumed smoking within four months. Of 21 variables, only 'smoked in bed' significantly differentiated the two groups. Other items pointing to poor results were drinking, rare church attendance, and an attitude that treatment will help 'if you believe it'.

Discussion   Sadly, without a control group it is impossible to guess whether the healer helped by healing, suggestion, or indeed if he helped at all beyond strengthening the will of the smokers to cease.

Some healers hold healing meetings for large numbers of people. These are often healers with particular religious beliefs who highlight prayer in the healing service. Much of this seems designed to heighten the emotional pitch of the audience, which may even reach emotional frenzies. This vastly enhances the suggestibility of participants and may well help them be more open to changes initiated by healers' suggestions and healing powers.

I review the work of KATHRYN KUHLMAN, of this healing tradition, because several investigations of her healing are available.

H. Richard Casdorph – The Miracles

H. R. CASDORPH, a physician, describes in detail ten cases in which patients were cured with healing, most of them by the late KATHRYN

KUHLMAN. These are detailed case presentations, including confirmation of organic disease by examining physicians, with laboratory and X-ray reports (reproductions in the book) prior to and following healing treatments, and personal reports by the healed and their families.

Casdorph includes cured cases of: reticulum cell sarcoma of right pelvic bone; chronic rheumatoid arthritis with severe disability; malignant brain tumor (glioma) of the left temporal lobe; multiple sclerosis; arteriosclerotic heart disease; carcinoma of the kidney (hypernephroma) with diffuse bony metastases; mixed rheumatoid arthritis and osteoarthritis; probable brain tumor vs. infarction of the brain; massive gastrointestinal hemorrhage with shock; and osteoporosis of the entire spine with intractable pain requiring bilateral cordotomies.

Casdorph holds that a belief in Jesus and the Holy Spirit played an important part in these healings. In his opinion, the 'full healing syndrome' generally includes:

1. There is usually, but not always, a friend or relative of the patient who feels a burden for their healing.
2. ... the correction of the physical deformity caused by the illness.
3. ... spiritual healing. I refer to a change in the personality and the spirit of the individual.
4. Typically, those who have been miraculously healed start teaching and talking about Jesus.
5. ... when miraculously-healed people give their testimonies before groups, there are spontaneous healings in the audience and souls are saved for the Lord Jesus Christ.

He discusses the possibility that healing abilities reside in every person, and provides examples of untrained, 'normal' people who appeared to act as agents for healing.

> The inescapable conclusion is that God uses us to help others. There are times when He gives us a specific burden for another individual and, if we do not obey that call, the task may possibly never be done.

Discussion   Casdorph's investigation provides an interesting contrast with those of W. A. NOLEN and ALLEN SPRAGGETT, below.

Although the cases CASDORPH refers to have been collected retrospectively, they are carefully supported with reports from physicians who examined healees before and after healings. The medical documentation of individual cures presented here is the most precise and convincing collection of all the healing literature reviewed in this book.

Schmeidler/Hess review Casdorph's work and add support to its credibility.

Allen Spraggett – Kathryn Kuhlman: The Woman Who Believes in Miracles

ALLEN SPRAGGETT, a journalist, describes the healing services of the late *KATHRYN KUHLMAN*. He discusses many healings, with medical evaluations to support the claims of unusual physiological changes. He outlines in a sketchy way possible explanations for these occurrences.

Criteria for healings are included in a detailed section of this book:

> (1) The disease should be a medically diagnosed organic or structural disorder.
> (2) The healing should be rapid, preferably quasi-instantaneous, and involve changes of a type not normally considered attributable to suggestion.
> (3) The healing should be permanent.

Diagnoses included:
* post-traumatic corneal (eye) scarring with severely reduced vision – vision restored;
* corneal laceration with prolapse of iris – medically unaccountable rapid healing;
* a single case of slow-healing (10 months) clavicular (collar-bone) fracture, sinusitis, unilateral deafness (etiology and type not described) – all cured;
* heart condition with mitral stenosis with murmur, left atrial enlargement and right ventricular enlargement – cured;
* massive occlusion of basilar artery (to brain) – cured;
* club foot – cured.

Spraggett also reports on several less detailed and documented healings.

How do these miracles occur? Kuhlman believed it was the power of God acting through her (not her own powers) which produced the healings.

Discussion   Although pleasant and easy to read, this book is technically much weaker than Casdorph's. It is obvious, the author is not trained in medicine or research and did not have proper medical consultation in writing his review.[17]

Rex Gardner – Miracles of healing in Anglo-Celtic Northumbria as recorded by the Venerable Bede and his contemporaries: A reappraisal in the light of twentieth century experience *(British Medical Journal 1983)*

REX GARDNER, a British physician, describes healings recorded by *SAINT BEDE THE VENERABLE*, who is a respected historian of the seventh to eighth centuries. Gardner points out that there is a tendency in modern times to dismiss first-hand observations and records of healings from earlier centuries as exaggerations or distortions which can be given little credence.

GARDNER argues for attending to such reports. He describes a number of remarkable modern healings which initially reached him as questionable reports but for which he subsequently tracked down first-hand observations from reliable reporters.

Case 1: An 11-month-old boy was admitted to Royal Victory Infirmary, Newcastle upon Tyne, in August 1977, "a wasted, miserable little scrap, severely dyspnoeic at rest, with pronounced lower costal and intercostal recession". (In layman's terms, he had difficulty breathing even without exertion, with pronounced retraction of his chest wall on breathing, indicating severe airway obstruction.) He had had measles at age eight months and never fully recovered. Chest X-rays revealed "diffuse confluent mottling with a small right pneumothorax" (indicating chronic infection and air escaping from the lung into the chest cavity). "...a definitive diagnosis of advanced fibrosing alveolitis was established by biopsy of the lung... The prognosis for fibrosing alveolitis starting in the first year of life is almost uniformly fatal." He was treated with antibiotics, to which he did not respond. He was then given steroids for 12 weeks together with azathioprine (which suppresses the body's immune responses) during the latter six of the 12 weeks but he did not show any improvement.

The doctors told his mother the prognosis was hopeless since his disease appeared to be progressive and unresponsive to treatment. He was discharged.

The child's practitioner suggested the fam-

ily might take him to a Pentecostal healing service. Five days following the healing treatment he appeared to be happier and more ready to play. Two weeks later he was clearly stronger, even able to stand up by himself for the first time in four months. He continued to improve steadily. By the age of five years and two months he had fully recovered.

Case 2: In 1975 a general practitioner trainee contracted meningococcal septicemia with meningitis and was admitted in moribund condition to hospital with an illness diagnosed as Waterhouse-Friderichsen syndrome. "No such case had ever survived in that hospital." Four healing groups simultaneously but separately prayed for her and

... believed that their request that she might be healed with no residual disability had been granted. At the same time, 8:30 pm, there was a sudden improvement in her condition, though it was four days before she regained consciousness. Physicians were unable to explain how her chest X-ray film, which had showed extensive left sided pneumonia with collapse of the middle lobe, could, 48 hours later, show a normal clear chest. The ophthalmologist saw and photographed a central scotoma [scar] in the left eye caused by intraocular haemorrhage affecting the macula, and assured the patient that there was permanent blindness in that eye. Her faith that God had promised her that she would be made 'completely whole' was quite reasonably met with his, 'You have got to face the medical facts.' When she did in fact develop perfect vision in that eye, and no residual intraocular disease could be found, he was understandably left unable to offer any explanation, and could only say, 'Do you realise you are unique?'

Case 3: A 35-year-old woman came to a physician (known personally to Gardner) in Pakistan in about the eighth month of pregnancy with the report of intermittent bleeding and abdominal pains for five months, in this, her seventh pregnancy. A low segment Caesarian section was performed under local anesthesia.

A low transverse incision in the lower uterine segment went right through the placenta which was found to be extremely adherent to the lower uterine flap and was raggedly removed. Copious dark blood was released on entering the uterus... Heavy blood loss at time of operation and profuse loss postoperatively – not clotting. Deep pools of unclotted blood between the patient's thighs and pad – heavy and prolonged trickling. Oxytocin was added to the dextrose saline drip, and then we prayed with the patient after explaining to her about Jesus in whose name we had prayed for her before the operation, and who was a great healer. I also told her that we were not going to worry. I had seen Jesus heal this condition before and was sure He was going to heal her. We then managed to get 2 pints blood for her – brisk bleeding continued. First clot was seen 48 hours after operation. Heavy loss had continued till then but her general condition gave no cause for concern after the initial postoperative examination at two hours. We prayed again with her on the night of the operation and then to thank Jesus for her healing when she went home with her baby on the 10th day.

GARDNER muses on the fact that his initial impression upon hearing a third-hand report of this case had been skeptical but that he had full confidence in the reliability of the medical report presented above.

Gardner then proceeds to present paired cases of similar medical problems from the *BEDE* records and from his own experience. (Only one pair is summarized below.)

Bede... records a story... A woman, because of possession by an evil spirit, had contracted hideous ulcers (of the skin). As long as she remained silent nothing could be done for her; but when she had told all that had happened she was cured by prayers and by application of holy salt, together with the doctor's medical aid. Only one stubborn ulcer remained, against which no remedies prevailed. At last, by her own suggestion, based on previous experience, oil blessed for the sick was applied, whereupon the remaining ulcer immediately responded to treatment by priest and doctor.

From Gardner's own experience:

About 1970 the captain of the Girls' Brigade at ... had a deterioration in a large varicose ulcer of the leg which had been troubling her for many years. Each morning her bandage was soaked with pus. Her doctor told her to give up her activities. She asked for prayer at the monthly charismatic prayer meeting. A general practitioner present examined the leg and judged that even were the ulcer to heal, it would require skin grafting. The pastor requested one of the women present to join him in praying for the patient. By next morning almost the whole ulcer had dried up with healthy skin covering; but one spot continued to exude pus. One week later one of the Girls' Brigade lieutenants called on the pastor and with embarrassment stated that she felt she should have joined in the prayer for the patient. They immediately visited the patient and the lieutenant laid hands on the area and prayed. Healing became immediately complete.

This story is so bizarre that it would not have been included were I not one of the doctors who examined the patient's leg at the next monthly prayer meeting, and were not all the people who had been present available for interrogation. Against the background of such cases one can no longer shrug off the miracles of the sixth and seventh centuries.

Discussion   Healing appears to promise to help diseases for which medical treatment in the west is still inadequate (e.g. fibrosing alveolitis, meningococcal meningitis, chronic stasis ulcers).

The cases observed by GARDNER seem to me most convincing; those for which he vouches somewhat less so; those of BEDE far less so. Gardner's point is well made. First-hand testimony of a physician can clearly be given greater credence. However, reports of unknown persons – even though they be educated, competent and of good reputation – are still somewhat suspect. Reports filtered through second-hand observers, especially from many years past, are easily subject to exaggeration or inaccurate diagnoses. Yet as Gardner points out, with careful clarification one may confirm that a reported healing of dubious certainty may actually prove as impressive as it is claimed to be.

What Gardner does not point out is that the converse is also true. Cases of doubtful nature may prove to be hysterical (conversion) reactions, misperceptions, misdiagnoses or exaggerations.

W. A. Nolen – Healing: A Doctor in Search of a Miracle

W. A. NOLEN, an American surgeon, presents discursive, somewhat overly-detailed descriptions of his investigation into the work of KATHRYN KUHLMAN, NORBU CHEN and many of the better known Philippine psychic surgeons. Via direct observation and follow-up of treated cases Nolen reaches the conclusion that no paranormal physical effects could be demonstrated in any of the cases and that all of the positive results could be explained by mechanisms of suggestion or normal fluctuations in disease processes.

Nolen makes a good case for the gullibility of a wide variety of average people. He suggests reasons for seeking psychic healers:

1. Enthusiasm of others who claimed they were cured through healing;
2. Wish to avoid unpleasant and/or risk-laden medical treatment;
3. Neurotic anxieties about medical/surgical treatment;
4. Inadequate explanations of illness and/or procedures proposed by physicians, which often produce or exacerbate (2) and (3).

Nolen points out dangers in delaying conventional treatment. He speculates that healers may stimulate patients' self-healing and discusses possible forms that suggestion could take within a person, which could have unusual effects. He also considers the unpredictability of cancer and its treatment.

Discussion   NOLEN's discussion contrasts markedly with reports by KRIPPNER/VILLOLDO, MEEK, STELTER, SPRAGGETT, CASDORPH and others, who studied some of the same healers and reached different, often opposite conclusions to Nolen's.

Stelter contradicts Nolen on specific information concerning Philippine healers. He suggests that Nolen is selecting and distorting evidence to support his contention that psychic surgery is fakery.[18]

Harry Edwards – Thirty Years a Spiritual Healer

During a worldwide epidemic of Asian 'flu', the epidemiological progress of the disease was clear from country to country. It was calculated when the disease was likely to reach the U.K., and the public was warned.

HARRY EDWARDS experimented on how to use healing as a preventive against contracting the virus.

> ... we published... an invitation for our readers to join in this experiment. In addition, we enclosed in some twenty thousand letters sent out to the many who were at that time receiving absent healing a notice to the same effect.
>
> The notice said that we would be holding a mass absent healing intercession for all our patients and readers in order that they might be protected from the disease. We asked our patients and readers to inform us at once if they caught Asian 'flu', or had its symptoms.

Edwards estimated his experiment covered 40,000 people. The epidemic was severe in Britain, forcing many factories and schools to close as well as causing many deaths.

> The result of our experiment was surprising. The number of letters we received telling us that our readers, patients and their families had been infected was very few indeed – about a score. Considering the number of people involved in the experiment and that many of them lived in badly infected areas, by all normal reckoning we should have received reports from 500 to a 1,000 infected cases.
>
> One school head mistress wrote to ask if we would place her school children within the protective influencing of spiritual healing... The result was, that while every other school in the area had to close down, this particular school had no need to, for the number of children who became ill was surprisingly few, and even those were very mild cases.

None of Edwards' staff contracted influenza either.

Discussion   Edwards' experiment is an important application for healing. Unfortunately, because of the looseness of the experimental design, clear conclusions from this experiment cannot be drawn. For instance, patients may have neglected to advise the researchers that they had 'flu' symptoms, either consciously or unconsciously, out of loyalty to Harry Edwards. A better arrangement would have been to take random samples of subjects and not to rely merely on the subjects' self-reporting.

If the results prove valid, knowing whether the 'mass intercession' involved single healers sending healing to large numbers of people simultaneously or whether a one-to-one distant healing was required in each case would be of interest. (See also the earlier review of TURNER's report of preventive healing.)

Harry Edwards – The Evidence for Spirit Healing

This is the sort of book which makes me want to cry. Edwards makes poor apologies for healers' not keeping records of healings, claiming that this would take up too much time. He presents a book full of exceedingly brief excerpts of written testimonials from healees' reports of successful healings, including cancer and other growths; surgery; tuberculosis; spinal diseases; disseminated sclerosis; paralysis; rheumatism; arthritis and limb diseases; infantile ailments; sight and hearing; heart and blood conditions; breathing disorders; internal disorders; hernias; ulceration; skin diseases; mental diseases; epilepsy and nervous disorders; and more.

Though Edwards unquestionably was a powerful healer with a wealth of experience, he presents such brief excerpts in this book as to leave many possible alternative explanations for any of the cases he mentions. He claimed he engaged in spiritual healing, not faith healing. It is unfortunate that he forces the reviewer to rely only on faith for interpretation of this data.

In his defense, one would have to point out that he took only a few minutes to give healings to any one person. Writing the records might have taken longer than giving the treatment. Nevertheless, he did have secretaries answering mail and keeping records of absent healings, so he could probably have done better with his reports He was also untrained in medical diagnosis and had no help from doctors in his assessments.

This note is primarily to point out the benefits which might accrue with broader cooperation between healers and research oriented doctors.[19]

Piero Cassoli – The healer: Problems, methods and results *(European Journal of Parapsychology 1981)*

PIERO CASSOLI discusses difficulties in defining a healer and enumerates pertinent problems for research. He recommends controlled clinical studies, pointing out that it is deplorable that the need for such studies has been recognized for many years but that none has been done. He suggests healing be renamed *pranotherapy*. He does not describe exactly who or what type of healer(s) he studied, but mentions touch and distant healing. Cassoli appears to have wide clinical experience. He makes the following recommendations:

> Considering the healer's action from the antalgic [sic][20] point of view, we have brilliant results on chronic incurable headaches in many women, on arthritic and arthrosic processes, on neuralgias refractory to treatment (trigeminal, sciatica, occipital, intercostal; the last one especially post-herpetic), on pains from metastasis of malignant neoplasms, and on colics of every kind (biliary, menstrual, reneal)...
>
> Quite recently I have observed pain relief in coronaropathies [heart problems], but the scientific – or even clinical – demonstration of this last result is possible only with a large sample... Further, it is possible to make a listing, based on my clinical experiences, of the diseases which seem to have received the most benefit from pranotherapy. First there are the epilepsies...
>
> I would further suggest the use of pranotherapy in every case of 'sepsis' with chronic course, typically found in urinary infections. Similarly, I recommend to

persevere wherever there is a suspicion of latent microbiosis (sinusitis, adnexitis, chronical otitis and synusitis, chronical appendicitis). Verrucas or warts often find a definitive relief, as they do also by hypnosis, while medical treatments are disappointing and painful. I would point out that some handicapped children, even mongoloids, have received considerable help from pranotherapy. On the contrary it seems to not be worth while to attempt pranotherapy in some neurological diseases like spastic cerebropathies, and in some degenerative illnesses of the nervous system like lateral amiotrophic sclerosis. I mention these because I have found many cases of these hopeless patients who were treated by pranotherapists. There were never any positive results, even temporary. I would always try pranotherapy if it is early enough, in the so-called and frequent muscular progressive dystrophies. Here I venture to say I have got some results in malignant neoplasms. Against the scepticism of many people, I think this illness must be treated from the beginning by selected pranotherapists as a support for orthodox treatments, especially after a destructive operation like mastectomy. Cases of this kind, where patients have been relieved of pain, are steadily increasing...

Discussion   This is a rather sketchy clinical report, unsupported by case descriptions. It appears to have useful hints from someone who has thought about this field for many years and has apparently practiced or had others assist him in practicing healing on a wide variety of medical problems in Italy.

Other healers may have success with a different range of illnesses. I know of several who have seen improvements with spastic children and degenerative neurological illnesses (especially multiple sclerosis), for instance.

Benson Herbert – Near and distant healing *(International Journal of Paraphysics 1973)*

BENSON HERBERT described his personal experience with psi healing for severe pains caused by a muscle sprain on his shoulder blade. He also reviewed successful healings by SUZANNE PADFIELD. The following points are noteworthy:

1. Padfield performed several successful distant healings without the healees' knowledge.

2. Healer visualizations in distant healing include:

* seeing the patient in perfect health;
* imagining oneself by the patient's bed, hearing her say she is getting well; and
* feeling as though one's self is being projected into the patient's mind.

3. In touch healing of headaches, with her hands pressing gently on the patient's temples, Padfield visualizes "a current or vortex flowing from my hands into the head...the pain receding as the vortex speeds up".

4. In other pains, Padfield relates:

> I relax and visualize exactly where in the body is the pain; I seem to see the body as a sort of transparent negative; in the area where the trouble is I see a cloudy disturbance, congealing in one spot. By this means I locate the focal point of the disease. I then proceed to visualise this par-

ticular area as becoming clear and healthy, and as in the case of headaches I mentally formulate a vortex which I can only describe as clearing the blockage in the currents flowing through the body until gradually the whole body appears perfectly clear and free from cloudiness, that is, if the treatment is successful.

5. There are some dangers to the healer in healing:

* If both of Padfield's hands touch the patient, this seemingly closes a circuit and illness may be transmitted to the healer. (Padfield once became 'violently sick' after touching with both hands a person suffering from 'nervous hysteria'.)
* With visualization, images of illness must be rapidly dismissed, to prevent the patient's symptoms passing to the healer. Padfield prefers not to become too sympathetic with the patient.

Herbert measured Padfield's electrical skin resistance, finding it was about one-quarter of the mean of six other people. Her skin potentials fluctuated at least twice as widely as others in the group under similar conditions. He postulated that her low skin resistance would make her more sensitive to electromagnetic potentials in her environment. In this he was supported by Padfield's report that she is unusually sensitive to slight shocks from electrical appliances.

Herbert further theorized that patients undergoing an "hysterical attack may evidence excessive potential fluctuations between skin contact points and that Miss Padfield reacts to these. If a patient not wearing anti-static garments acquired an electrostatic charge, Miss Padfield would feel a shock with only one hand touching the patient."

From a survey of European healers, Herbert generalizes:

1. All subjects claiming PK ability also claim healing ability;
2. On the contrary, many healers do not claim PK ability, and many discount its importance; and
3. Not all, but the majority of healers, claim absent-healing ability.

Discussion: PADFIELD's report of successful healings without healees' knowledge that healing was being attempted has been echoed by other healers. HERBERT's cases are described in more detail and better documented than many other reports.

It is unclear whether Padfield's unusual bioelectrical activity is related specifically to her healing or whether the mechanisms for her healings are different from those of other healers who do not have the same bioelectrical activity.

A survey showed that 70 percent of people with unusual electrical experiences also had psi abilities (SHALLIS).

Unusual electrical phenomena in healers have been detailed by others.[21]

Franklin Loehr – The Power of Prayer on Plants

FRANKLIN LOEHR describes a series of controlled experiments, ranging from very loose to carefully supervised ones. The basic design used several groups of seeds (usually corn or wheat) planted in identical pans. Earth was thoroughly mixed prior to filling the pans. Equal watering, light and other conditions were carefully provided for the various pans. The experimenters then prayed over one pan for more rapid germination and growth of the seeds while ignoring the second pan. In many cases a third pan of seeds was included, over which they prayed for retardation of growth. In some cases prayer or healing was directed to the earth or water used to water the plants.

Results were about three times out of four (though not consistently) in the desired directions. Seeds receiving positive prayer generally both germinated and grew more rapidly than control seeds. Negative prayer tended to retard germination and growth, frequently leaving seeds that did not sprout at all and sometimes plants that withered and died. The percent of spread between pans, in millimeters of growth, ranged from single digit to (frequently) 30–40%. Occasional spreads of 100–200% were obtained.

Similar results were obtained with ivy cuttings and silkworm eggs. The experimenters generally did not report blinds or statistical analyses.

Discussion Though attempts were made to provide careful controls in some of the experiments, procedures are not sufficiently described to permit inclusion of these studies in the well-controlled category. More important, it is not clear if any of these experiments included proper blinds. Thus it is impossible to accept the results at face value.

Despite these criticisms, this is a thoughtful book which is highly recommended.

Spindrift, Inc. *(Eds)* – Prayer and Healing: Tests With Germinating Seeds

SPINDRIFT is a Christian Science group which has invested fifteen years in studying healing in various ways. They have published summaries of their extensive work privately. Un-

fortunately, they are admittedly so untrained in rigor of design and/or reporting as to make it impossible to assess their findings with satisfying degree of confidence. These reports come to several findings may lead to further productive investigation of healing effects on plants.

Spindrift's research is based on certain assumptions about healing.

'Qualitative thought' of a healer is described as not being goal directed and having the capacity to return biological systems from physiological deviations towards more normative patterns. 'Non-qualitative thought' of a healer is goal directed and 'pushes' a biological system towards a pre-conceived direction of change determined by the healer.

A number of these experiments have most far-reaching implications. The experimenters set contingencies for choosing which of several series of plant batches were to receive healing. Healers and experimenters were blind to which were the chosen plants. Despite this, the chosen plants often germinated much faster than the controls. For instance,

1. In our first experiment of this kind we used three cups of mung beans. We placed a penny in a closed box, thoroughly shook the box, and placed it aside until the experiment was over. The cups were labeled C (for control), H (for heads), and T (for tails). Treatment was given to the beans in the cup designated by the penny in the closed box. From … the results … it was conclusded the penny was heads and when the box was opened this was the case.

In several repetitions of this design, the determining factor was varied to include a die in a closed box, decks of cards, and dollar bills of various currencies in sealed envelopes. Highly significant results were obtained, though statistical analyses are not reported as probabilities.

> 2. Faith, or strong belief, comes in many forms; experimenter effect, faith healing, placebo effect and so on. It is present along with qualitative thought (either as belief in one's healing ability or as disbelief in one's healing ability) in every prayer. It can, therefore, under proper measurement conditions, be measured in conjunction with qualitative thought.
>
> In the following ... tests a belief system was in place for a limited time which permitted such measurements...
>
> One of the theoretical conceptions of he healing method used in these experiments is that matter is a subjective and objective form of certain elements of consciousness, in other words a mode of consciousness or form of thought. It was reasoned that, as unconscious thought-forms, the physical mechanisms which trigger seed germination might respond to the thought force, structured will, or survival instincts of other living things.
>
> To test this our researcher used two different forms of living things, plants and yoghurt. Rye grass seeds were sown and germinated...[in trays of vermiculite with a controlled water table] but a plant or a small jar with active yoghurt in it was correlated with one-half of each tray of seeds. The correlation was mental, although the trays and jars and plants were marked accordingly.
>
> Each jar or plant was promised (this is the mental link, and by promised we mean that the intention was formed in thought) a reward if seed germination was greater in the designated tray areas than in the control areas. The plants were promised more

> light and the yoghurt was promised fractional teaspoons of milk for each percentage increase in germination of the experimental area over the control area of the tray.
>
> ... we had no way of knowing whether or not we were viewing some hitherto unsuspected ability in the plants and yoghurt or whether we were seeing the effect of our own unconscious thought.

3. The same design produced measurable differences when a dresser drawer was removed from a dresser and the mental intention was made to return the drawer only if a designated group of seeds germinated more rapidly than the controls.

4. In some experiments *additive effects* of healing appeared when healers separately treated two groups of seeds, where a portions of one seed group was presented to the healers in overlapping fashion with a portion of the second seed group.

Significant differences were noted when contingencies such as the above were included in the experiments but not when paired sets of seeds were all left as controls (that is, without contingence designations).

Discussion   This is a most tantalizing, yet frustrating, set of studies. It closely parallels GERRY SOLFVIN's study of malarial mice, where it appeared that 'super-esp' was evident. That is, it seems likely that the participants in the SPINDRIFT studies scanned the experimental elements with either telepathy, clairsentience, or precognition and then applied healing to the designated plants.

Because of this possibility, it appears impossible to support the contentions of the Spindrift group that distinctly different types of healing, such as *qualitative* and *non-qualitative thought* were at play.

The reports do not separate speculations and beliefs from experimental hypotheses or presentations of the results. Individual experiments are not clearly delineated, so that it is impossible to know in many cases whether blinds were employed. Methods for establishing blinds are not described. These are some of the problems which make it extremely difficult to assess the results of these fascinating experiments.

Robert N. Miller – The positive effect of prayer on plants
(Psychic 1972)

ROBERT MILLER reports a unique experiment in which he measured and recorded the growth rate of ordinary grass with exquisitely sensitive electronic equipment. He states:

> Under the constant conditions of lighting, temperature and watering selected for the test, the growth rate was approximately 0.006 inch per hour. At no time did the growth exceed 0.010 inch per hour in any of the preliminary experiments.

He then arranged for OLGA and AMBROSE WORRALL, who were 600 miles away at the time, to

> … hold the seedlings in their thoughts at their usual 9:00 P.M. prayer time. One hour later they 'prayed' for the plant by visualizing it as growing vigorously in a white light.
>
> All through the evening and until 9:00 P.M. the trace was a straight line with a slope which represented a growth rate of 0.00625 inch per hour. At exactly 9:00 P.M. the trace began to deviate upward and by

8:00 A.M. the next morning the grass was growing 0.0525 inch per hour, a growth rate increase of 840 percent. (Instead of growing the expected 1/16 of an inch in a ten hour period the grass had sprouted more than 1/2 inch.) The recorder trace was continued for another 48 hours. During that time the growth rate decreased but did not fall back to the original rate.

During the experiment the door of the room had been locked, the temperature was constant at 70–72 degrees F, the fluorescent lights were on continuously, and there was no known physical variable which could have caused any large variation in the growth of the rye grass.

Discussion   This is one of the few impressive direct effects of healing measured. Unfortunately, no independent controls were used to rule out other factors which might have affected the plant growth. It would also be useful to have an independent, mechanical measurement as a check on whether the healer might have been affecting the measuring instrument by PK rather than the plant. Worrall was not generally known for PK effects, but Miller himself noted she could influence a cloud chamber. Replication with other healers seems clearly warranted and should be relatively simple.

Larissa V. Vilenskaya – A scientific approach to some aspects of psychic healing
(International Journal of Paraphysics 1976)

LARISSA VILENSKAYA reports on several of her experiments which clarify the effects

and possible mechanisms of healing:
1. 'Normal humans with no specific gifts' were taught to see auras generated by Vilenskaya 'between two fingers of their hand'.
2. Aura diagnosis of physical problems by touch was likewise taught.
3. Vilenskaya had an opportunity of conducting

> ... research using a sensitive astatic magnetometer with sensitivity ranging about 0.01 gamma-units (1 gamma = 0.00005 Oersted units). The experiments proved that the magnetic field of the human hand varies with the physical and emotional state of the patient...
>
> If the subject is prepared to perform healing, the intensity of the hand's magnetic field increases. At the same time, if a person just contracts the muscles of the arm, the intensity of the field decreases rapidly.
> ... during an influence of a healer over a patient a decrease in the magnetic field of the latter was also detected. Thus, a person ill with radiculitis [peripheral nerve pain] had an initial intensity of magnetic field 0.096 gamma; after the healer's influence over a period of 3 minutes (the author was performing it) the intensity became 0.018 gamma. The patient was relieved of pain.
>
> As both the healing and the electrical stimulation of the acupuncture points create a better condition for the patient's organism, a conclusion can be made that a normal stably-functioning human organism has no tendency towards radiation of energy; on the contrary, an ill person (or a healer) emits much more energy (whereas a healer does this in a controlled manner, but an ill person is unable to check it).
>
> We can assume that the ability to diagnose through the energetic field can be caused by the ability of some persons to perceive very weak changes in the biomagnetic field, though it does not explain the paranormal diagnostics completely.

4. VILENSKAYA investigated healing influence upon the seeds of plants:

> Cucumber seeds were used for the experiment. The results of the first series of experiments have shown that the optimal duration of the plant's exposure to bioenergetic influence was 10 to 15 minutes; a longer duration of exposure resulted in a deterioration of growth and development of plants as compared with the results after the optimal exposure... the most remarkable feature of this is that whenever the author used psychic healing, the sessions never lasted longer than 15 minutes, though there was nowhere an indication to be found of any kind of optimal duration. The author considered it natural, that the only index when to stop was her own feeling of the state of the biological field radiated by the patient.
>
> In the second experimental series it was found that the optimal duration of the healing influence was about 5 to 10 minutes. Compared to the first series it shows that the effect is very much dependent on the condition of the healer. Besides, it also turns out that in the first few days after the germination the effect of the influence is more pronounced than in the days to follow.

Discussion   Though interesting, the above results are reported with insufficient data for proper evaluation. In (1) and (2), no numbers are given; in (3) and (4), conclusions are based on studies of only four subjects.

If valid, these observations are of interest and concern for healing. Such experiments should be repeated, with duration of healing extended beyond 30 minutes. This would establish whether harm can come from prolonged healing, which possibility is implied by the reduced growth indicated in seeds treated between 15 and 30 minutes. If we extend the growth curve graph, at 45 minutes the experimental plants may weigh less than the controls. This would imply by analogy that potential for harm may exist as a result of healing being carried out beyond an optimal period. This is an important point, especially for student healers who may not have developed the often-reported sense Vilenskaya mentions for when a healing is completed.

I should add that reports of negative effects of healing, when positive effects are desired, have been found only in laboratory experiments with growth of plants and with malaria in mice. Neither healers nor doctors or nurses working with healers have ever reported negative clinical healing effects in humans or animals

John Hubacher, Jack Gray, Thelma Moss, and Frances Saba – A laboratory study of unorthodox healing *(Proceedings of the Second International Congress on Psychotronic Research 1975)*

This report describes in detail three cases of healings using 'magnetic passes'. These were the most successful of a series of 11 patients, of whom six showed sustained improvements; two had initial dramatic improvements but then returned to the original symptoms; and three did not respond.

Case 1: A 21-year-old man with severe multiple leg fracture was told by his physicians that repair was impossible and incessant pain inevitable unless the leg were amputated. Jack Gray, the healer, noted an exquisite sensitivity of the patient to his (the healer's) hands. When they were at a distance of one foot from the patient's body, he complained of severe pain!

Repeated, prolonged treatments with slow improvement were given over eight months, at which time X-rays demonstrated healing in the bones. After two years, the patient could walk, unaided by crutch or brace.[22]

Case 2: A 42-year-old man had total paralysis of his right arm and hand following a bullet wound in his neck, which cut through a major artery and irreparably severed several nerves. A neurologist informed him that the arm would never move again. With three months' treatments (primarily consisting of magnetic passes), he regained some use of his arm and hand. Use of his thumb did not return until eight months later. The neurologist could not explain this recovery. "In fact, on his last medical visit, the patient was told there would be 'no charge' because the neurologist had seen something he had not believed possible: movement not apparently prompted by neuronal connecions."

Case 3: A 21-year-old woman suffered from advanced scleroderma (hardening skin) – barely able to walk and so limited in hand movements she could not even take care of her own toileting. Sporadic improvement was noted over ten months' treatment, with increased ability to care for herself, and decreased pain.

Kirlian photography consistently demonstrated an increase in coronal flares and emanations from healees' fingers after treatments. A deep altered state of consciousness was experienced by patients during the 'magnetic passes'. Healer and healees reported intense sensations of heat and cold during treatments.

Discussion   These startling results are found in a small percent of healings. Unfortunately, descriptive details are limited and it is difficult to evaluate these reports. It would be helpful to know more about the 'magnetic passes', the specifics of diagnoses, criteria for improvement, etc.

The controlled studies of healers' diagnostic abilities did not focus on their methods for arriving at intuitive impressions. One method that healers report is to observe the colors in the aura, an apparent energy field around the body.

Shafika Karagulla and Dora van Gelder Kunz – The Chakras and the Human Energy Field

DORA KUNZ, a gifted clairvoyant healer, sat over several years with SHAFIKA KARAGULLA, a neuropsychiatrist, to observe the auras and chakras of patients with various illnesses. They report that the aura provided information which was highly correlated with the physical diagnoses. Occasionally Kunz was able to diagnose problems which had been unknown to the patients and doctors. Detailed descriptions of the patterns and colors reported by Kunz are reported, along with the medical diagnoses.[23]

Discussion   This method appears to offer a non-invasive complement to conventional medical diagnostic tests.

One must be cautious in interpreting such aura readings. In two pilot studies I ran with eight aura sensitives who simultaneously observed a series of four patients with known diagnoses, the divergences in aura observations and their interpretations were far greater than the overlaps. Yet the patients resonated with most of the readings, different as they were. It appears that sensitives may resonate with partial aspects of the people they observe. We would thus have to be careful of false negative reports. (BENOR 1991)

Francis Geddes – Healing Training in the Church (Doctoral dissertation, San Francisco, Theological Seminary 1991)

GEDDES provides a history of healing in the church from biblical to modern times. He points out that Christ used a variety of healing techniques and that he taught them to his disciples.

For his doctoral work, Francis Geddes studied healers doing healing. He trained groups of people from four congregations in techniques of healing, per the LeShan methods, in a five-day seminar.

These groups met weekly for present and distant healings of 206 persons. Case records were obtained for only 79 subjects. Of these, 13 reported dramatic acceleration in their rate of recovery from illness, ranging from minutes to two or three days; 31 reported some acceleration in the pace of recuperation within several days or weeks; and 35 reported no change in the recovery rate. Geddes speculates that the 127 who did not respond also experienced no change and were therefore unmotivated to report. Recovery ratings are based on patients' reports, since physicians treating them were uncooperative in providing records.

The following are excerpts from six case records in the group that demonstrated the most marked results -

1. Severe hepatitis – rapid return of abnormal blood studies to normal ranges, rapid return of strength, and greater feeling of 'closeness with my creator';
2. Blindness [cause unstated] – prior to healing vision had been limited for several months to dim perception of black and white, but following healing some perception of red and blue returned for two days;
3. Post-surgical pain 'of some years' duration (after intervetertebral disc removal)' – able to sleep and to ambulate free of pain for most of day, with marked improvement in outlook on life;
4. Arthritis of spine – prior to healing had to wear support collar and could not move head from left to right or raise or lower head without pain, but following healing had no pain (lasting until 18-month follow-up);
5. Depression with insomnia, alcoholism, and very poor self-image – healing enhanced inner peace and stability for several weeks; and
6. Diabetes – prior to healing had been maintained on 55-60 units of insulin daily for a long period, but after healing had an immediate drop in insulin requirement and within four days was taking only 25 units.

GEDDES notes that dramatic positive changes were experienced by the healers themselves as a result of their participation in the healing groups over the six months of the study. These included a greater sense of well-being; increased sensitivity to others; improved self-awareness; greater energy; closeness to God and/or universe; a more focused everyday life; ability to push through old barriers; sense of joy; clearer sense of direction; increased self-discipline; improved ability to cope; and instances of self-healing. In a few cases, the healers experienced breakthroughs of old emotions. Some healers did not perceive any change. "The author was surprised to discover the variety and depth of personal transformation and spiritual growth in the twenty-eight subjects."

Discussion The improvements probably represent impressive results of healing. The lack of medical inputs limit the value of such reports. Laymen often misunderstand and therefore misrepresent their illnesses, as may lay experimenters.

Geddes's focus on the transformative nature of healing for healers is a helpful contribution to our appreciation of the effects of healing. I have personally had similar experiences when giving healing treatment and have heard these echoed by other healers.[24]

Negative Effects of Healing

We must be cautious with healing as with any other modality which is untested in conventional medical practice. Though no permanent negative effects of healing have been noted, there is certainly a possibility that it could be used injudiciously. For instance, it could be substituted for conventional therapies without, or against, medical advice. CO-AKLEY/MCKENNA give the instance of a woman who discontinued thyroid hormone after attending a faith healing ceremony at her church. She had a recurrence of delusions, hallucinations and thought disorders which required psychiatric hospitalization. Return to hormone replacement produced a cure which had lasted six years (to the time of publication).

In the UK, the Code of Conduct of the Confederation of Healing Organisations stipulates that healers will not give healess diagnoses and will not begin treatment without referring a person first to their physician for evaluation of their problems.

Minor exacerbations of symptoms, especially pains, have been reported occasionally. These are usually transient. Some healees have discontinued treatments when this happened, and healers have not studied this systematically, making it impossible to know the natural course of this development. Improvements usually follow within days or weeks when healing is continued. Thus the temporary worsening of symptoms is viewed by healers as a positive development, similar to other sensations perceived during healing, such as heat, cold and tingling.

Surveys of Healees

Surveys of healees have focused on subjective assessments of results and satisfaction with treatment. I am of mixed opinions regarding the surveys. On the one hand, it is absolutely essential to consider healees' points of view. Surveys often provide qualitative information which the more scientific studies omit – tending, as the latter do, to Type II research errors.

On the other hand, while I do not wish to devalue anyone's opinion of the help they have received from healing, I feel that such surveys have limited scientific value. Heal-

ees report subjective relief from healing in almost every survey made. They have little appreciation for placebo effects and might as easily praise any nostrum whose effects derive from suggestion rather than any value inherent in the treatment itself. They tend to Type I errors. However, placebo reactions regularly produce improvements in about 33% of subjects. Since healing is subjectively reported to be effective in a greater percent of cases, these surveys appear to indicate overwhelming healee satisfaction with healing treatments.

JOHANNES ATTEVELT, as part of his doctoral dissertation at the State University of Utrecht in the Netherlands, performed two studies of healees. Reports of 4,379 healees were gathered from 'treatment cards' of 65 Dutch healers. The first study surveyed healers' and healees' subjective assessments of effects of healings immediately following the end of a period of treatment; the second obtained healees' opinions on the efficacy of healings six months following the termination of treatment.

The average age of healees was 47.5 years. The average duration of illnesses for which they sought treatment was seven years. Two-thirds were women. The most frequent diseases for which healing was sought were – skeletal-locomotory, 24–25%; neurological, 20–21%; heart and arterial, 9%; respiratory and pulmonary, 7–8%; rheumatic, 5–8%; and skin diseases, 5–7%. A total of 4,656 complaints were listed, demonstrating that healees often came for more than one problem. Pain was a factor in 51%. Psychological complaints totaled 1,397 cases, of which 50% were 'nervousness'.

Healer and healee assessments correlated closely (p < 0.001). Their opinions were that 42% were much improved; 24% rather improved; 18% somewhat improved; 14% not improved; and under 1% deteriorated. No correlation was found between improvement and age, sex or duration of disease.

Repeated questioning of healees, at intervals of one and three months following treatment, showed variability of responses ranging from slight to 50% changed. The presence of the healer during the interview led to 16% higher assessments of improvement by healees.

Attevelt also found that subjective healee assessments correlated well with objective measures of improvement, as reported in the last chapter.

DAVID HARVEY presents another thorough discussion on this subject (1983). He focuses on benefits derived from treatment, on circumstances under which these occurred and on healees' experiences during treatments. He states:

> Up until now, medicine has tended to regard the condition, rather than the patient, as the focal point of interest; but we are currently seeing a pendulum swing away from this extreme...
>
> Quality of life, freedom from pain and related considerations cannot be weighted and calibrated, but they are probably the most important factors from the patient's point of view...

Of 175 questionnaires mailed by Harvey 151 responses were obtained (86%). An impressive number reported they felt significant improvement – complete recovery 30%; partial recovery 25%; and improved ability to cope with symptoms 24%. However, Harvey's selection was based on a request to nine healers to each choose 20 patients who had shown positive responses to healing. This does not leave us with a clear idea of the percent of people in general who might benefit from

healing treatment. Harvey's survey is still recommended for its thorough, book-length discussion of numerous aspects of healees' subjective reports.

LOUISE RISCALLA, for her doctoral dissertation, interviewed a series of people engaged in religious healing, "considered as healing of the whole person – body, mind, and spirit through the use of prayer, anointing with oil, and/or laying-on-of-hands". Her aim was to study "the motivations of individuals seeking religious healing and their perceptions of what happens as a result of the ministrations of a healer..."

Riscalla selected churches at random near her home, attending services without revealing that she was conducting a study. They included Episcopal, Presbyterian, Roman Catholic and non-denominational churches. She conducted open-ended interviews, recording information on sex, age, occupation, marital status, types of problems to be healed, feelings experienced when seeking healing and (if any) with the process of healing.

Twenty-three people were interviewed (ages 9 to 65; 17 female; 17 married; and two divorced). A range of occupational levels was represented. They sought help for physical and emotional problems, separately or in combination. These included cancer, blindness, deafness, colds, colitis, headaches, ulcers, alcoholism, feelings of resentment and hurt and "difficulties coping". When seeking healing, 65% were under the care of a physician.

"It appears that the service itself creates an atmosphere conducive to receptivity for healing..." Of 17 experiencing touch healing, 82% reported the sensation of warmth during treatment; 6% experienced vibrations; 12% felt nothing. Riscalla reports 57% noted "variation in emotional improvement" and 28% in physical recovery, "which suggests that religious healing seems to focus on emotional conditions and on emotional aspects of physical illness which may, in many instances, be a major component". Greater improvement was reported from those attending less structured services.

The survey showed physicians' help had been sought more often by men than by women and more often for physical than for emotional problems or a combination thereof. Those reporting physical improvement were more likely to be older, under a physician's care and of lower occupational level. Those reporting emotional improvement were younger and had more emotion-related problems. Changes in emotional condition were only slightly related to physical improvement. In the latter group, physical change was associated with youth. Those who experienced improvement sometimes felt their lives had changed. Some attributed their improvements to powers of Jesus or God. Failure to recover was occasionally interpreted as insufficient faith or as God's will that they bear their illness.

Thirteen healers were interviewed (ages 28 to 62; 7 male; 85% married). All prayed for healing during the services. Of 11 who used the laying-on-of-hands method two felt tingling, two experienced vibrations, two were aware of strength and power and two "experienced the strength of God". Two reported they instantly knew when healing occurred, though they could not explain how they knew. Five reported praying in tongues (glossolalia), feeling this was a gift from God. Responsiblity for healing was attributed to God. Everyone considered cooperation with physicians as important.

An evaluation of healing efficacy in RISCALLA's survey is difficult. People commonly report improvement from all treatments, including placebos. The heterogeneity of treated conditions and lack of control group leave the possibility that selection for improvement may have occurred on some basis unrelated to healing.

KATHERINE BOUCHER studied 11 healees for her doctoral dissertation. Nine showed varying degrees of benefit, with eight having marked physical improvement.

PATRICIA WESTERBEKE studied the belief systems and the healing process of people visiting Philippine healers (WESTERBEKE, GOVER/KRIPPNER). Of 85 approached, 62 completed a series of questionnaires before and during their visit to the healers. Only 11 returned one or both questionnaires mailed to them 6 and 12 months later. She summarizes:

> The data suggest that one's post-session confidence in psychic healing (as recorded on the second questionnaire) is positively correlated with several items on the first questionnaire – stated willingness to change one's way of life if it meant being healed ... ($p < 0.01$), personal experience with psi phenomena ... ($p < 0.02$), and one's pre-session confidence in psychic healing ... ($p < 0.01$).
>
> The healee's post-session report on help obtained from the healer (on the second questionnaire) appears to be positively correlated with such items on the first questionnaire as pre-session confidence in psychic healing ... ($p < 0.01$) and personal experience involving purported psi phenomena ... $p < 0.02$). In other words, a healee's confidence in psychic healing is, perhaps, preconditioned by experience with presumptively paranormal events.

Healees' long-term changes correlated significantly with these items in the questionnaires at the time of healing: confidence in healing before their treatments, beliefs they received help from the healer and "perceived change in body *energy*" (all p < .01) and with "personal experience with purported psi phenomena" (p < .02). This study begins to explore which factors may predict positive outcomes. Its greatest flaw seems to be in the self-selection of 11 out of 85 healee respondents.

STANLEY KRIPPNER used the same questionnaire for a similar survey of experiential reactions of 10 (out of 16) healees to a Brazilian healer, *IRMAO (BROTHER) MACEDO* (1990).

> ... the individuals on this study tour were not seriously ill but joined it for other personal or professional reasons.
> ... One question asked, 'If regaining health necessitates changing your personality or style of living, to what extent would you be willing to make a change?' Five types of response were possible ranging from 'I would not be willing to change my life' to 'I would make any changes at all if it meant getting well'. These responses were significantly and positively related to professed improvement in one's spiritual viewpoint...
> The perceived change in 'energy and vitality' 6 months after the healing session was significantly related to a shift (at 12 months) toward a positive spiritual viewpoint...'

ERLENDER HARALDSSON/ORN OLAFSSON randomly surveyed 1,000 persons from the National Registry in Iceland by questionnaire and telephone follow-up. The 902 responses indicated that 34% felt healing was very helpful; 57% somewhat beneficial; and 9% that it was of no use. There was some correlation with religiosity and positive response.

No attempts were made to verify objectivity versus subjectivity of any changes brought about by the healings.

RICHARD WHARTON/GEORGE LEWITH summarized 145 responses to a questionnaire received from 200 general practitioners in Avon, England, on their involvement with spiritual healing in 1986. The survey found that 6% believed it is very useful; 4% useful; 31% no opinion; 16% not useful; and 10% harmful. This confirms that healing is becoming an adjunct to conventional medical practice in the U.K.

JOHN COHEN, at the request of a group of healers, referred 44 patients for healing from his National Health Service general practice of medicine in London. Of these, 17 had musculoskeletal pains and 11 had psychological problems.

> Of the 44 people who attended during the 20 weeks of the study, 31 (70 per cent) were women and 13 (30 per cent) were men. Ages ranged from 18 to 75 years (mean 45.5 years). The number of visits varied between one and 22 (mean 3.8); 16 (37 per cent) came only once and six (14 per cent) came more than eight times. The total number of healing sessions received was 167...
> ...35 (80 per cent) received counselling and support as well as healing when they attended while nine (20 per cent) received healing alone; six (75 per cent) of these attended for a 'booster' session after previously successful healing.
> Improvement was rated by patients as 'great deal better' 12%; 'good deal better' 36%; 'a little better' 20%; 'a bit better' 12%; 'no different' 20%.

Healers' expectations of improvement correlated closely with the observed healee reports.

Further analysis showed that:

> The greater the number of visits the greater the benefit
> * Those who did not feel they were going to respond visited only once
> * More women than men found the healing beneficial

DR. COHEN appears to believe that the benefits to his patients derived primarily from physical touch and compassionate attention.

In some instances, the point of view of investigaters may be radically different from that of healees. E. MANSELL PATTISON, et al. interviewed and also administered psychological tests to 43 fundamentalist Pentacostalists who received 71 faith healings. The researchers reported, "...our psychological data demonstrate the extensive use of denial, externalization, and projection with...disregard of reality..." Pattison, et al. suggest that the psychological beliefs and defense mechanisms of these subjects helped them adapt to their culture. The healings in this particular setting were not necessarily designed to decrease symptoms but seemed more oriented to reinforcing the religious community's belief systems. This points out the multiplicity of functions healing may serve.[25]

The greatest weaknesses of these surveys are that criteria for improvement are unspecified and that medical assessments to allow for comparison with populations of patients in other settings are not included. Still, the overall picture is that the majority of people are satisfied with healing treatments they receive in such settings.

Shamanic Healing

A rich literature is available on healing in non-industrial cultures, usually under the hands of shamans (medicine men).[26] Much of this literature views shamanistic healings as little more than superstitious, mystical rituals, of value primarily in their suggestive effects rather than in any intrinsic healing effects.

KAJA FINKLER, for example, describes spiritualist healers in a Mexican temple. Many patients she queried reported that they experienced heat and tingling during spiritualistic treatments and that they considered these portions of the treatment to be the most important in the healing.

Finkler attributes little significance to this or to the one-third of the patients who responded positively to 'cleansing' passes and who identified these in particular with relief of symptoms. The healings seemed to increase pain tolerance. She interprets these results as the products of suggestion, a response to cultural symbols employed by the temple healers. Her conclusions are that "...the healing requisites of patients are rooted in cultural imperatives mediated symbolically by the curing act".

One must seriously question whether yardsticks for measuring medical and healing effectiveness in one culture are appropriate or sufficient for assessing it in another. I agree with Victor Barnuow, who said, "The notion that modern Europeans or Americans are essentially more rational than members of non-literate societies must be classified as one of western man's irrational assumptions."

I learned a lesson on this theme in my clinical years in medical school. A person might complain of particular symptoms, such as a stomach ache with some weakness and generalized malaise. I was responsible as the examining student physician to ask the relevant questions that would allow me to arrive at a correct differential diagnosis. The patient, uneducated in medical syndromes, did not know which of his bodily sensations or symptoms might be relevant or causal in his illness and might not report vital information if I did not think to inquire about it. For example, with the patient who had abdominal pain, if I did not ask about aches elsewhere I might miss the facts that he had a lesser ache in his left jaw and that these symptoms all started when he was shoveling snow from his front walk. Without my pointed questioning one could easily have construed his symptoms to be of gastric origin. Taking into consideration the additional information elicited by focused, direct questions, the diagnosis of myocardial infarction (heart attack) was far more likely (and indeed was confirmed by cardiogram). I had to think of this possible diagnosis in order to ask the questions.

Similarly, a person unfamiliar with psi healing may see only the suggestion dimension of a healing interaction. Had Finkler known something of psi healing, she might have asked other questions and might also have reached somewhat different conclusions and interpretations thereof.

> If all you have is a hammer, then everything looks like a nail.
>
> *Abraham Maslow*

A few academics are more aware of the actuality of healing and other psi capabilities of shamans (HEINZE; ACHTERBERG 1985). MICHAEL HARNER (1980), STANLEY KRIPPNER/ALBERTO VILLOLDO (VILLOLDO/ KRIPPNER) are worthy of special mention. They not only studied shamanic practices by observation but actually trained in their methods. They were able to verify through their personal experiences much of what shamans report of their subjective states of consciousness during their work and to effect healings as well. Harner now teaches these methods to interested westerners. Villoldo has led groups of people to study under various shamans. Krippner has lectured and written voluminously on these topics. KRIPPNER/ WELCH have a particularly good discussion on the spectrum of healing in non-industrial and industrial societies.

It is refreshing to see how people trained in western science can accept the fact that so-called primitive cultures have much wisdom to offer to those who are open to learning. These cultures may be less advanced than ours in technology but they are far more advanced in application of psi skills, especially intuitive awareness and healing. Their methods warrant careful scrutiny so that both sides may learn: we – what may complement our modern medical methods, and they – to distinguish what might be the essential parts of their teachings from what may be mere magical and superstitious beliefs. We may all gain insight into mechanisms whereby healing functions.

Let me give a very speculative example from my own observations of archaeological excavations near the temple mount in Jerusalem. There is a *mikve* (Jewish ritual bath) here with a small reservoir (about 2x4x3 feet) adjacent, connected to it by a hole (about 3 inches in diameter), which reportedly had been plugged with a bung. According to tradition the reservoir used to be filled with rainwater and then blessed by the temple priests. Whenever the *mikve* bathwater was drained and refilled with fresh water the new bathwater was consecrated by opening up the bung between the reservoir and the mikve, allowing a little of the consecrated water to flow into the mikve. Fresh rainwater was added to the reservoir as needed to prevent it from drying out. As long as the reservoir did not dry out it was considered consecrated.

By conventional western logic, one would speculate that the originally consecrated water in the reservoir must become diluted fairly quickly, to the point that little of the original water would remain. Any effects of the consecration would appear to have been purely symbolic, especially following such serial dilutions. Let us assume that the priests were aware of some healing effects of their blessings upon water. Recent research suggests that healing effects inherent in blessed water may be transmitted through vibrations or other energy phenomena that may not follow conventionally accepted, western laws of chemical dilutions. A small quantity of water treated by healing might, therefore, confer full healing potency to a bottle or to an entire reservoir of untreated water. This speculation of course must be properly tested in the la-

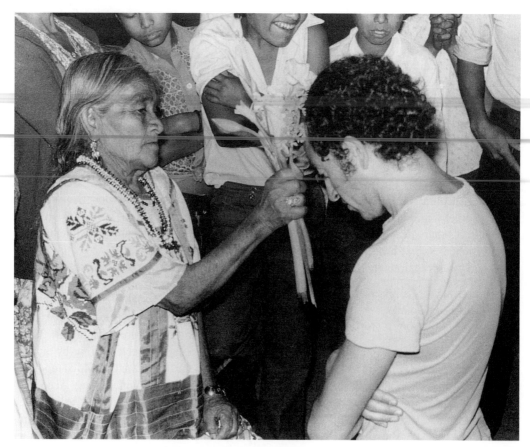

Fig. I-11. Maria Sabina, a Mexican shaman who uses hallucinogenic mushrooms, rituals and other methods of healing. Photography by courtesy of Bonni Colodzin Moffet

boratory. Homeopathy may have further observations to contribute on these matters.[27]

Much of the literature on shamanism and eastern medicine (e.g. KAPTCHUK) elaborates world views in which human beings constitute a small part of the cosmos, linked with nature via a vast web of interactions, including psi and spiritual interactions. Descriptions of these interconnections vary widely with the particular culture and may seem to western eyes so alien as to constitute mere superstitious belief. The fact is that people in each culture believe wholeheartedly in their cosmologies and respond to elements within them.[28] A shaman may therefore be able to draw upon imagery and beliefs from his culture in order to facilitate psi healings. In fact, it may be impossible for a healer from one culture to heal a patient from another because of dissimilar frames of reference.[29]

If we allow that in various cultures healing may appear entirely different from healing in western society, we might then be in a better position to re-examine the attitude of patients in our own culture toward their healings. Investigators within western culture have tended to discount these beliefs as being at least unimportant or certainly inessential to the actual, mechanical processes of healing. If we agree that alternative views may apply to healings in other cultures should we not consider the perspectives of those undergoing healing treatment in our own culture as being relevant to their responses to healing, even if they differ from those of our scientist subculture? (BERMAN is especially cogent in arguing these points.)

Non-industrialized cultures are universally more in tune with their environment than the industrialized world. There is a reverence for nature which comes from many generations of experience in learning from and accommodating to nature – rather than dissecting, conquering and subjugating nature. Shamanic practices, including healing (MCFADDEN) and trance states (ELIADE; HARNER 1980), bring about a personal and immediate awareness of nature and of one's relationship to nature. At this time, when excesses of materialism include global despoiling of resources and wanton pollution which plague and even threaten our existence, we have an urgent need to learn from nonindustrial societies how to heal ourselves and our planet.

CONCLUSION

The anecdotal material on healing suggests that healers can, by a wide variety of techniques, accelerate recuperation from illness even in cases where no cure seems possible through conventional medicine. The difficulty with such data is that they may mislead us by representing healing as the agency for improvement when in fact other processes or agencies were partially or totally responsible. This is less likely when the illnesses treated successfully by healers were chronic and unresponsive to conventional therapies.

Many of the psychological modes whereby symptoms may be relieved and changes brought about within the human body are considered in Chapter II-1. *Self-healings* via visualizations have been reported, explained by mechanisms such as alterations of the immune system, enhanced functions of white blood cells or other, unknown processes such as those involved in biofeedback, hypnosis or multiple personality. These might explain some but not all cases of healing in humans.

Two thirds of the controlled studies reviewed in Chapter I–4 demonstrate that psi healing is effective. When enzymes, yeasts, and bacterial cells in laboratory culture, plants and animals respond significantly to healing (leave aside that this is in controlled studies), either something more than sugges-tion is taking place or we must allow for attributes of sentience in lower organisms which would make them suggestible and thus also able to produce self-healing.

I submit that it is adequately demonstrated that healing is an effective treatment modality. Healing offers a potent complement to conventional therapies. We must get on with making healing available to those in need.

The next step will be to explore how healing works. The mystery called life challenges us to explore further. People suffering from illness and pain will benefit from this sleuthing. Further, our world views will be broadened, to return us to awareness of our intimate interrelationships with nature.

Psi healing contradicts currently popular scientific paradigms. It challenges the materialistic world view, pointing out that this is apparently a limited-case explanation for the cosmos. This closely parallels and in many ways overlaps the relationship of classical physics and modern physics. The natural laws which apply to the material world are accurate and helpful in understanding and manipulating that domain, but not appropriate for other dimensions of perception and interaction with non-material aspects of the world.

Healing points out that our bodies can be understood as energy in addition to understanding them as matter. VOLUME II explores this dimension.

Healing opens both healers and healees to spiritual awareness. Again this pushes the boundaries of materialistic beliefs. These dimensions are impossible to appreciate through words and reason alone. It is like when a traveller to a far land returns with descriptions of tastes of exotic fruit. Yet research shows in linear analyses that evidence exists for survival of the spirit and for reincarnation. VOLUME III delves into these dimensions.

Healing is not yet explained by existing theories. There are many clues and speculations at to what it is and how it happens. VOLUME IV presents theories for healing and organizes the clues so that patterns begin to emerge. It also includes my personal education, development and experiences in learning healing.

Each of us in the course of our life stands before the doors which open to healing. We have only to examine and experience the world in new ways to find the keys to unlock them. And if we learn some of the methods of healing and psi we may find we can enter without physical keys.

We must be prepared to come up with more questions than answers. LAURENS VAN DER POST framed this nicely (1973): "...the light the fire throws does not diminish the aboriginal mystery because of its power to illuminate some of the night. On the contrary, the mystery grows with the growth of consciousness."

APPENDIX A
Healing in the Bible

Jesus' individual healings	Healing type	Matthew	Mark	Luke	John
Simon's mother-in-law, fever	Touch; rebuked	8:14–15	1:29–31	4:38–39	
Leper	Touch	8:1–4	1:40–45	5:12–16	
Paralytic, carried by four	Sins forgiven	9:1–8	2:1–12	5:17–26	
Centurian's servant	Distant, synchronous	8:5–13		7:1–10	
Demonics at Gadara	Demons transferred to pigs	8:28–34	5:1–20	8:26–36	
Woman, bleeding	Touch-garment; faith	9:20–22	5:25–34	8:43–48	
Jairus' daughter raised	Belief; command	9:18–26	5:21–43	8:40–56	
Two blind men	Touch; faith	9:27–31		20:30–34	
Dumb, possessed (devil)	Drive out	9:32–34			
Withered hand	Command	12:9–14	3:1–6	6:6–11	
Man blind, deaf, possessed	(Drive out demon?)	12:22–30		11:14–26	
Daughter of Canaanite, possessed (demon)	Distant, synchronous	15:22–28	7:24–30		
Epileptic boy	Prayer; exhort	17:14–21	9:14–29	9:37–42	
Unclean spirit	Exhortation		1:21–28	4:31–37	
Deaf, speech impaired	Touch; spit; command		7:32–37		

Continued on next page

Jesus' individual healings	Healing type	Matthew	Mark	Luke	John
Blind Bartemus	Faith		10:46–52	18:35–43	
Widow's son raised from dead	Touch of coffin; command			7:11-17	
Woman bent double by spirit	Touch			13:10-17	
Man with dropsy	Took hold			14:1-6	
Ten lepers	Suggestion; faith			17:11-19	
Nobleman's son	Distant, synchronous				4:46-54
Sick man at pool	Exhortation; caution: to stop sinning				5:2-18
Man blind from birth	Spit; mud; bathe in Siloam pool				9:1-15
Raising of Lazarus	Call; faith; precognition				11:1-14

Jesus heals many problems	Diseases and healing types	Matthew	Mark	Luke
Throughout Galilee	Every disease and sickness; demons; seizures; pain; paralytics	4:23–24		
At Simon's door	Touch; demons driven out 'with a word'	8:16	1:32–34	4:40–41
By Capernaum	Touch; people touching Jesus	12:15	3:7–12	6:17–19
Jesus tells of his healings	Blind see; lepers cured; lame walk; deaf hear; dead are raised; cures evil spirits, sicknesses	11:2–5		7:21–22
At Gennesaret	Touching him; edge of his cloak	14:35–6	6:55–56	
Before feeding 4,000	Lame, blind, mute, crippled healed	15:30–31		
In the temple	Blind and lame	21:14		
In home town, Nazareth	Touch; sick (miracles few, lacking faith)		6:5	

Jesus' healings of crowds	Diseases and healing types	Matthew	Mark	Luke
Before feeding 5,000		14:14		9:11
Beyond the Jordan		19:2		
In towns and villages	Every disease and sickness	9:35		

Jesus 'gives authority' to others to heal	Diseases and healing types	Matthew	Mark	Luke
Twelve disciples	Heal sick; raise dead; cleanse leprosy; drive out demons	10:8		
Seventy-two believers	Heal sick; speak in tongues; pick up snakes; drink poison; touch-heal		16:17–8	10:1–9

Healings by Apostles	Diseases and healing types	Book, Chapter, Verses
Ananias	Paul regains sight bedridden eight years; exhorted	Acts 9:1–19; 22:6–13
Peter	Aeneas, paralytic	Acts 9:33–35
Peter	Dorcas raised by prayer; exhorted	Acts 9:36–41
Paul	Man lame from birth; faith; exhorted	Acts 14:8–10
Paul	Stops slave girl's precognition	Acts 16:16–19
Paul	Raises Eutychus who fell from third storey	Acts 20:9–12
Paul	Resists poison snake	Acts 28:3–6

Apostles' healings of crowds	Diseases and healing types	Book, Chapter, Verses
Philip	Paralytics, cripples; evil spirits came out with shrieks	Acts 8:6–7
Paul at Ephesus	Touch-handkerchiefs and aprons cured illnesses and evil spirits left	Acts 19:11–12
Paul at Melita	Sick	Acts 28:9
Seven sons of Sceva evoking Jesus' name	Driving out spirits	Acts 19:13–16

Old Testament healings	Diseases and healing types	Book, Chapter, Verses
Elisha and Shunamite's son	1. Staff on face (not done) 2. Touch-lying on boy	II Kings 4:18–27
Elisha and Naaman	Leprosy; washing seven times in Jordan	II Kings 5:1–19
Isaiah and King Hezekiah	Poultice of figs to boil when King was dying and prayed to God; (shadow goes back ten steps)	II Kings 20:1–11

APPENDIX B
Sources of Help and Information

Healing Organizations in the United Kingdom

Laying-on-of-hands healing locally and absent healing sent regularly; requests accepted from anywhere

Confederation of Healing Organisations
113 High Street
Berkhamsted, Herts. HP4 2DJ
Tel.(0442) 870660
Includes a wide variety of member organizations, listed below. Disseminates information on healing.

The Atlanteans
2 Runnings Park
West Malvern, Worcs. WR14 4BP
Phone (06845) 68017
Non-denominational healing

British Alliance of Healing Associations
(Referrals: Mrs. V. Pat Hissey)
26 Highfield Avenue
Herne Bay CT6 6LM
Phone (0227) 373804
Spiritual healing

Guild of Spiritualist Healers
36 Newmarket,
Otley, W. York LS21 3AE
Phone (0943) 462708
Spiritualist healing

National Federation of Spiritual Healers
Old Manor Farm Studio
Church Street
Sunbury on Thames, Middx. TW16 6RG
Phone (09327) 83164/5
Non-denominational. Largest of the CHO members. Extensive courses teaching about healing and how to develop healing gifts. Most extensive referral system to healers

Spiritualist Association of Great Britain
33 Belgrave Square, London W1
Phone (071) 235 3351
Spiritualist healing

Spiritualists' National Union
Redwoods, Stansted Hall,
Stansted, Essex, CM24 8UD
Phone (0279) 816363
Spiritualist Church

World Federation of Healing
(Referrals: Mr. Gilbert Anderson)
Brook Farm Cottage
Walsham Le Willows
Bury St. Edmunds,
Suffolk 1P31 3AP
Phone (03598) 665
Non-denominational

The White Eagle Lodge
Brewells Lane
Rake
Liss Hants GU33 7HY
Phone (0730) 893300
Non-denominational Christian

Jewish Association of Spiritual Healers
23 Magnolia Court
Headley Road East
Woodley, Reading, Berks. RG5 4SD
Phone(0734) 442281

The Seekers Trust
Addington Park nr Maidstone
Kent ME19 5BL
Phone (0732) 843589

Association of Therapeutic Healers
(Referrals: Elizabeth St. John)
Flat 5
54-56 Neal Street
London WC2
Phone (071) 831 9377
*Non-denominational. Most healers
are also trained in other therapies.*

Centre for Health and Healing
(Referrals: Beverly Martin)
Coordinator St. James' Church
197 Piccadilly
London W1V 9LF
Phone (071) 734 4511; 437 7118
Christian and Non-denominational

College of Healing
Referrals: Henley Thomas
3 Runnings Park
Croft Bank, West Malvern WR14 4BP
Phone (06845) 65253
Non-denominational

College of Psychic Studies
16 Queensberry Place
London SW7 2EB
Phone (071) 589 3292
Non-denominational. Large library

Other Sources for Help in the United Kingdom

Wirral Cardiac Rehabilitation Programme
St. Catherine's Hospital
Church Road
Birkenhead
Phone (051) 6785111 Ext. 3489
Holistic approaches, including healing

Cancer Link
17 Britannia Street, London WCIX 9JN
Phone (071) 833245
*Conventional and self-help, holistic cancer
treatments*

New Approaches to Cancer
5 Larkfield
Egham, Surrey TW20 ORB
Phone (0784) 433610
*Information on holistic treatments of cancer,
especially for self-help*

M.E. Action
PO Box 1302
Wells BA5 2WE
Information on approaches to treatment

The Natural Medicines Society
Edith Lewis House
Back Lane
Ilkeston, Derbys. DE7 8EJ
*Disseminates information on natural
medicines and lobbies for same.*

Immune Development Trust
4 Chatsworth Road
London NW2 4BN
Phone (081) 4593002
*Disseminates information on holistic
treatments for AIDS and other chronic
illnesses.*

Natural Health Network
The Lodge
Chardstock House
Chard, Somerset TA20 2TL
Phone (0460) 62662
List of Natural Health Centers around the UK

Findhorn Foundation
The Park
Forres IV36 ORD
Phone (0309) 72288 or 39311
Residential workshops on aspects of energy medicine and healing. Worldwide network of past participants

Holistic London, Brainwave
33 Lorn Road
London SW9 OAB
Phone (071) 7337883
Therapists and courses from Aromatherapy to Zen

Self-Help Organizations in the United Kingdom

12-STEP recovery programmes

Alcoholics Anonymous
London Service Office,
(071) 3523001
PO Box Stonebow House,
York YO1 2N
Tel: (0904) 644026

Alanon Family Groups
(UK and Eire)
61 Great Dover Street
London SEI 4YF
Phone (071) 4030888

Narcotics Anonymous
PO Box 417

London SW 10 ORS
Phone (071) 3516794

Codependents Anonymous
PO Box 1292
London N4 2XX
Phone (071) 3595810 & (081) 3486313

Debtors Anonymous
(*Call* Lorraine)
Phone (071) 3284802

Emotions Anonymous
c/o Society of Friends
120 Heath Street
London NW3
Phone (071) 2375161

Families Anonymous
Phone (071) 4313537 (help-line)
Phone (071) 4313536 (meetings)

Gamblers Anonymous
17/12 Blantyre St. Cheryl Walk
London, SW10
Phone (071) 3523060

Gamma Anonymous
Families and Friends of Gamblers
Phone (071) 3523060

Overeaters Anonymous
SAE to 27 Verdant Court
Verdant Lane
London SE6 1LE
Phone (081) 9819363

Sex and Love Addicts Anonymous
Write to: The Augustine Fellowship
PO Box 2040,
London W12

Adult Children of Sex Addicts and
Sexually Dysfunctional Families
(ACSA)
PO Box BM 3157
London WC1N 3XX

Sex Addicts Anonymous
Phone (071) 4027278

**Concerned with international focus on
healing the planet**

Fountain International
Lelant Garden Centre
Nut Lane
Hayle, Cornwall TR27 6J
Phone (0736) 754573

The Life Cancer Centre
Maristowe House
Dover Street
Bilston, W. Midlands WV14 6AL
Information and holistic treatments

The Life Cancer Centre
15 Holyhead Road
Bangor Wales, Gwynedd LL57 2EG
Phone (0248) 3700764

Healing Organizations in the United States of America

International Society for the Study of
Subtle Energies and Energy Medicine
(ISSSEEM)
C. Penny Hiernu, Executive Director
356 Goldco Circle
Golden, CO 80401 USA
Phone (303) 278 2228
*Principal US organization, interested in
healing, especially research. Journal
"Subtle Energies", and Newsletter. Annual
conference at end of June*

Spiritual Emergence Netword
Institute of Transpersonal Psychology
250 Oak Grove Avenue
Menlo Park, CA 94025
*Consultations on overlaps of spiritual
awakening and psychological confusion*

Association for Transpersonal Psychology
PO Box 3049
Stanford, CA 94309 USA
Phone (415) 327 2066
*Journal; newsletter; annual conference;
membership list*

FOOTNOTES

INTRODUCTION

[1] First a note on footnotes. As a reader of others' footnotes, I have been frustrated by not knowing whether I will find information or a reference when I get to the back of the book, and annoyed when I found whichever I was not interested in. For readers of this book there is the following code: Footnotes in ordinary numerals are bibliography references when more than two sources are cited. Those *italicized* are cross-references within the four volumes of HEALING RESEARCH and may contain ordinary references as well. Those in **bold** contain information, and occasionally bibliography references, too.

[2] See Chapter II - 1 on **psychoneuroimmunology** (PNI) (Roman numerals indicate VOLUME number.)

[3] See reviews of Capra, Dossey, Koestler, Zukav, and myself (Chapters II - 6, II - 8) for a taste of this.

[4] I brought this research (which promises with simple techniques to reduce post-surgical pain, nausea, vomiting, urinary and bowel problems, and to shorten hospital stay) to the attention of numerous surgeons. It has been dismaying to hear most of them decline under various excuses (e.g. that they would be embarrassed to be seen speaking to their patients as they are coming out of anesthesia - and presumably therefore unable to respond to the surgeon's intervention). See Evans and Richardson 1988 for recent application of these methods.

[5] It took close to two years to find funds for a carefully designed controlled study of healing in surgical patients. Most foundations and other funding sources indicated that such research is outside their field of interest. I am now living in England because I have found the doctors here more open to collaborative research on healing.

[6] I have used 'healee' in preference to 'patient' because the latter is taken (in conventional Western medicine) to be a person who receives treatment from someone else for his ailments in a passive manner. The term healee indicates a person who shares in the responsibility for doing something about his condition, even though his participation may be unconscious, through various mind-body-spirit connections elucidated in this book. LeShan (1974a) was the first to use this term. Siegel (1990) suggests the term 'respant', meaning responsible participant .

[7] Numerous observers through the ages have speculated on life forces or energies which may be associated with healing.

Ch'i (also spelled *Chi* and *Ki*)	Ancient Chinese
Prana	Ancient Hindu
Mana	Pacific civilization and, in part, ancient Europe
Pneuma	Pythagoras
Vis medicatrix naturae	Hippocrates
Archaeus	Paracelsus
Gana	South America
Astral light	Kabbalists
Vital fluid	Hermes Trismegistus
Universal fluid	Jan Baptista van Helmont; Franz Anton Mesmer
Odic Force	Baron Karl von Reichenbach
Orgone energy, *Od,* or *Odyle*	Wilhelm Reich
N-Rays	Professor Blondlot
X-Force	L. E. Eeman
Invisible emanations	Erich Konrad Müller
Life beams; *Spiritus*	Robert Fludd
Hidden forces	Emile Boirac
Prephysical energy	George de la Warr
Eloptic energy	T. Galen; Hieronymus
Di-electric Biocosmic energy	Oscar Brunier

L-Fields	Harold S. Burr; Leonard Ravitz
T-Fields	Edward Russell
DC Fields	Robert Becker
Telergy	Macedo
Paraelectricity	Ambrose Worrall
Psychotronic energy and Bioplasma	Various Soviet and Eastern European researchers
Biothermal reaction	Alexei Sergeyev
Zoophoretic light	Gordon Turner

After laboring on the aforelisted collection I found a far more comprehensive one in White/Krippner, which I highly recommend. There are thorny problems with the use of any name for healing. 'Healing' alone, or 'natural healing,' may refer to physiological processes of wound healing or to any other aspect of recuperation from illness. 'Faith' healing in the United States suggests something which is done by evangelical preachers in a tent or large auditorium, with much emotionality; or, on both sides of the Atlantic, cures brought about by faith or suggestion alone. 'Prayer' healing implies that without prayer healing may not occur, or that it is ne-cessarily tied to religious beliefs or practices. 'Psychic' healing in England, and 'Spiritual' or 'Spirit' healing in the United States, evoke images of seances, spiritualist and mediumistic phenomena. 'Mental' healing implies that what occurs may be only in the mind; may be due simply to suggestion; or may be due to 'wrong thinking', as taught by Christian Science and by some religious groups. 'Intuitive' healing suggests it is merely the product of the healer's subconscious instincts. 'Shamanic' healing implies that only within particular cultures where shamans officiate may healing be found or be effective. 'Miracle' healing suggests that every healing should produce a miraculous cure, whereas mild to moderate acceleration of normal recuperation is far more commonly seen. 'Paranormal' healing suggests something abnormal or unnatural. 'Charming', used in parts of Ireland seems to imply use of suggestion or even deception. 'Curing', also used in Ireland, may have some merit, but is not widely used there or elsewhere. 'Divine' healing suggests God is the agent for it. 'Magnetizing' suggests the use of magnets and/or techniques employed by the early hypnotists. 'Non-medical' healing seems silly to me, as healing probably is a part of every human caring interaction, especially those of dedicated health professionals. 'Laying-on-of-hands' and 'distant', 'remote', or 'absent' healing are descriptions of subtypes of healing practices. 'Bioenergotherapy' (abbreviated to BET), used in Eastern Europe, has merit but is quite a mouthful, and may imply healing energy is strictly from the body of the healer. 'Pranotherapy', suggested by Pierro Cassoli, of Italy, suggests a particular Eastern cosmology.

I am grateful to Allan Cooperstein for discussions which helped to clarify my thoughts on this subject. He suggests

a new term, 'transpersonal healing', which I like, but fear could be mistakenly identified with the transpersonal psychology movement, many of whose practitioners are uncomfortable with psi healing.

While none of these seems sufficient in and of itself, all touch upon some part-truths in a phenomenon which HEALING RESEARCH will explore in depth.

The term *psi healing* (or 'healing' for short) will be used in this book as hopefully the most neutral. It is derived from the Greek letter ψ (pronounced 'sigh'), which is used in parapsychology to denote phenomena such as telepathy, clairsentience, psychokinesis (PK, or mind-over-matter), and pre- or retro-cognition. Psi healing appears to me to be a part of other psi phenomena. This is discussed in detail in Chapter I-3. Alfred Stelter is the first to have used the term psi healing.

---

[8] For the sake of convenience I have used masculine singular pronouns. There is no intention here to emphasize gender in positive or negative fashion. In fact I have several times had to catch myself when talking of healers (of whom, in my acquaintance, the majority are women), and to use the masculine pronoun for the sake of consistency.

---

[9] This **historical review** is taken from portions of Dossey; Coddington; Pierrakos 1976; and Meek (chapter by Rindge). Pierrakos has the best historical overview and bibliography. Dossey has the best discussion on **Cartesian influences on western medicine.** For discussions on **paradigm shifts** related to psi in general Kuhn is a must and Harman (1988) is highly recommended. See also Braude (1986); Collins/Pinch; and H. Evans (1982). Brested and Estes are interesting for **ancient Egyptian concepts of healing.** Krippner/Welch provide an excellent discussion on shamans, medicine men, and spiritual dimensions in healing.

---

[10] See Appendix A for a table of **Biblical references to healing;** also Cerutti and Meek for lists of Bible references to incidents involving psi as well as healing. See also Gardner (1986a; b) on healings of the Venerable Bede. Chapters III-8 and III-11 discuss religions and healing.

CHAPTER I-1
Healers' Views of Healing

---

[1] See more on **Visualization** in Chapters I-3; II-2.

---

[2] Ivanova 1978; 1980; 1983; 1986 adds further details on her theories and experiences. 'Telesomatic reaction' is a

term coined by B. Schwarz 1967.

3 J. Smith; Grad 1965, personal communication.

4 See study of Estebany's use of cotton wool for healing mice (Grad 1965), reviewed in Chapter I - 4; discussion in Chapter IV - 3 under **storage** and **linger** effects.

5 See McRae for a detailed discussion on the **military potential of psychic weapons**; Targ and Harary for a more general discussion of East-West competition on the psi frontiers.

6 'Margaret,' described briefly later in this chapter.

7 See Chapter III - 11 on spiritual and spirit healings.

8 For thorough discussions of **connections between emotions and physical symptoms** see Dethlefsen and Dahlke; Harrison; Hay; Rossi; Steadman .

9 See Chapter III - 3; III - 4; III - 5; III - 11.

10 See more on Victor Krivorotov in Church and Sherr.

11 See Chapter IV - 2.

12 See Chapter II - 1: Studies of Collins; Fedoruk; Ferguson; Heidt; Krieger; Lionberger; Meehan; Parkes; Quinn; Randall; Wirth.

13 For further descriptions of **Therapeutic Touch** see Boguslaski 1980; Borelli and Heidt; Lionberger; MacRae; Melloy; Quinn 1979; 1988; 1989; Randolph 1984; Raucheissen; Rowlands; Witt.

14 Shubentsov; Tarpey (described in Volume II by Westlake) also report the use of **healee-held photographs for drawing healing to themselves.**

15 For discussion of **kundalini** phenomena see Greenwell; Sanella 1978. For photos of Cain at work see Harvey 1982.

16 See also Ray 1983 for discussion of theoretical bases for **Reiki**; Arnold and Nevius for practical descriptions of methods.

17 See also Angelo; White and Swainson for other views of **spirit communication regarding healing**, and Beard on the general subject of spirit communication.

18 Vogel, in public talks, seemed prone to exaggerations and Type I errors.

19 For references to **shamanic practices** see Footnote 26 in Chapter I - 5.

20 **Psi phenomena** are reviewed in Chapter I - 3.

21 See the Bhagavad Gita, especially the Judge translation; also the Upanishads.

22 Discussed in Chapter II - 1.

23 Dorie D'Angelo, Charles Cassidy, Rosita Rodriguez, Harold Plume, Etel deLoach, The Fullers, Bob Hoffman, Dorothy Vurnovas, Rev. William Brown, Alberto Aquas, William McGarey (a physician who is exploring methods recommended by Edgar Cayce).

24 See also Crenshaw; Fry; A. Taft; Valley Times for further details and Stemman 1983 for photographs of Willard Fuller.

25 For detailed biographies of Cayce see Bolton; H. L. Cayce; Stearn 1967; Sugrue. These are highly recommended for a view of the range of possibilities with applied psi. For Cayce remedies see Karp.

26 Numerous **shrines** around the world are alleged to promote healing. The most famous is the one at Lourdes, France. See Chapter I - 5. It is unclear whether the cures should be attributed to the waters usually present at such shrines, to self-healing initiated by healee expectations, or to other causes. This report by Stelter provides the only reference I have found which suggests that human interventions may be causally connected with these cures as well. For a review of *Lourdes* and other shrine healings see Footnote 5. See review in Chapter IV - 2.

27 Theories for healing are considered in Chapter IV-2.

28 Including: Josephina Sison, Rolling Thunder, Dona Pachita (also described by Puharich (described in Chapter III - 10), Olga Worrall, Hernani Andrade, Fausto Valle, and Josef Zezulka.

29 Reviewed in Chapter III - 7.

30 See Chapter II - 3.

31 For **further general reading on healing**: **Descriptive** – Annual - *Science of Mind*; Anonymous 1895; Barbanell 1962; 1953; Barns; Beard 1951; Beasley; Beck/Peper; Bibb/Weed; B. Bloomfield 1984; 1990; Bogulawski; Bramly; Brennan; Brody; Burns; Cavallini; Cassoli 1979 (Italian); Church/Sherr; Colinan (French); Cuddon 1963; Cuevedo; Davis/Davis; Delsanto de Simic; Ding-ming; Ed-

wardes/McConnell; Elliott; England; Feild; Flammonde; Fricker; Garret 1957; Graves; Gray; Gregorczick; Gresik; Hammond; D. Harvey; R. Harvey; Hebda; Herbert 1975; Hickey/Smith; Holmes; Holzer; Horstman; F. Huxley [poor]; Ivanova 1986; P.Y. Johnson; Jurak; Kemp; Keni; Kirkpatrick; Ko; Korth; Krieger 1987; Kuhlman; Leek; Levesque; Locker; Magaray; Markides; Mir/Vilenskaya; Montagno; R. Moss; V. Moss; Nanko; Nichols; Nixon [poor]; Omananda; Oursler 1957; Playfair 1985; Polyakov; Poulton; Regush; Rehder (German); C.A. Roberts; E. Roberts; Robinson 1983; Rogo 1983a; b; E. Salmon; Schmeidler/Hess; Shepard; Sheppard; Shine; W. Smith; Snel/Millar 1984; A. Taylor; Tebecis; Tester; Theosophical; Vilenskaya 1985(c-e); Wallace/Henkin; C. Wilson (describing 18th Century healers, 'The Convulsionnaires', who subjected themselves to strange tortures but were unharmed); Winn.

Methods – *General methods* – Butler; Colinon (French); Dean (in press); DiOrio; Ebon; Manning; Murphy; Regan/Shapiro; Weinman; *Reiki* – Arnold/Nevius; *Polarity therapy* – K. Gordon; Teschler; Polarity and nutritional – Burke [poor]; *Psychological* – Steadman; C. Lee; Lin. *Therapeutic Touch* – Borelli/Heidt; Krieger; MacRae; Rawnsley; Rogers 1970; 1984; Rogo 1986b; Sandroff; Wright; *TT and LeShan healing* – Malloy; Denham on Harry Edwards; Hutton on *Leah Doctors and their spirit assistants;* and with **aura surgery** Chapman 1973; 1978, and much more on this in Volume III of HEALING RESEARCH. King on the *Aetherius Society;* Reilly on the *Cayce methods;* Raphaeli on *crystals;* see also Chapter I - 3 on *self-healing*. On *Qi Gong* – China Sports Magazine; Dong; Shen; Takahashi/Brown; Vilenskaya 1985; Yan; Zeng. For a sample of lore on *herbs, amulets, numerology* and the like, C.J.S. Thompson is representative, and Croke provides a sample of common practices with the 'storage' phenomenon, discussed in this chapter by Estebany. The use of *music* in healing is discussed by Bonny/Savary; the use of hallucinogens by de Rios.

General Reviews on Healing – Benor 1984a; 1986; Carlson; T. N. Davis; Hastings, Fadiman/Gordon; Howe; Kittelson; Krippner/Solfvin; L. A. Miller; Nash 1972; Solfvin 1984; White/Krippner.

Speculations – Bailey 1972; Balint; Benor 1984b; 1985; 1988; 1990 (also in Chapter IV-3 as 'Reasons healing has not been accepted'); Challoner; Ikin; Levesque; The Medical Group; Ponder, McCausland; Parapsychology Foundation 1957; Roberts 1964; J. E. Rush; Sanford 1949; Solfvin 1982; A. Worrall.

Spirituality and religions in healing – Volume III. *Healing unto death:* Doctor-Healer Network, Newsletter 1992, No. 4; Jackson and Mueller.

Dangers of Healing – No dangers are reported with healing per se. However, it is possible that healees may delay conventional treatments which might have been of value if given earlier. See Coakley; Oakley/MacKenna; D. M.

Smith; Zlatos for such cases and Haviland for a discussion of the relative safety of healing (including the healers' code of ethics and the fact that healers' annual malpractice insurance in England is less than £2/year). *Healing fraud* is another possible indirect danger, discussed by Armstrong; Bishop; Randi. Other skeptics: Cuevedo (Portuguese); J. Davis.

Theories – Discussed in great detail in Chapter IV - 2, IV - 3.

How to find a healer – Appendix B; Chapter IV - 3; Herzberg.

[32] See Chapter IV-2 for a dicsussion of theories of healing and IV-3 for topical discussions andanalyses of aspects of healing.

CHAPTER I-2
Measurements of Healers' Effects on the Physical World

[1] See discussions on these below and in Chapters IV-2 and IV-3: He also found that this water had a specific peak at 1000 cm-1 on Raman spectroscopy. Water treated with a different caduceus ol with a repetition rate of 30kHz producrd changes in ultraviolet spectroscopy. This effect was retained by the water over several months.

[2] Patrovsky 1978; 1979; 1983b.

[3] See descriptions of *Picardi experiments on percipitates* in Gauquelin 1968, reviewed in Chapter III - 4.

[4] See more on variability with **geomagnetic and apparent planetary influences** in Chapter I - 3, Footnote 12, and in Chapter II - 4.

[5] See also Frydrychowski et al. on a study of **human serum photon emission**, reviewed in Chapter I - 4.

[6.] Watkins 1979, reviewed in Chapter I - 4. *PK (psychokinesis)* denotes influences of mind over matter. Healing is considered by some researchers to be a type of PK. Their term for *healer* is *PK subject*.

[7] More on **fields and energies associate with healing** in Chapters II - 3; IV - 2; IV - 3.

[8] See Wilson and Barber for a discussion of people who are are gifted with psi, healing and visual imaging abilities; Reviewed in Chapter II - 1.

[9] See discussion of **chakras** in Chapter II - 2.

[10] theses are waves postulated to exist around caducens coils, which as yet are unmeasurable on any instrument but seem to produce biological effects. More on these in Chapters II - 3, IV - 2, IV - 3.

[11] More on **Kirlian photography** and **other photographic effects of healers** in Chapter II - 3 .

CHAPTER I-3
Psi Phenomena

[1] Rhine 1961; 67; 78.

[2] Jahn & Dunne 1987; Puthoff & Targ; Schmidt; and others in Edge, et al.

[3] Haraldsson; Hislop; Murphet 1972; 1978; Sandweiss.

[4] See also Pulos 1982 for further material on Thomas. McClure reports on a similar case of **light phenomena.** An excellent review of biological light phenomena is presented by Alvarado.

[5] Houck 1984b discusses electron microscopy of **metal bent by PK.** Hasted et al.; Isaacs 1985 discuss piezoelectric studies of PKMB. Kelly discusses **psychotronics,** the term used in (former) Eastern Block countries for mind-machine interactions. There are several early reports of bending of plastic cutlery in the same manner as metal is bent. As the molecular structure of plastic is very different from that of metals, this may add an important dimension to our clues regarding PK mechanisms. There are also some less well studied **related PK effects,** of plywood and of leather rings which have been joined by PK into chains, further broadening the PK horizons (Isaacs 1981). For discussions on paradigm shifts implied by macro-PK see Braude 1979a; b; 1986; Collins/Pinch.

[6] The originator of this approach is Jack Houck 1983; 1984a.

[7] For more on the **Batcheldor approach** see also Isaacs 1982; 1984; Batcheldor 1983; 1984; Brookes-Smith and Hunt; Owen/Sparrow; Playfair 1985. See Chapter II - 6 for further discussion of mediumistic phenomena, especially the work of Crawford.

[8] For other good reviews of **poltergeist** material see Fodor 1958; Podmore; Thurston. Rogo 1974a discusses issues of the poltergeist and psychotherapy. Manning 1974 has a nice personal description of his experiences in producing poltergeist phenomena. Goss 1979 presents an annotated bibliography on poltergeists.

[9] For a contrast with **spirit phenomena** see Chapters III - 4 and III - 5.

[10] Stanford 1974a; b; 1975; 1978.

[11] Braud 1979; 1980; McCarthy 1979.

[12] For more on **psi abilities in psychics and healers,** see Garrett 1949; Heywood; Karagulla; Kucharev/Vilenskaya; Manning; McCaffery; Murphet; Playfair 1975; L. Rhine 1970; Ullman 1974a; b; Uphoff 1987; Uphoff/Uphoff 1980a; b; Vasiliev 1963; 1965; Vilenskaya 1981a; b; **psi in animals** – Rhine/Feather; Vilenskaya 1986. Interesting **reviews of psi** can be found in Edge et al. 1986 excellent overall review; Fodor 1966; Haynes 1961; Inglis 1977; Moore 1976; Moss 1974; Murphy 1970 Nash 1978; 1986 [excellent overall reviews]; Pratt 1973; Robinson 1981; Schmidt 1975; Sudre 1960 [translates much foreign language literature]; Taylor 1975a; Ullman 1974; Watson 1979. Considerations of **aspects of research in psi** are provided by Ashby; Beloff 1974; 1977; Braude 1979a; b; Cadoret; Carington; Edge 1978a; Ehrenwald 1976a; Gauld 1976; Humphrey/Nicol; Irwin 1978; 1979; 1985; Jahn 1982; 1984; Jahn/Dunne 1987; Kreitler/Kreitler; Marshall; Millar 1978; Nash 1978; 1986; Rao 1977; Rauscher 1983; Richards; Schmidt 1974; Stanford 1977; Tart 1963; 1972; 1975; Wolman 1977. On **psi, psychotherapy and psychopathology** see Benor 1986; Burg; Eilbert/Schmeidler; Krippner 1969; Mintz/Schmeidler; Pederson-Krag; Peterson 1975; 1987; Rogo 1974. On **hypnosis and psi** see LeCron; **other states of consciousness and psi** – Neppe; Osis/Bokert; Tart 1972. For discussions of **fears of psi** see Benor 1990 (also Volume IV - 3, under 'Reasons healing has not been accepted'); Eisenbud 1983; Tart 1984; 1986a; Chapter III - 13. Inglis 1986 discusses **retrocognitive dissonance,** whereby people seek to distort their memories of psi events to make them consonant with conventional reality. Bloch; Estes/Worth; Freud 1963 are of interest as **historical notes on psi. Psi in archaeology** is presented by S. Schwartz 1983; **military applications of psi** in Harary; McRae; Targ. On **conformance Theory** – Gruber; McCarthy et al. 1979; Braud 1980; Stanford/Fox. On **physiological reactions to ESP**– Dean 1962; Lloyd 1973; Schouten 1976; Sieveking 1981; Targ/Puthoff 1974; Tart 1963. On **brain functions, hemispheric laterality and psi** – Braud 1975; Broughton; Ehrenwald; Lloyd. On the search for **electromagnetic fields to account for ESP** see Balanovski/Taylor. On **gravity and psi** see Gallimore; **geomagnetic influences on psi** – Persinger 1985; 1987; Rogo 1986a; Schaut/Persinger; Polyakov; Sergeyev; Tunyi. See Newton-Smith; Shallis for further discussion of **time,** and Barrington; Gribbin for discussion of apparent slips or warps in time. A movement among American **fundamentalists against 'New Age' thought,** including psi and consciousness research, holistic approaches, etc. is brewing, represented by J. Carr; Cumbey; Groothius. On **negative reactions by the science**

establishment to psi see Mc Connell/Kuzmen; Palmer, Honorton/Utts. On **fraudlent psychics**: Bishop; Keene; Randi.

13 For more on **modern physics** see Chapter IV - 2.

14 On the **fallacy of trying to measure one science with the yardstick of another** see H. Smith; LeShan/Margenau 1980; 1982; Wilbur 1979.

15 See Chapter II - 1; Naranjo/Ornstein on right and left brain functions.

16 See Chapter I – 4 reviewing the Solfvin 1982 experiment on malarial mice.

17 See for instance the **joining techniques** of Neurolinguistic Programming through synchronizing breathing (Bandler/ Grinder).

18 See Chapter III - 6.

19 See Chapter II - 4, for more on **geobiological effects**.

20 Chapter IV - 3 considers many such **factors relevant to healing**.

21 **Skeptics** Alcock; Hansel; Neher and review by A. Hyman; skeptic Alcock reviewed by Morris; skeptics J. Booth; K. Frazier; M. Harris; P. Kurz and review by D. Stokes; skeptic Nolen criticized by Stelter; Randi and review by Benor 1989; U.S. National Academy of Sciences and McConnell and Kuzmen Clark.

CHAPTER I-4
Controlled Studies

1 See discussion on **suggestion and placebo effects** in Chapter II - 1.

2 Tables of such variables are presented in Chapter IV - 3. See also Benor and Ditman on suggestions for research reports.

3 See summary of **vehicles for healing** in Chapter IV - 3

4 See summary in Chapter I - 2.

5 See Rein's **theoretical discussion on Non-Hertzian fields** as mediators for healing in Chapter IV - 2.

6 Spindrift work with plants is summarized in Chapter I - 5.

7 See discussion of **extraneous factors which may influ-**

ence healing and psi effects in Chapter IV - 3 and Tables IV - 5 to IV - 10.

8 See review of Solfvin's study on malarial mice later this chapter.

9 For more on psi and psychological effects see Footnote 12, Chapter I - 3.

10 See Chapter II - 3 on Gurvich's work on **mitogenetic radiations**.

11 In brief, **Stanford's conformance theory** postulates that psi works best on elements that are randomly in flux (discussed in Chapter I - 3). When a reproductive cell divides, the chromosome pairs split into single strands, half of which go to each of the two gametes (egg or sperm) that are produced. The genes of the parent cell distribute themselves randomly between the single-stranded sets of chromosomes of the gametes. Psi or healing might work well at this stage of the life cycle. Evidence for this hypothesis can be found in the successes of Luther Burbank in producing over 800 new varieties of fruits, vegetables, flowers, trees and other plant stock (Benor 1987), and from research by Cox 1957 on the gender of the fifth child in families where the first four were all male.

12 Instrumentation is discussed by Timosenko. See also Bose; McCullough; Retallack for further discussion on **awareness in plants.** Luther Burbank's work with plants, suggesting a psi influence over hereditary changes, is reviewed in Kraft/Kraft and similar work in Sauvin. Kammerer's work with animals suggesting the same is discussed by Koestler 1971. See also Cox; McDougall.

13 Adamenko 1972a briefly mentions experiments with **plant memory and conditioned reflexes**. This certainly seems a feasible and logical extension of findings in this chapter.

14 '**Harmonizing of experimenters and subjects** in healing studies appears to me very important. See also the study of V. Hunt, reviewed in Chapter II - 2, on harmonizing in studies of Kirlian photography and aura readings during Rolfing massage.

15 Summarizes also Grad 1964a; b; 1963; 1961.

16 See summary of **vehicles for healing** in Chapter IV - 3.

17 This study is reviewed only because it has been cited by many other reviewers.

18 See discussion on **dowsing and radionics** in Chapter II - 4.

[11] See also Knowles 1971 for similar discussion.

12 See discussion on self healing in Chapter II - 1; Roud for similar experiences.

[13] The absence of skin temperature change despite strong sensations of heat during healing has been a consistent finding with most researchers.

[14] For more on TT see also Boguslawski; Borelli/Heidt; Krieger 1979b; Miller; Quinn 1988; 1989; Randolph 1984; Raucheisen; Rowlands; Witt; Wright.

[15] Rose 1955 briefly outlines some of this same material.

[16] See also Kowey/Friehling/Marinchak; and later in this chapter Casdorph/Gardner.

[17] This work is also reviewed briefly in Vilenskaya 1976a, with some comments by Herbert.

18 Psychic surgery is reviewed in Chapter II - 7.

[19] A Doctor-Healer Network has been started in the UK. In regular meetings of healers, doctors, nurses and other involved therapists, discussions focus on healees, methods and theoretical issues.

[20] I have left the original odd spellings lest I misinterpret them.

[21] Agpaoa (in Stelter; Motoyama); Hochenegg (in Playfair 1988); Kraft (also in MacDonald et al.); Krivorotov (in Adamenko 1970).

[22] This case is also reported in Moss 1979 in slightly greater detail.

[23] See also B. Brennan; Pierrakos 1987.

[24] Other references which examine healing with some semblance of scientific approach include: Anonymous 1887; 1895; Davitashvili 1983; Dresser; Elliotson; Ferda; Goodrich 1976; Haynes 1977a; b; Herbert 1970 [too brief to be helpful]; 1979; Holzer 1974b; 1979; Ilieva-Even; Krippner 1973; MacRobert 1955; Roland; Vu. Interesting case reports are presented by Kowey; Thorley. These could easily have appeared as cases of 'spontaneous regression' had the authors not known to inquire about healing. Some brief abstracts on healing: *Parapsychology Abstracts International* 1987, 5(2), nos. 2477-8; 2481-5 from the Polish *Psychotronika*.

[25] Millar/Snel review several Dutch surveys of healers.

[26] Technically, a medicine man is defined as a native healer. **Shamans** are **medicine men**, but not all medicine men are shamans. Shamans serve in many other capacities within their culture in addition to their duties as healers, such as in mediating disputes, officiating at religious holidays and rites of passage, etc. References in related disciplines which deal with **shamanic healing,** and **healing in the context of Western sub-cultures and other cultures**: Achterberg 1985; Ayishi; R. J. Beck; Bhandari et al.; F. Bloomfield; Boshier; Boyd; Calderon; Constantinides; Dieckhofer; Dirksen; Dobkin de Rios 1972; 1984a; b; Eliade [a classic]; Fabrega; Raquel Garcia; Raymond Garcia; Garrison; Geisler 1984; 1985; Glick; Golomb; Halifax; Harner [a classic]; Heinze 1984; 1985 [excellent surveys]; Hiatt; Hill; Hood; Hultkrantz; Humphrey; Joralemon; Kakar; Kapur; Katz; Kerewsky-Halpern; S. King; Kleinman [essential to cross-cultural understanding of diagnosis and treatment]; Koss; Krippner 1980b; Krippner/Welch; Krippner/Villoldo; Kuang et al.; Landy; J. Long; M. Long 1976; 1978; Machover; C. Miller; Morley/Wallis; J. Nash; Orsi; Osumi/Ritchie; Oubre; Packer; Peters/Price-Williams; R. Prince 1972; Rauscher 1985; St. Clair 1970; 1974; Sandner; Scharfetter; P. Singer; Singer et al.; Sneck; Swan 1986; Takaguchi; Torrey; Peters; Ullrich; Villoldo/Krippner; Webster; Winkelman; A. Young 1976; Zimmels.

Achterberg/Heinze focus most clearly on psi healing. Kakar; Kleinman; Romanucci-Ross et al.; Servadio (reviewed in Chapter I - 4); provide excellent discussions on the importance of factors in the healers' cultures in explaining their effectiveness.

[27] Dean 1985 observed, for instance, that the **alterations in UV spectrum produced by healers in water** was more pronounced when the water container had a greater air space in it. This may have been a fortuitous finding, but may possibly represent a further property of healing energy yet to be elucidated. See review in Chapter I - 2. See also Chapter II - 2 on homeopathic dilutions.

[28] e.g. Chesi 1980; 1981; Finkler 1985.

[29] Berman; Finkler 1985; Kiev 1964; 1968; Kleinman 1980; Phoenix.

REFERENCES

Achterberg, Jeanne: *Imagery in Healing: Shamanism and Modern Medicine.* Boston and London: New Science Library/ Shambala 1985.

Adamenko, Victor: Electrodynamic systems. *Journal of Paraphysics* 1970, (4), 113-121.

Adamenko, Victor: Living detectors. *J. Paraphysics* 1972 (a), 6(1), 5-8.

Agnellet, M.: *Accept These Facts: The Lourdes Cures Examined.* London 1958.

Alcock, James E.: *Parapsychology: Science or Magic?* New York: Pergamon 1981.

Alvarado, Carlos S.: Observations of luminous phenomena around the human body: A review. *Journal of the Society for Psychical Research* 1987, 54, 38-60.

Andrade, H.G.: *A Corpuscular Theory of Spirit.* Sao Paulo: Privately published 1968.

Angelo, Jack: *The Healing Spirit: The Story of Dennis Barrett.* London: Rider 1990.

Annual – *Science of Mind: The New Age of Healing.* Los Angeles: Science of Mind 1979. [Briefs from conference.]

Anonymous: A recent case of faith healing. *Journal of the Society for Psychical Research* 1895. (Also in: *British Medical Journal* Nov, 16, 1895.) From Corliss, W. R.: *The Unfathomed Mind: A Handbook of Unusual Mental Phenomena.* Glen Arm, MD: The Sourebook Project 1982. [Case of follicular infection on beard responding to healing].

Armstrong, O.K.: Beware the commercialized faith healers. *Reader's Digest* 1971 (June), 179-186.

Arnold, Larry E./ Nevius, Sandra K.: *The Reiki Handbook.* (Psi) 1982. Harrisburg, PA: Para Science International.

Ashby Robert H.: *A Guidebook to the Study of Psychical Research.* New York: Weiser 1973.

*Attevelt, J.T.M.: Research into Paranormal Healing. *Doctoral dissertation,* State University of Utrecht, The Netherlands 1988.

---

* indicates report of controlled study reviewed in Chapter I-4

Backster, Cleve: Evidence of a primary perception in plant life. *International Journal of Parapsychology* 1968, 10(6), 329-348.

Baer, Randal N./ Baer, Vicki: *The Crystal Connection: A Guidebook for Personal and Planetary Ascension.* San Francisco: Harper and Row 1986.

Bailey, Alice A.: *Esoteric Healing,* V. VI. New York: Lucis 1972.

Balint, Mic.hael: Notes on parapsychology and parapsychological healing. *International Journal of Parapsychology* 1955, 36, 31-35.

Bandler, Richard/ Grinder, John: *Frogs into Princes: Neurolinguistic Programming.* Moab, Utah: Real People 1979.

*Baranger, P./ Filer, M.K.: Amulets: The protective action of collars in avian malaria. *Mind and Matter.* Oxford, England: Radionics Centre 1967(March) [Excerpt from *Acta Tropica* 1953, 10(1)].

Barbanell, Maurice: *Harry Edwards and His Healing.* London: Psychic Book Club 1953.

Barbanell, Maurice: *I Hear a Voice: A Biography of E.G. Fricker, the Healer.* London: Spiritualist 1962.

*Barrington, Mary Rose: Bean growth promotion pilot experiment. *Proceedings of the Society for Psychical Research* 1982, 56, 302-304.

Barrington, Mary Rose: A slip in time and place. *Fate* 1985 (October), 88-94.

*Barros, Alberto, et al.: Methodology for research on psychokinetic influence over the growth of plants. *Psi Communicacion* 1977, 3(5/ 6), 9-30 (Summary, translated from Spanish, from: *Parapsychology Abstracts International* 1984, 1(2), 80, Abstr. No. 662).

*Barry, Jean: General and comparative study of the psychokinetic effect on a fungus culture. *Journal of Parapsychology* 1968, 32, 237-243.

Batcheldor, K.J.: Report of a case of table levitation and associated phenomena. *Journal of the Society for*

Psychical Research 1966, 43(729), 339-356.

Batcheldor, K.J.: Contribution to the theory of PK induction from sitter-group work. In: Roll, W.G./ Beloff, J./ White, R. (Eds): *Research in Parapsychology 1982.* Metuchen, NJ: Scarecrow 1983, 45-61. (Also in: *Journal of the American Society for Psychical Research* 1984, 78(2), 105-132.)

*Baumann, S./ Lagle, J./ Roll, W.: Preliminary results from the use of two novel detectors for psychokinesis. In: Weiner, Debra H./ Radin, Dean I. (Eds): *Research in Parapsychology 1985.* Metuchen and London: Scarecrow 1986, 59-62.

Bayless, Raymond: *The Enigma of the Poltergeist.* New York: Ace 1967.

Beard, Rebecca: *Everyman's Search.* Chichester, England: Science of Thought Press 1951.

Bechterev, W.: Direct influence of a person upon the behavior of animals. *Journal of Parapsychology* 1948, 13, 166-176.

Beck, Rene/ Peper, Eric: Healer-healee interactions and beliefs in therapeutic touch: Some observations and suggestions. In: Borelli, Marianne/ Heidt, Patricia, (Eds): *Therapeutic Touch.* New York: Springer 1981, 129-137.

Bek, Lilla/ Pullar, Philippa: *The Seven Levels of Healing.* London: Century 1986.

Beloff, John: *New Directions in Parapsychology.* London: Unwin/ Gresham 1974.

Beloff, John: Psi phenomena: Causal versus acausal interpretation. *Journal of the Society for Psychical Research* 1977, 49(773), 573-582.

Benor, Daniel J.: Psychic healing: Research evidence and potential for improving medical care. In: Salmon, J. Warren (Ed): *Alternative Medicines: Popular and Policy Perspectives.* London: Tavistock/Methuen 1984(a).

Benor, Daniel J.: Meta-awareness and meta-emotions as related to psychic healing. *Paper presented at* Hospitality Suite Section of the American Psychological Association Meeting, Transpersonal Psychology Interest Group, Toronto 1984(b).

Benor, Daniel J.: Believe it and you'll be it: Visualization in psychic healing. *Psi Research* 1985, 4(1), 21-56.

Benor, Daniel J.: Research in psychic healing. In: Shapin, Betty/ Coly, Lisette (Eds): Current Trends in Psi Research. *Proceedings of an International Conference, New Orleans, LA, 1984.* New York: Parapsychology Foundation 1986.

Benor, Daniel J.: The overlap of psychic 'readings' with psychotherapy. *Psi Research* 1986, 5(1,2), 56-78.

Benor, Daniel J.: Lamarckian genetics: Theories from psi research and evidence from the work of Luther Burbank. *Research in Parapsychology (p3) 1987, 1988.*

Benor, Daniel J.: A psychiatrist examines fears of healing. *Journal of the Society for Psychical Research* 1990, 56, 287-299.

Benor, Daniel J.: Individual variability in intuitive diagnosis. *Paper presented at* First Annual Conference of the International Society for the Study of Subtle Energies and Energy Medicine, Boulder, CO 1991.

Benor, Daniel J./ Ditman, Keith S.: Clinical psychopharmacological research: Problems, questions and some suggestions in analyzing reports. *Journal of Clinical Pharmacology* 1967, 7, 63-76.

Berman, Morris: *The Reenchantment of the World.* New York: Bantam 1984.

*Beutler, Jaap J./ Attevelt, J.T.M., et al: Paranormal healing and hypertension. *British Medical Journal* 1988, 296, 1491-1494.

Bibb, Benjamin O./ Weed, Joseph J.: *Amazing Secrets of Psychic Healing.* West Nyack, NY: Parker 1976.

Bishop, George: *Faith Healing: God or Fraud?* Los Angeles: Sherbourne 1967.

Bloch, M.: *The Royal Touch: Sacred Monarchy and Scrofula in England and France (translated from French).* London: Routledge and Kegan Paul; Montreal: McGill University 1973 (10 pp. refs.).

Bloomfield, Bob: *The Mystique of Healing.* Edinburgh, England: Skilton and Shaw, 1984.

Bloomfield, Bob: *Linda Martel: Little Healer.* Tasburgh, England: Pelegrin Trust/ Pilgrim 1990.

Bloomfield, Frena: Asking for rice: The way of the Chinese healer. *Shaman's Drum* 1985, 1, 33-36.

Boguslawski, M.: The use of therapeutic touch in nursing. *Journal of Continuing Education in Nursing* 1979, 10(4), 9-15.

Boguslawski, Marie: Therapeutic touch: A facilitator of pain relief. *Topics in Clinical Nursing* 1980, 2, 27-37.

Bolton, Brett: *Edgar Cayce Speaks.* New York: Avon 1969.

Bonnell, John Sutherland: *Do You Want to be Healed?* New York: Harper and Row 1968.

Bonny, Helen L./ Savary, Louis M.: *Music and Your Mind, Listening with a New Consciousness.* Port Townsend, WA: ICM 1983; Orig., New York: Collins Associates 1973.

Borelli, Marianne D./ Heidt, Patricia (Eds): *Therapeutic Touch: A Book of Readings.* New York: Springer 1981.

Bose, Jaqadis C.: Awareness in plants. In: Muses, Charles/ Young, Arthur M. (Eds): *Consciousness and Reality.* New York: Outerbridge and Lazard/ Dutton 1972.

Boucher, Faith Katherine: The Cadences of Healing: Perceived Benefits from Treatment Among the Clientele of Psychic Healers. *Doctoral dissertation, University of*

California, Davis 1980.

Boyd, Doug: *Rolling Thunder.* New York: Delta/Dell 1974.

Bramly, Serge: *Macumba: The Teachings of Maria Jose, Mother of the Gods.* New York: Avon 1979.

Braud, William G.: Conformance behavior involving living systems. In: Roll, W.G., et al. (Eds): *Research in Parapsychology 1978.* Metuchen, NJ: Scarecrow Press 1979, 111-115.

Braud, William G.: Lability and inertia in conformance behavior. *Journal of the American Society for Psychical Research* 1980, 74, 297-318.

*Braud, William G.: Distant mental influence of rate of hemolysis of human red blood cells. In: Henkel, Linda A./ Berger, Rich E. (Eds): *Research in Parapsychology 1988.* Metuchen, NJ, and London: Scarecrow 1989(a), 1-6.

Braud, William G.: Using living targets in psi research. *Parapsychology Review* 1989(b), 20(6), 1-4.

*Braud, William/ Davis, Gary/ Wood, Robert: Experiments with Matthew Manning. *Journal of the Society for Psychical Research* 1979, 50, 199-223.

*Braud, William/ Schlitz, Marilyn: Psychokinetic influence on electrodermal activity. *Journal of Parapsychology* 1983, 47(2), 95-119.

*Braud, William/ Schlitz, Marilyn: Possible role of intuitive data sorting in electrodermal biological psychokinesis (Bio-PK). In: *Research in Parapsychology 1987, 1988,* 5-9.

*Braud, William/Schlitz, Marilyn: A methodology for the objective study of transpersonal imagery. *Journal of Scientific Exploration* 1989, 3(1), 43-63.

*Braud, William, et al.: Further studies of the Bio-PK effect: Feedback, blocking, specificity/generality. *Presentation at* Parapsychological Meeting 1984.

Braude, Stephen E.: The observational theories in parapsychology: A critique. *Journal of the American Society for Psychical Research* 1979(a), 73, 349-366.

Braude Stephen E.: *ESP and Psychokinesis: A Philosophical Examination.* Philadelphia, PA: Temple University Press, Philosophical Monographs 1979(b).

Breasted, J.H.: *The Edwin Smith Surgical Papyrus.* Chicago: University of Chicago 1930.

Brennan, Barbara: *Hands of Light.* New York: Bantam 1987.

*Brier, Robert: PK on a bio-electrical system. *Journal of Parapsychology* 1969, 33, 187-205.

*Brier, R./ Savits, B./ Schmeidler, G.: Experimental tests of Silva Mind Control graduates. In: Roll, W.G./ Morris, R.L./ Morris, J.D. (Eds): *Research in Parapsychology 1973.* Metuchen, NJ: Scarecrow Press 1974, 13-15.

Brookes-Smith, C./ Hunt, D.W.: Some experiments in psychokinesis. *Journal of the Society for Psychical Research,* 1970, 45, 265-280.

Broughton, R.S.: Possible brain hemisphere laterality effects on ESP performance. *Journal of the Society for Psychical Research* 1976, 48, 384-399.

Brown, William C.: *A Treatise on Etheric Surgery.* Toccoa Falls, GA: Privately printed, nd, 16pp.

Burbank, Luther: *Quote* from Tompkins, Peter/ Bird, Christopher: *The Secret Life of Plants.* New York: Harper and Row 1972, 134.

Burg, Bob: The puzzle of the psychic patient. *Human Behavior* 1975 (September), 25-30.

Burke, Abbot George: *Magnetic Therapy: Healing in Your Hands.* Oklahoma City: St. George 1980.

Burns, Jean: Consciousness and psi. *Psi Research* 1986, 5(1,2), 166-205.

Butler, Patrick: *The Healing Hand Book: Training and Developing the Power to Heal.* London/ New York: Quantum 1990.

*Byrd, Randolph C.: Positive therapeutic effects of intercessory prayer in a coronary care population. *Southern Medical Journal* 1988, 81(7), 826-829.

Cade, C. Maxwell/ Coxhead, N.: *The Awakened Mind: Biofeedback and the Development of Higher States of Awareness.* New York: Delacorte Press/ Eleanor Friede 1978.

Cadoret, Remi J.: The reliable application of ESP. *Journal of Parapsychology* 1955, 19, 203-227.

*Cahn, Harold A./ Muscle, Noel: Towards standardization of laying-on of hands investigation. *Psychoenergetic Systems* 1976, 1, 115-118.

Campbell, Anthony: 'Treatment' of tumours by PK. *Journal of the Society for Psychical Research* 1968, 44, 428. (Summary of Elguin, Gita H./ Onetto, Brenio; in: *Acta Psiquiat. Psicol. Amer. Lat.* 1968, 14, 47.)

Capra, Fritjof: *The Tao of Physics.* Boulder, CO: Shambala 1975.

Carington, Whately: *Telepathy.* London: Methuen 1946.

Carlson, Rick J. (Ed): *The Frontiers of Science and Medicine.* Chicago. IL: Henry Regnery 1975.

Carr, Joseph: *The Twisted Cross.* Shreveport, LA: Huntington House 1985.

Carrel, A.: *Voyage to Lourdes.* New York 1950.

Carter, Mary E./ McGarey, William A.: *Edgar Cayce on Healing.* Anderson, IN: Warner 1972.

Casdorph, H. Richard: *The Miracles.* Plainfield, NJ: Logos International 1976.

Cassee, Th. P.: Oubevoegde genezers en hun patienten: Afwijkend gedrag in de gezinidheidszerg. *Sociologische Gids* 1970, 17, 399-410.

Cassoli, Piero: *Il Guaritore* (Italian). Milan, Italy: Armenia 1979.

Cassoli, Piero: The healer: Problems, methods and results. *European Journal of Parapsychology* 1981, 4(1), 71-80.

Cavallini, Giuliana: *Saint Martin de Porres.* Rockford, IL: Tan 1979.

Cayce, Hugh Lynn: *Gifts of Healing.* Virginia Beach, VA: Association for Research & Enlightenment, nd. (From Melton).

Cayce, Hugh Lynn (Ed): *The Edgar Cayce Reader [1].* New York: Paperback Library, 1969.

Cayce, Hugh Lynn: *The Edgar Cayce Reader [2].* New York: Paperback Library 1969.

Cerutti, Edwina: *Mystic With the Healing Hands: The Life Story of Olga Worrall.* New York: Harper and Row 1975.

Challoner, H.K.: *The Path of Healing.* Wheaton, IL: Theosophical 1972.

Chapman, George: *Extraordinary Encounters.* Aylesbury, Bucks, England: Lang 1973.

Chase, Edgar: Personal communications 1988.

Chesi, Gert: *Voodoo: Africa's Secret Power* (translated by Klambauer, Ernst). Austria: Perlinger 1980.

Chesi, Gert: *Faith Healers in the Philippines.* Austria: Perlinger 1981.

China Sports Magazine (Ed.): *The Wonders of Qigong: A Chinese Exercise for Fitness, Health and Longevity.* Los Angeles: Wayfarer 1985.

Chopra, Deepak: *Quantum Healing: Exploring the Frontiers of Mind/Body Medicine.* London/ New York: Bantam 1989.

Church, Dawson/ Sherr, Alan: *The Heart of the Healer.* New York: Aslan 1987.

Clark, Philip E./ Clark, Mary Jo: Therapeutic touch: Is there a scientific basis for the practice? *Nursing Research* 1984, 33(1), 37-41.

Coakley, D./ McKenna G.W.: Safety of faith healing. *Lancet* 1986, (8478), 444, February 22.

Coddington, Mary: *In Search of the Healing Energy.* New York: Warner/Destiny 1978.

Cohen, John: Spiritual healing: A complementary role in general practice. *Modern Medicine* 1990 (September), 663-665.

Colinon, M.: *Les Guerisseurs* (French). Paris: Grosset 1957.

Collins, H.M.: *Changing Order, Replication and Induction in Scientific Practice.* London: Sage 1985.

*Collins, J.W.: The Effect of Non-contact Therapeutic Touch on the Relaxation Response. *Unpublished master's thesis,* Vanderbilt University, Nashville, TN 1983. (Quoted from Ferguson).

Collip, P.J.: The efficacy of prayer: A triple blind study. *Medical Times* 1969, 97(5), 201-4.

Constantinides, P.: Women heal women: Spirit possession and sexual segregation in a muslim society. *Social Science in Medicine* 1985, 21 (6), 685-692.`

Cooperstein, M. Allan: The Myths of Healing: A Descriptive Analysis and Taxonomy of Transpersonal Healing Experience. *Unpublished doctoral dissertation,* Saybrook Institute, California 1990.

Cox, W.E.: The influence of 'applied psi' upon the sex of offspring. *Journal of the Society for Psychical Research* 1957, 39, 65-77.

Crenshaw, James: Reverend Fuller's ministry of healing. In: *Fate Magazine; Exploring the Healing Miracle,* Highland Park, IL: Clark 1983, 115-139 (Orig. in: *Fate Magazine,* March/April 1975).

Croke, Piers: A shower of roses. *The Unexplained,* 1981, 3(36), 704-707.

Cuddon, Eric: The relief of pain by laying-on of hands. *International Journal of Parapsychology* 1968, 10(1), 85-92 Also in: Angoff, A. (Ed): *The Psychic Force.* New York: Putnam's 1970.

Cuevedo, Oscar G.: The problem of healers: Part II. (Portuguese). *Revista de Parapsychologia* 1973, 1(4), 4.

Cumbey, Constance: *The Hidden Dangers of the Rainbow.* Shreveport, LA: Huntington House 1984.

Cumbey, Constance: *A Planned Deception.* East Detroit, MI: Pointe 1985.

Davis, Bruce/ Davis, Genny Wright: *The Heart of Healing.* Fairfax, CA: Inner Light 1983.

Davis, Thomas N.: III, Can prayer facilitate healing and growth? *Southern Medical Journal* 1986, 79(6), 733-735.

Davitashvili, Juna: Results in healing: Selected documents. In: Vilenskaya, Larissa (Translator and Editor): *Parapsychology in the USSR, Part III.* San Francisco: Washington Research Center 1981, 55-60.

Davitashvili, Dzhuna: Verification of biotherapy by contemporary technology. *Proceedings of the 5th International Conference on Psychotronic Research* 1983, 2, 12-19.

Dean, Douglas: The plethysmograph as an indicator of ESP. *Journal of the American Society for Psychical Research* 1962, 41, 351-352.

Dean, Douglas: Research in healing: Effects on water. *Presentation at* Workshop on Healing Research at the Combined 100th Society for Psychical Research and 25th

Parapsychologyical Association Meeting, Cambridge, England, August 1982.

*Dean, Douglas: An Examination of Infra-Red and Ultra-Violet Techniques for Changes in Water Following the Laying-on of Hands. *Unpublished doctoral dissertation,* Saybrook Institute, CA 1983.

Dean, Douglas: Personal communication 1985, 1987.

Dean, Douglas: *Presentation at* Scientific and Medical Network Annual Meeting, Dartington 1989.

Dean, Douglas/ Brame, E.: Physical changes in water by laying-on of hands. *Proceedings of the Second International Conference on Psychotronic Research, Monaco 1975,* 200-201.

Dean, S.R./ Plyer, C.O., Jr./ Dean, M.L.: Should psychic studies be included in psychiatric education? *American Journal of Psychiatry* 1980, 137(10), 1247-1249.

Delsanto de Simic, Nelly: Microstructural interactions of biotherapist. *Proceedings of the 6th International Conference on Psychotronics 1986,* 133- 134.

Dethlefsen, Thorwald/ Dahlke, Rüdiger: *The Healing Power of Illness: The Meaning of Symptoms and How to Interpret Them.* Longmead, UK: Element 1990 (Original German 1983, Translation Peter Lerresurier).

Dieckhofer, K. (German): Treatment of epilepsy in the Middle Ages and by Paracelsus: On hagiotherapy and pharmacology in the 'falling disease'. *Fortschritte der Medizin* 1986, 104(11), 232-235.

Dingwall, Eric John: *Abnormal Hypnotic Phenomena: A Survey of 19th Century Cases.* London: Churchill 1968.

Dirksen, Murl Owen: Pentecostal Healing: A Facet of the Personalistic Health System in Pakal-Na, a Village in Southern Mexico. *Unpublished doctoral dissertation,* University TN 1984.

Dobkin de Rios, Marlene: *Visionary Vine: Hallucinogenic Healing in the Peruvian Amazon.* Prospect Heights, KS: Waveland 1972.

Dobkin de Rios, Marlene: The Vidente phenomenon in Third World traditional healing: An Amazonian example. *Medical Anthropology* 1984, Winter, 60-70.

Dobkin de Rios, Marlene: *Hallucinogens: Cross-Cultural Perspectives.* Albuquerque, NM: University of New Mexico 1984(a).

Dong, Paul: *The Four Major Mysteries of Mainland China.* Englewood Cliffs, NJ: Prentice-Hall 1984.

Dossey, Larry: *Space, Time and Medicine.* Boulder, CO: Shambala 1982.

Dowling, St. John: Lourdes cures and their medical assessment. *Journal of the Royal Society of Medicine* 1984, 77, 634-638.

Dresser, Horatio (Ed.): *The Quimby Manuscripts.* New

Hyde Park. New York: University Books 1969.

*Dressler, David: Light touch manipulative technique. *Journal of Alternative and Complementary Medicine* 1990.

Duval, P.: Exploratory experiments with ants (Abstract). *Journal of Parapsychology* 1971, 35, 58.

Edge, Hoyt L.: A philosophical justification for the conformance behavioral model. *Journal of the American Society for Psychical Research* 1978(a), 72, 215-231.

Edge, Hoyt L.: Plant PK on an RNG and the experimenter effect. In: Roll, W.G (Ed.): *Research in Parapschology 1977.* Metuchen, NJ: Scarecrow Press 1978(b), 169-174.

*Edge, Hoyt L.: The effect of laying-on of hands on an enzyme: An attempted replication. In: *Research in Parapsychology, 1979.* Metuchen, NJ: Scarecrow 1980, 137-139.

Edge, Hoyt L., et al.: *Foundations of Parapsychology: Exploring the Boundaries of Human Capability.* Boston & London: Routledge & Kegan Paul 1986.

Edwardes, Phil and McConnell, James, *Healing for You: The Story of Phil Edwardes, a Healer with Remarkable Powers.* Wellingborough, Northamptonshire, England: Thorsons 1985.

Edwards, Harry, *The Science of Spirit Healing.* London: Rider 1945.

Edwards, Harry, *The Evidence for Spirit Healing.* London: Spiritualist Press 1953.

Edwards, Harry, *Thirty Years a Spiritual Healer.* London: Herbert Jenkins 1968.

Ehrenwald, Jan: Parapsychology and the Seven Dragons: A neuropsychiatric model of psi phenomena. In: Schmeidler, Gertrude (Ed.): *Parapsychology: Its Relation to Physics, Biology, Psychology.* Metuchen, NJ: Scarecrow Press 1976(a), 246-263.

Eisenberg, David/ Wright, Thomas Lee: *Encounters with Qi.* New York: W.W. Norton 1985.

Eisenberg, H.: *Inner Spaces: Parapsychological Explorations of the Mind.* Toronto: Musson Book Co. 1977.

Eisenbud, Jule: *The World of Ted Serios.* New York; Pocket Books 1967.

Eisenbud, Jule: *Parasychology and the Unconscious.* North Atlantic Books 1983.

Eisenbud, Jule/ Stillings, Dennis: Paranormal film forms and paleolithic rock engravings. *Archaeus* 1984, 2(1), 9-18; 18-26.

Eliade, Mircea: *Shamanism: Archaic Techniques of Ecstasy* (Translator: W. Trask). London: Routledge and Kegan Paul 1970.

Elliotson, J.: Remarkable cure of intense nervous

[19] Bechterev; Braud 1979; Duval; Etra; Gruber; Nash and Nash 1980; Osis 1952. Review of animal studies in Sulvin 1984.

[20] e.g. Turner Aug. 1969; 1970 (reviewed in Chapter I - 5); Shine.

[21] See Chapter II - 1 on **experimenter effects**.

[22] See discussion on **biofeedback** in Chapter II - 1.

[23] See Chapter I - 3.

[24] In another experiment based on the **conformance hypothesis**, using rye seeds and a random number generator, no statistically significant results were found (Munson).

[25] **Reiki healing**, originating in Japan, is now taught in many parts of the world. See description of Reiki healing in Chapter IV - 1.

[26] See **LeShan** 1974a, reviewed in Chapter IV - 2; healer explanatory systems of LeShan and Goodrich in I - Introduction.

[27] **Subjective sensations during healing** are also noted earlier in this chapter in the experiment with Reiki healers (Schlitz and Braud); also in Turner 1969c, reviewed in Chapter I - 5.

[28] Clark and Clark review some of the same **TT** material and conclude that there is insufficient evidence to support a belief in healing. I agree with Rogo 1986 that Clark and Clark take far too limited a look at the available evidence and, consequently, their conclusions are unwarranted.

[29] See also unpublished Ph.D. dissertation of Heidt 1979, New York University.

[30] Solfvin 1984 mentions the following **unpublished manuscripts on healing research** which I have been unable to obtain: S. B. Harary; Heaton.

[31] Experiment 2 is sketchily described in this article.

[32] **Psi diagnosis** is reported very frequently by healers. Particularly worth reading are Ivanova 1983; Ivanova/Mir; Krieger; Polyakov; Safonov; B. Schwarz; Vu; - regarding the learning and practice of methods of psi diagnosis. Many suggest that **a person may also diagnose his own illness**, such as with cancer, on an unconscious basis, including Dethlefson/Dahlke; Nash 1987. Art therapy and clinical use of drawings (e.g. Kübler-Ross 1981; Siegel 1986) demonstrate a deep awareness of the unconscious mind regard-

ing a person's own health status. Much of the latter is reviewed in Chapter II - 1.

CHAPTER I-5
Uncontrolled Studies

[1] This chapter is clearly more open to **type I errors**, but is meant to counterbalance Chapter I - 4, which is more prone to **type II errors**. See Tunnell for a discussion on the need for field research.

[2] See Chapter I - 1, Footnote 30; Footnote 17 of this chapter for **anecdotal descriptions of healing** not reviewed individually.

[3] See Chapter II - 1 on **hypnosis**.

[4] *Journal of the Statistical Society,* Vol. xxii, p. 355.

[5] See reviews of **Lourdes and other shrine cases** also in Adgnellet; Carrel; Dowling; Fulda; Garner; F. Huxley; Lafitte; Lange; Larcher; Leuret/Bon; McClure; Myers/Myers; Sheldon; Swan; West 1948. See Thornton for Catholic shrines in the USA and Canada. For a review of Lourdes cases, see Dowling; Leuret/Bon; Fulda for a detailed description of a single case. For related cases at other shrines see Lange; McClure; .
Various *geographic locations are said to possess particular powers.* See for instance Westwood for a review of these; also geobiological effects in Chapter II - 4.

[6] These measurements show changes similar to those brought about in water by healers. (Research is summarized in Chapter I - 2.)

[7] A more detailed report on this project, by the same author, has appeared in German in two parts in the *Zeitschrift für Parapsychologie und Grenzgebiete der Psychologie* (Zur Frage der "Geistigen Heilung", Vol. II, No. 1; Vol IV, No. 1).

[8] See review of Turner's views and experiences in Chapter I - 1. **Two Worlds**, still in publication, kindly granted permission for the extensive quotes.

[9] Eisenbud 1967; Eisenbud/Stillings; Fukurai.

[10] e.g. Hochenegg, in Playfair 1988. Hochenegg's attraction of plant leaves visually suggests an electrostatic effect, as when an electrostatically charged rod attracts bits of paper.

affections, etc. *Zoist* 1847-1848, 234-253.

Elliott, G. Maurice: Spiritual healing. *Parapsychology Foundation Newsletter* 1960 (July-August), 4-6.

Engel, Hans G.: *Energy Healing: Research Report.* Los Angeles, CA: Ernest Holmes Research Foundation 1978, 1-15.

England, Ann (Ed): *We Believe in Healing.* Crowborough, England: Highland 1986.

Estebany, Oszkar: Personal communication 1982.

Evans/ Carlton/ Richardson: Improved recovery and reduced post operative stay after therapeutic suggestions during general anaesthesia. *Lancet* 1988, 11, 491-493.

Evans, Hilary: Spontaneous sightings of seemingly autonomous entities: A comparative study in the light of experimental and contrived entity fabrications. *Presentation at* 25th Annual Convention of the Parapsychological Association/100th Convention of the Society for Psychical Research at Cambridge 1982.

Fabrega, Horacio, Jr.: The study of medical problems in preliterate settings. *Yale Journal of Biology and Medicine* 1971, 43, 385-407.

Fabrega, Horacio, Jr.: *Disease and Social Behaviour: An Elementary Exposition.* Cambridge, Massachussets: MIT 1974.

Fadiman, James: The prime cause of healing: The process of exploring and experiencing it. *Journal for Holistic Health* 1977, p.11.

*Fedoruk, Rosalie Berner: Transfer of the Relaxation Response: Therapeutic Touch as a Method for the Reduction of Stress in Premature Neonates. *Unpublished doctoral dissertation,* University of Maryland 1984.

Feild, Reshad: *Here to Heal.* Shaftesbury, England: Element 1985.

Fenwick, Peter/ Hopkins, Roy: An examination of the effect of healing on water. *Journal of the Society for Psychical Research* 1986, 53, 387-390.

Ferda, Frantisek J.: *Paraphysics* 1979, 13(5/6) 129: Abstract-clairvoyant DX and healing at distance of 50 km. *Paper given at* 4th International Congress on Psychotronic Research 1979.

Ferguson, Cecilia Kinsel: Subjective Experience of Therapeutic Touch (SETTS): Psychometric Examination of an Instrument. *Unpublished doctoral dissertation,* University of Texas at Austin 1986.

Finkler, Kaja: *Spiritualist Healers in Mexico.* New York: Praeger 1985.

Flammonde, Paris: *The Mystic Healers.* New York: Stein and Day 1975.

Fodor, Nandor: *On the Trail of the Poltergeist.* New York Citadel Press 1958.

Fodor, Nandor: *Encyclopedia of Psychic Science.* USA: University Books, Inc. 1966. [Large number of people catalogued.]

Frazier, Kendrick: *Science Confronts the Paranormal.* Buffalo, NY: Promethius 1986.

*Fong, Li-da: The effects of external qi on bacterial growth patterns. *China Qi Gong Magazine* 1983, 1, 36 (Quoted in: Eisenberg, David/ Wright, Thomas Lee: *Encounters with Qi,* New York: W.W. Norton 1985, 213.

Freud, Sigmund: *Studies in Parapsychology.* New York: Collier 1963.

Fricker, E.G.: *God is My Witness: The Story of the World-Famous Healer.* London: Eyre and Spottiswoode 1979.

Fry, Daniel W.: *Can God Fill Teeth?* Lakemont, GA: CSA Press 1970.

*Frydrychowski, Andrzej F./ Przyjemska, Bozens/ Orlowski, Tadeusz: An attempt to apply photon emission measurement in the selection of the most effective healer. *Psychotronika* 1985, 82-83. Abstract, translated from Polish by Alexander Imich. In: *Parapsychology Abstracts International* 1987, 5(2), No. 2489.

Fukurai, T.: *Clairvoyance and Thoughtography.* New York: Arno Press 1975.

Fulda, Edeltraud: *And I Shall be Healed: Autobiography of a Woman Miraculously Cured at Lourdes.* New York: Simon and Schuster 1961.

Gagnon, T.A./ Rein, G.: The biological significance of water structured with non-Hertzian time-reversed waves. *Journal of the US Psychotronics Association* 1990 4, 26-29.

Gallimore, J. G.: Relationship Between Parapsychology and Gravity; *V.3 of Handbook of Unusual Energies.* Mokelumne Hill, CA: Health Research 1977.

Galton, F.: Statistical studies into the efficacy of prayer. *Fortnightly Review* 1872, 12, 125-135 (Reprinted in: Roland, C.G.: Does prayer preserve? *Archives of Internal Medicine* 1970, 125, 580-587).

Garcia, Raquel: Healed by a Santera. *Fate, Exploring the Healing Miracle.,* Highland Park, IL: Clark 1983 (Orig. April 1974).

Garcia, Raymond L.: 'Witch doctor?' A hexing case of dermatitis. *Cutis* 1977, 19(1), 103-105.

Gardner, Nancy/ Gardner, Esmond: *Five Great Healers Speak Here.* Wheaton, IL: Quest/ Theosophical 1982. (Reprinted by permission of The Theosophical Publishing House, Wheaton, IL 1982 [Copyright Nancy & Esmond Gardner].)

Gardner, Rex: Miracles of healing in Anglo-Celtic Northumbria as recorded by the Venerable Bede and his contemporaries: A reappraisal in the light of twentieth century experience. *British Medical Journal* 1983

(December 24-31), 287, 1927-1933. Also reviewed in: Rogo, D. Scott: The power of prayer, *Fate* 1986 (August), 43-50.

Garner, Jim: Spontaneous regressions: Scientific documentation as a basis for the declaration of miracles. *Canadian Medical Association Journal* 974, 111, 1254-1264.

Garrett, Eileen Jeanette: *Adventures in the Supernormal: A Personal Memoir.* New York: *Garrett Publications* 1949.

Garrett, Eileen Jeanette: *Life is the Healer.* Philadelphia, PA: Dorrance 1957.

Garrison, Vivian: Doctor, espiritista or psychiatrist? Health-seeking behavior in a Puerto Rican neighborhood of New York City. *Medical Anthropology* 1977, 1, 65-180.

Gauld, Alan: ESP and attempts to explain it. In: Thakur, S. (Ed): *Philosophy and Psychical Research.* London: Allan and Unwin 1976, 17-46.

Gauquelin, Michel: *The Scientific Basis of Astrology: Myth or Reality.* New York: Stein and Day 1969.

Geddes, F.: Healing Training in the Church. *Unpublished Ph.D. dissertation,* San Francisco Theological Seminary 1981.

Geisler, Patrick V.: Batcheldorian psychodynamics in the Umbanda ritual trance consultation; Part I. *Parapsychology Review* 1984, 15(6), 5-9.

Geisler, Patrick V.: Batcheldorian psychodynamics in the Umbanda ritual trance consultation; Part II. *Parapsychology Review* 1985(a), 16(1), 11-14.

Geisler, Patrick V.: Parapsychological anthropology II: A multi-method study of psi and psi-related processes in the Umbanda ritual trance consultation. *Journal of the American Society for Psychical Research* 1985(b), 79(2), 113-166.

Glick, Deborah Carrow: Psychosocial wellness among spiritual healing participants. *Social Science Medicine* 1986, 22(5), 579-586.

Gmur, M./ Tschopp, A.: Factors determining the success of nicotine withdrawal: 12-year follow-up of 532 smokers after suggestion therapy (by a faith healer). *International Journal of the Addictions* 1987, 22(12), 1189-1200.

Goddard, Henry H.: The effects of mind on body as evidenced by faith cures. *American Journal of Psychology* 1899, 10, 431-502.

Goldsmith, Joel S.: *The Art of Spiritual Healing.* New York: Harper and Row 1959.

Golomb, L.: Curing and sociocultural separatism in South Thailand. *Social Science in Medicine* 1985, 21(4), 463-468.

*Goodrich, Joyce: Psychic Healing - A Pilot Study. *Doctoral dissertation,* Graduate School, Yellow Springs,

Ohio 1974.

Goodrich, Joyce: Studies in paranormal healing. *New Horizons* 1976, 2, 21-24.

Goodrich, Joyce: The Psychic Healing Training and Research Project. In: Fosshage, James L./ Olsen, Paul: *Healing: Implications for Psychotherapy.* New York: Human Sciences 1978, 84-110.

Goodrich, Joyce: Personal communication 1982-1985.

Gordon, Richard: *Your Healing hands: The Polarity Experience.* Santa Cruz, CA: Unity Press 1978.

Goss, Michael: *Poltergeists: An Annotated Bibliography of Works in English, circa 1880-1975.* Metuchen, NJ, and London: Scarecrow 1979.

Gough, W.: Joint US-China Experiment on the Effect of External Qi on Molecular Structure Using Raman Spectroscopy. *Unpublished report,* Foundation for Mind-Being, cited in Rein 1992.

Grabiec, S./ Frydrychowski, A.F./ Przyjemska, B.: Photon emission as an indicator of the degree of activation by the 'biofield'. *Psychotronika* 1985, 80-82. (Translated from Polish by Alexander Imich.)

*Grad, Bernard R.: A telekinetic effect on plant growth; I. *International Journal of Parapsychology* 1963, 5(2), 117-134.

*Grad, Bernard R.: A telekinetic effect on plant growth; II. Experiments involving treatment of saline in stoppered bottles. *International Journal of Parapsychology* 1964(a), 6, 473-498.

*Grad, Bernard R.: A telekinetic effect on plant growth; III. Stimulating and inhibiting effects. *Research brief, presented to the* Seventh Annual Convention of the Parapsychological Association, Oxford University, Oxford, England September 1964(b).

*Grad, Bernard R.: Some biological effects of laying-on of hands: A review of experiments with animals and plants. *Journal of the American Society for Psychical Research* 1965(a), 59, 95-127. (Also reproduced in: Schmeidler, Gertrude (Ed): *Parapsychology: Its Relation to Physics, Biology, Psychology and Psychiatry.* Metuchen, NJ: Scarecrow 1976.)

*Grad, Bernard R.: PK effects of fermentation of yeast. *Proceedings of the Parapsychological Association* 1965(b), 2, 15-16.

Grad, Bernard R.: The laying-on of hands: Implications for psychotherapy, gentling and the placebo effect. *Journal of the Society for Psychical Research* 1967, 61(4), 286-305. (Also reviewed in: Schmeidler, Gertrude (Ed.): *Parapsychology: Its Relation to Physics, Biology, Psychology and Psychiatry.* Metuchen, NJ: Scarecrow 1976.)

*Grad, Bernard R./ Cadoret, R.J./ Paul, G.I.: The

influence of an unorthodox method of treatment on wound healing in mice. *International Journal of Parapsychology* 1961, 3, 5-24.

Graves, Charles: *The Legend of Linda Martel.* London: Icon, 1968.

Gray, Isa: *From Materialization to Healing: Evidence of Both.* New York: Regency 1972.

Green, Peter: *Heal, My Son: The Amazing Story of John Cain.* Gerrards Cross, England: Van Duren 1985.

Gregorczuk, Bozena: Combining various methods of assistance in biotherapy. *Proceedings of the 6th International Conference on Psychotronics 1986,* 135- 136.

Gresik, Vlademar: My experience with diagnostics. *Proceedings of the 6th International Conference on Psychotronics 1986,* 124.

Gribbin, John: *Time Warps.* New York: Delacorte/ Eleanor Friede 1979.

Groothuis, Douglas: *Unmasking the New Age.* Downers Grove, IL: Intervarsity.

Gruber, E.R.: Conformance behavior involving animal and human subjects. *European Journal of Parapsychology* 1979, 3(1), 36-50.

*Gulak, Jan: Lowering the anxiety levels in persons undergoing bioenergotherapy. *Psychotronika* 1985, 6-9. (Translated from Polish by Alexander Imich).

*Guo/ Ni: Studies of qi gong in treatment of myopia (nearsightedness). (Cited in: Eisenberg, David/ Wright, Thomas Lee: *Encounters with Qi.* New York: W.W. Norton 1985, 202-203.)

Halifax, Joan, *Shaman: The Wounded Healer.* New York: Crossroads 1982.

Hammond, Sally: *We Are All Healers.* New York: Harper & Row 1973.

Hansel, C.E.M.: *ESP: A Scientific Evaluation.* New York: Charles Scribner's Sons 1966.

Hansen, George: Deception by subjects in psi research. *JASPR* 1990, 84(1), 25-80, 19pp. Refs.

Haraldsson, Erlendur: *Miracles are my Greeting Cards: An Investigative Report on the Psychic Phenomena Associated with Sathya Sai Baba.* London: Century 1987.

Haraldsson, Erlendur/ Olafsson, Orn: A survey of psychic healing in Iceland. *Christian Parapsychologist* 1980, 3(8), 276-279.

*Haraldsson, E./ Thorsteinsson, T.: Psychokinetic effects on yeast: An exploratory experiment. In: Roll, W.C./ Morris, R.L./ Morris, J.D. (Eds): *Research in Parapsychology 1972.* Metuchen, N.J.: Scarecrow Press 1973, 20-21.

Harary, S.B.: A Pilot Study of the Effects of Psychically

Treated Saline Solution on the Growth of Seedlings. *Unpublished manuscript,* Psychical Research Foundation, 1975.

Harman, Willis: *Global Mind Change.* Knowledge Systems 1988.

Harner, Michael: *The Way of the Shaman.* New York: Bantam/ Harper and Row 1980.

Harrison, John: *Love Your Disease, It's Keeping You Healthy.* London: Angus and Robertson 1984.

Harvey, David: Taking the Cain cure. *The Unexplained,* 1982, 9(108), 2154-2157.

Harvey, David: Healing at a stroke. *The Unexplained,* 1983, 13(153), 3046-3049.

Harvey, David: *The Power to Heal: An Investigation of Healing and the Healing Experience.* Wellingborough, Northamptonshire, England: Aquarian 1983.

Harvey, Ruth S.: Three healings to a gallon of tea. In: *Fate Magazine: Exploring the Healing Miracle.* Highland Park, IL: Clark, 1983 (Orig. in: *Fate Magazine* Nov 1978).

Hasted, John: *The Metal-Benders.* Boston: Routledge and Kegan Paul 1981.

Hasted, John B./ Robertson, David/ Arathoon, Peter: PKMB with piezoelectric sensors. In: Roll, William G./ Beloff, John/ White, Rhea: *Research in Parapsychology 1982.* Metuchen, NJ and London: Scarecrow 1983, 39-42.

Hastings, J. (Editor): Ordeal. In: *Encyclopedia of Religion and Ethics,* Vol IX: 507. New York: Scribner's 1955.

Haviland, Denis: Safety of faith healing. *Lancet* 1986 (March 22), 1(8482), 684.

Hay, Louise L.: *You Can Heal Your Life.* Santa Monica, California: Hay House 1984.

Haynes, Renee: *The Hidden Springs: An Enquiry into Extrasensory Perception.* London: Hollis and Carter 1961.

Haynes, Renee: Faith healing and psychic healing: Are they the same? *Parapsychology Review* 1977(a), 8(4), 10-13.

Haynes, Renee: Miraculous and paranormal healing. *Parapsychology Review* 1977(b), 8(5), 25-27.

Heaton, E.: Mouse Healing Experiments. *Unpublished manuscript,* Foundation for Research on the Nature of Man 1974.

Hebda, Hillard: An Inquiry into Unorthodox Healing: Psychic Healing and Psychic Surgery. *M.A. thesis,* Governors State University (Human Learning and Development) 1975. (Abstract from *Parapsychology Abstracts International,* 1983, 1(2), No. 479, 58 Refs.).

*Heidt, Patricia: An Investigation of the Effect of Therapeutic Touch on the Anxiety of Hospitalized Patients. *Unpublished Ph.D. dissertation,* New York University 1979.

*Heidt, Patricia: Effects of therapeutic touch on the anxiety level of hospitalized patient. *Nursing Research* 1981, 30, 30-37.

Heinze, Ruth-Inge: *Trance and Healing in Southeast Asia Today: Twenty-One Case Studies*. Berkeley, CA: University of California 1983.

Heinze, Ruth-Inge (Ed): *Proceedings of the International Conference on Shamanism, St. Sabina Center, San Rafael, CA, 1984*. Berkeley, CA: Center for South and Southeast Asia Studies, University of California May 1984.

Heinze, Ruth-Inge: *Proceedings of the Second International Conference on the Study of Shamanism, San Rafael, CA, 1985*. Berkeley, CA: Center for South and Southeast Asia Studies 1985.

Herbert, Benson/ Alexei Krivorotov: Russian "healer". *Journal of Paraphysics* 1970, 4(4), 112.

Herbert, Benson: Near and distant healing. *Journal of Paraphysics* 1973, 7(5), 213-218.

Herbert, Benson: Theory and practice of psychic healing. *Parapsychology Review* 1975 (November/December), 6, 22-23.

Herbert, Benson: Biogravitation: Experimental evidence. In: *Proceedings of the 4th International Conference on Psychotronic Research, Sao Paulo, Brazil* 1979(b), 149-152.

Herzberg, Eileen: *Spiritual Healing: A Patient's Guide*. Wellingborough, UK: Thorsons 1988.

Heywood, Rosalind: *ESP: A Personal Memoir*. New York: E.P. Dutton 1964.

Hiatt, J.: Spirituality, medicine and healing. *South Medical Journal* 1986, 79(6), 736-743.

Hill, Scott: Paranormal healing in Russia. *Fate* 1981 (August).

Hislop, John S.: *My Baba and I*. San Diego: Birth Day 1985.

Holmes, A. Campbell: *The Facts of Psychic Science*. New Hyde Park, NY: University Books 1969.

Holzer, Hans: *Beyond Medicine: The Facts About Unorthodox and Psychic Healing*. New York: Ballantine/ Random House 1974(b).

Holzer, Hans: *Psychic Healing: All the Facts About the Alternate Way to Good Health and Happiness*. New York: Manor 1979.

Honorton, Charles: Psi and internal attention states. In: Wolman, B.B. (Ed), *Handbook of Parapsychology*. New York: Van Nostrand Reinhold 1977, 435-472.

Hood, Mariya: *Magic Power to Heal*. Hicksville, NY: Exposition 1976.

Horowitz, Kenneth A./ Lewis, Donald C./ Gasteiger, Edgar L.: Plant "primary perception": Electro-physiological unresponsiveness to brine shrimp killing. *Science* 1975, 189, 478-480.

Horstmann, Lorna: *An Introduction to Spiritual Healing*. London: Rider and Co. 1964.

Horstmann, Lorna: *A Handbook of Healing*. Middlesex, England: National Federation of Spiritual Healers, undated pamphlet, purchased 1985.

Houck, Jack: Conceptual model of paranormal phenomena. *Archaeus* 1983, 1(1), 7-24.

Houck, Jack: Psychic healing. *Archaeus Project Newsletter* 1984(a), 3(1), 13-14.

Houck, Jack: PK party history. *Psi Research* 1984(b), 3(1), 67-83.

Houck, Jack: Surface change during warm-forming. *Archaeus* 1984, 2(1), 27-50.

Hsu Ding-ming: *The Chinese Psychic Healing*. Taipei: Parapsychological Association 1984, 6.

Hubacher, John/ Gray, Jack/ Moss, Thelma/ Saba, Frances: A laboratory study of unorthodox healing. In: *Proceedings of the Second International Congress on Psychotronic Research, Monte Carlo, 1975*, 440-44.

Hultkrantz, A.: The shaman and the medicine-man. *Social Science Medicine* 1985, 20(5), 511-515.

Humphrey, Betty M.: Paranormal occurrences among preliterate peoples. *Journal of Parapsychology* 1944, 8, 214-229.

Humphrey, B.M./ Nicol, J.F.: The feeling of success in ESP. *Journal of the American Society for Psychical Research* 1955, 49, 3-37.

Hutton, J. Bernard: *The Healing Power: The Extra-ordinary Spiritual Healing of Mrs. Leah Doctors and 'Dr. Chang,' Her Spirit Guide*. London: Leslie Frewin 1975.

Huxley, Francis: The miraculous Virgin of Guadalupe. *International Journal of Parapsychology* 1959, 1(1), 19-31.

Ikin, Alice Graham: *The Background of Spiritual Healing: Psychological and Religious*. London: Allen and Unwin, 1937.

Ilieva-Even, Yanina: A case of shamanistic healing in Siberia. (Translated by Vilenskaya, Larissa [Ed.], in: *Parapsychology in the U.S.S.R.; Part III*. San Francisco: Washington Research Center 1981, 63-64).

Inglis, Brian: Retrocognitive Dissonance. *Theta* 1986 13/14 (1), 4-9.

Inglis, Brian: *Natural and Supernatural: A History of the Paranormal from Early Times*. England: Hodder and Stoughton 1977.

Irwin, H.J.: Psi, attention and processing capacity. *Journal of the American Society for Psychical Research* 1978, 72, 301-313.

Irwin, H.J.: *Psi and the Mind: An Information Processing*

Approach. Metuchen, NJ: Scarecrow 1979.

Irwin, Harvey J.: *Flight of Mind*. Metuchen, NJ: Scarecrow 1985.

Isaacs, Julian: The Batcheldor approach: Some strengths and weaknesses. *Presented at* 25th Annual Convention of the Parapsychological Association/ 100th Annual Convention of the Society for Psychical Research 1982. (Also published in: *Journal of the American Society for Psychical Research* 1984, 78(2), 123-132.)

Isaacs, Julian: A twelve session study of micro-PKMB training. In: Roll, William G./ Beloff, John/ White, Rhea: *Research in Parapsychology 1982*. Metuchen, NJ, and London: Scarecrow 1983, 31-35.

Isaacs, Julian D.: Psychotherapeutic intervention in piezo-PK training studies. In: Weiner, Debra H./ Radin, Dean I.: *Research in Parapsychology 1985*. Metuchen, NJ, and London: Scarecrow 1986, 175-176.

Ivanova, Barbara: Psycho- and auto-regulation. *International Journal of Paraphysics* 1978, 12(1 & 2), 20-21.

Ivanova, Barbara: Relation of paraphenomena to physical fields. *International Journal of Paraphysics* 1980, 14 (5 and 6), 110-112.

Ivanova, Barbara: Some training experiments in clairvoyance. In: *Proceedings of the 5th International Conference on Psychotronic Research*. Bratislava 1983, 162-167.

Ivanova, Barbara: *The Golden Chalice* (Mir, Maria/ Vilenskaya, Larissa; Eds). San Francisco, CA: H.S. Dakin 1986(a).

Ivanova, Barbara: Incarnation-regressions: Informational, educational and healing effects. *Psi Research* 1986(b), 5(1,2), 16-28.

Ivanova, Barbara: Reincarnation and healing. *Psi Research* 1986(c), 5(1,2), 28-33.

Jackson, Mary E. Mueller: The use of therapeutic touch in the nursing care of the terminally ill person. In: Borelli/ Heidt: *Therapeutic Touch*. New York: Springer 1981.

*Jacobson, Nils/ Wiklund, Nils: Investigation of claims of diagnosing by means of ESP. In: *Research in Parapsychology 1975*. Metuchen, NJ: Scarecrow 1976, 74-76.

Jahn, Robert G.: The persistent paradox of psychic phenomena: An engineering perspective. *Proceedings of the IEEE*. 1982 (February).

Jahn, Robert G./ Dunne, Brenda J.: *The Margins of Reality*. San Diego, CA and London: Harcourt, Brace Jovanovich 1987.

Johnson, P. Youlden: *Healing Fingers: The Power of Yoga Pranic Healing*. New York: Rider 1950.

Joralemon, D.: The role of hallucinogenic drugs and sensory stimuli in peruvian ritual healing. *Cultural*

Medicine and Psychiatry 1984, 8, 399-430.

*Joyce, C.R.B./ Welldon, R.M.C.: The objective efficacy of prayer: A double-blind clinical trial. *Journal of Chronic Diseases* 1965, 18, 367-77.

Jurak, Alois: Curative effects of bioenergy. In: *Proceedings of the 6th International Conference on Psychotronic Research 1986,* 108-110.

Kakar, Sudhir: *Shamans, Mystics and Doctors: A Psychological Inquiry into India and its Healing Traditions*. Boston: Beacon, 1982.

Kanthamani, H./ Kelly, E.F.: Awareness of success in an exceptional subject. *Journal of Parapsychology* 1974, 38, 355-382.

Kaptchuk Ted: *The Web that has no Weaver*. New York: Congdon and Weed 1984.

Kapur, R.L.: The role of traditional healers in mental health care in rural India. *Social Science and Medicine* 1979 (January), 138(1), 27-31.

Karagulla, Shafica/ Kunz, Dora van Gelder: *The Chakras and the Human Energy Field*. Wheaton, IL, Quest/ Theosophical 1989.

Karp, Reba Ann: *Edgar Cayce Encyclopedia of Healing*. New York: Warner 1986.

Katz, Richard: *Boiling Energy: Community Healing Among the Kalahari Kung*. Cambridge, MA: Harvard University 1981.

Keane, P/ Wells, R.: An examination of the menstrual cycle as a hormone related physiological concomitant of psi performance. *Paper presented at* Parapsychological Association Conference, St. Louis 1978.

Keene, M. Lamar (as told to) Spraggett, Allen: *The Psychic Mafia*. New York: Dell 1976.

Keller, Elizabeth Kolbet: Therapeutic touch: A review of the literature and implications of a holistic nursing modality. *Journal of Holistic Nursing* 1984, 2(1), 24-29.

*Keller, Elizabeth/ Bzdek, Virginia M.: Effects of therapeutic touch on tension headache pain. *Nursing Research* 1986, 35, 101-104.

Keni, Ram akant: *Psychic Healing: My Personal Experiences*. Bombay: Somaiya 1981.

Kerewsky-Halpern, B.: Trust, talk and touch in Balkan folk healing. *Social Science Medicine* 1985, 21(3), 319-325.

*Kief, Herman K.: A method for measuring PK with enzymes. In: Roll, W.G./ Morris, R.L./ Morris, J.D. (Eds): *Research in Parapsychology 1972*. Metuchen, NJ: Scarecrow 1973, 19-20.

Kiev, Ari (Ed): *Magic, Faith and Healing: Studies in Primitive Psychiatry Today*. New York: Free Press/ Macmillan 1964.

Kiev, Ari: *Curanderismo: Mexican-American Folk*

Psychiatry. New York: Free Press 1968.

King, George: *You Too Can Heal.* Los Angeles, CA: Aetherius 1976.

King, Serge: *Kahuna Healing: Holistic Health and Healing Practices of Polynesia.* Wheaton, IL: Quest/ Theosophical 1983.

Kirkpatrick, Richard A.: Witchcraft and lupus erythematosus. *Journal of the American Medical Association* 1981, 245, 1937.

Kleinman, Arthur M.:, Some issues for a comparative study of medical healing. *International Journal of Social Psychiatry* 1973, 19(3/4), 160.

Kleinman, Arthur: *Patients and Healers in the Context of Culture: An Exploration of the Borderland Between Antropology, Medicine, and Psychiatry.* Berkeley/ Los Angeles: University of California 1980.

Klos, Jethro: *Back to Eden.* Santa Barbara, CA: Woodbridge 1981.

Kmetz, John M.: An examination of primary perception in plants. *Parapsychology Review* 1975, 6(3), 21.

Kmetz, John M.: A study of primary perception in plant and animal life. *Journal of the American Society for Psychical Research* 1977, 71, 157-168.

*Knowles, F.W.: Some investigations into psychic healing. *Journal of the American Society for Psychical Research* 1954, 48(1), 21-26.

Knowles, F.W.: Psychic healing in organic disease. *Journal of the American Society for Psychical Research* 1956, 50(3), 110-117.

*Knowles, F.W.: Rat experiments and mesmerism. *Journal of the American Society for Psychical Research* 1959, 53, 62-65.

Knowles, F.W.: My experience in psychic healing and parapsychology. *New Zealand Medical Journal* 1971, 74, 328-331.

Ko Wen-hsiung: Superstition or ancient wisdom? *Fate* 1988 (February), 56-63.

Koestler, Arthur: *The Case of the Midwife Toad.* New York: Random House 1971.

Korth, Leslie O.: *Healing Magnetism: The Power Behind Contact Therapy.* Wellingborough, Northamptonshire, England: Thorsons 1974.

Koss, J.D.: Expectations and outcomes for patients given mental health care or spiritist healing in Puerto Rico. *American Journal of Psychiatry* 1987, 144(1), 56-61.

Kowey, Peter R./ Friehling, Ted D./ Marinchak, Roger A.: Prayer meeting cardioversion. *Annals of Internal Medicine* 1986, 104(5), 727-728.

Kraft, Dean: *Portrait of a Psychic Healer.* New York: G.P.

Putnams's Sons 1981. (Quotes reprinted by permission of author, copyright Dean Kraft.)

Kreitler, Hans/ Kreitler, Shulamith: Subliminal perception and extrasensory perception. *Journal of Parapsychology* 1973, 37, 163-188.

*Krieger, Dolores: The relationship of touch, with intent to help or to heal, to subjects' in-vivo hemoglobin values. In: *American Nurses' Association 9th Nursing Research Conference, San Antonio, TX, 1973.* Kansas City, MO: American Nurses' Association 1974, 39-58.

*Krieger, Dolores: Therapeutic touch: The imprimatur of nursing. *American Journal of Nursing* 1975, 7, 784-787.

*Krieger, Dolores: Healing by the laying-on of hands as a facilitator of bioenergetic change: The response of in-vivo human hemoglobin. *Psychoenergetic Systems* 1976, 1, 121-129.

Krieger, Dolores: *The Therapeutic Touch: How to Use Your Hands to Help or Heal.* Englewood Cliffs, NJ: Prentice-Hall 1979.

Krieger, Dolores: *Foundations for Holistic Health Nursing Practices: The Renaissance Nurse.* Philadelphia: J.P. Lippincott 1981.

Krieger, Dolores: *Living the Therapeutic Touch.* New York: Dodd Mead 1987.

Krieger, Dolores/ Peper, Eric/ Ancoli, Sonia: Therapeutic touch. *American Journal of Nursing,* 1979 (April), 660-665.

Krippner, Stanley: Investigations of 'extrasensory' phenomena in dreams and other altered states of consciousness. *Journal of the American Society of Psychosomatic Dentistry and Medicine* 1969, 16(1), 7-14.

Krippner, Stanley: Research in paranormal healing: Paradox and promise. *American Society for Psychical Research Newsletter* 1973, 19.

Krippner, Stanley: A suggested typology of folk healing and its relevance for parapsychological investigation. *Journal of the Society for Psychical Research* 1980(b), 50(786), 491-499.

Krippner, Stanley: A questionnaire study of experiential reactions to a Brazilian healer. *Journal of the Society for Psychical Research* 1990, 56, 208-215.

Krippner, Stanley/ Solfvin, Gerald: *Psychic Healing: A Research Survey.* 1984, 3(2), 16-28.

Krippner, Stanley/ Villoldo, Alberto: Spirit healing in Brazil. *Fate* 1976 (March).

Krippner, Stanley/ Villoldo, Alberto: *The Realms of Healing.* Millbrae, CA: Celestial Arts 1976; 3rd. Ed. Rev. 1986.

Krippner, Stanley/ Welch, Patrick: *Spiritual Dimensions of Healing: From Native Shamanism to Contemporary*

Health Care. New York: Irvington 1992.

Krivorotov, Victor: Some issues of bioenergetic therapy. In: Vilenskaya, Larissa (Translator and Editor): *Parapsychology in the USSR, Part III*. San Francisco: Washington Research Center 1981, 30-41.

Krivorotov, Victor K./ Krivorotov, Alexei E./ Krivorotov, Vladimir K.: Bioenergotherapy and healing. *Psychoenergetic Systems* 1974, 1, 27-30.

*Kuang, Ankun, et al.: Long-term observation on qigong in prevention of stroke: Follow-up of 244 hypertensive patients for 18-22 years. *Journal of Traditional Chinese Medicine* 1986, 6(4), 235-238. (Also in: Kuang, A.K., et al.: Comparative study of clinical effects and prognosis of 204 hypertensive patients treated with qigong in 20 years of follow-up and its mechanisms. *Chinese Integration of Traditional and Western Medicine* 1986, 1, 9.)

Kübler-Ross, Elisabeth: *Living with Death and Dying*. New York: Macmillan 1981; London: Souvenir 1982.

Kuhn, Thomas S.: *The Structure of Scientific Revolutions*. The University of Chicago Press, Vol II, No.2, 1962, 1970.

Kuhlman, Kathryn: *I Believe in Miracles*. New York: Pyramid 1969.

Kunz, Dora: *Healing Seminar*. Pumpkin Hollow, 1982.

Kurtz, Paul: *The Transcendental Temptation: A Critique of Religion and the Paranormal*. Buffalo, New York: Promethius 1986.

Lafitte, G.: The Lourdes cures: Osteo-articular disorders. In: Flood (Ed): *New Problems in Medical Ethics*. Cork 1953 (from West, D.J.: *Eleven Lourdes Miracles*, p.9; London 1957). [Instantaneous cure]

Landy, David: *Culture, Disease and Healing: Studies in Medical Anthropology*. New York: Macmillan 1977.

Lange, Walter R.: *Healing Miracles: The Story of the St. Rupertus Spring and its Miraculous, Health-Giving Water*. Brooklyn, NY: Walter R. Lange 1977.

Larcher, Hubert: Sacred places and paranormal cures. *Revue Metapsychique* 1981, 15(4), 19-28.

LeCron, Leslie: Hypnosis and ESP. *Psychic* 1970 (August).

Lee, C.: Qigong (breath exercise) and its major models. *Chinese Culture* 1983, 24(3), 71-79.

Leek, Sybil: *The Story of Faith Healing*. New York: Macmillan, 1973.

Leichtman, Robert R.: Afterword to the gift of healing. *Journal of Holistic Medicine* 1986, 8(1,2),67-78.

*Leikam, W.C.: A pilot study on the psychic influence of E. coli bacteria. *Unpublished manuscript,* 1981.

*Lenington, Sandra: Effects of holy water on the growth of radish plants. *Psychological Reports* 1979, 45, 381-

382. (Abstract in: *Journal of Parapsychology,* 1980, 44, 386-7.)

LeShan, Lawrence: *The Medium, The Mystic and The Physicist: Toward a General Theory of the Paranormal*. New York: Ballantine 1974(a); British edition - *Clairvoyant Reality*. Wellingborough, England: Thorsons. (Copyright 1966, 1973, 1974 by Lawrence LeShan. Quotations by permission of Viking Penguin, Inc.).

LeShan, Lawrence: *Alternate Realities*. New York: Ballantine 1976.

LeShan, Lawrence/ Margenau, Henry: An approach to a science of psychical research. *Journal of the Society for Psychical Research* 1980, 50, 273-283.

LeShan, Lawrence/ Margenau, Henry: *Einstein's Space and Van Gogh's Sky*. New York: Macmillan 1982.

Leuret, Francois/ Bon, Henri: *Modern Miraculous Cures: A Documented Account of Miracles and Medicine in the 20th Century*. New York: Farrar, Straus and Cudahy 1957.

Levesque, G.V.: *Miracle Cures for the Millions*. New York: Bell Publishing Company.

Lin, Kuo: *A New Methodology of Qigong Applied in Cancer Treatment*. Shanghai: The Scientific Press 1981.

*Lionberger, Harriet Jacqueline: An Interpretive Study of Nurses' Practice of Therapeutic Touch. *Unpublished doctoral dissertation,* University of California, San Francisco 1985.

*Liscia, Julio C. di: Psychic healing: An attempted investigation. *Psi Comunicacion* 1977, 3(5/6), 101-110 (Abstract, translated from Spanish. In: *Parapsychology Abstracts International* 1984, 2(1), 82, Abstr. No. 669).

Lloyd, D.H.: Objective events in the brain correlating with psychic phenomena. *New Horizon* 1973, 1, 69-75.

Locker, Leonard: *Healing All and Everything*. Shaftesbury, England: Element 1985.

Loehr, Franklin: *The Power of Prayer on Plants*. New York: Signet 1969.

Lombardi, Ethel: Personal communications 1981, 1984.

Long, Joseph K.: *Extrasensory Ecology: Parapsychology and Anthropology*. Metuchen, NJ, and London: Scarecrow 1977.

Long, Max Freedom: *The Secret Science Behind Miracles*. Marina del Rey, CA: DeVorss 1976 (Orig. 1948).

Long, Max Freedom: *Recovering the Ancient Magic*. Cape Girardeau, MO: Huna 1978 (Orig. 1936).

*MacDonald, R./ Dakin, H. S./ Hickman, J. L.: Preliminary studies with three alleged "psychic healers". In: Morris, J.D./ Roll, W.G./ Morris, R.L (Eds): *Research in Parapsychology 1976*. Metuchen, NJ, and London: Scarecrow 1977.

MacManaway, Bruce/ Turcan, Johanna: *Healing: The*

Energy that can Restore Health. Wellingsborough, England: Thorsons 1983.

MacRobert, R.G.: When is healing "psychic"? *Tomorrow* 1955, 3(3), 47-55.

Magaray, Christopher: Healing and meditation in medical practice. *Medical Journal Australia* 1981, 1, 338-341.

Manning, Matthew: *The Link.* New York: Holt, Rinehart and Winston, 1974.

Markides, Kyriakos: *The Magus of Strovolos: The Extraordinary World of a Spiritual Healer.* London & Boston: Arkana 1985.

Markides, Kyriakos: *Homage to the Sun: The Wisdom of the Magus of Strovolos.* New York & London: Arkana 1987.

Markides, Kyriakos C.: *Fire in the Heart: Healers, Sages and Mystics.* London: Arkana/Penguin 1991.

McCaffery, John: *Tales of Padre Pio, The Friar of San Giovannni.* Garden City, NY: Image/ Doubleday 1981. (Orig. *The Friar of San Giovanni.* U.K.: Darton, Longman & Todd 1978.)

McCarthy, Donald/ Keane, Patrice/ Tremmel, Lawrence: Psi phenomena in low complexity systems: Conformance behavior using seeds. In: Roll, W.G (Ed): *Research in Parapsychology 1978.* Metuchen, NJ, and London: Scarecrow 1979, 82-84.

McClure, Kevin: Miracles of the Virgin. *The Unexplained,* 1983, 11(131), 2614-2617.

McConnell, Robert/ Kuzmen Clark, Thelma: The enemies of parapsychology. *Presentation at* 33rd Annual Meeting of the Parapsychological Association, Chevy Chase, MD, 1990.

McCullough, J.: Plants and people: Some exploratory experiments. *Parascience Proceedings* 1973, 39-42.

McDougall, W.: Fourth report on a Lamarckian experiment. *British Journal of Psychology* 1938, 28, 321-345.

McGarey, William A.: *The Edgar Cayce Remedies.* New York: Bantam, 1983.

McRae, Ron: *Mind Wars: The True Story of Secret Government Research into the Military Potential of Psychic Weapons.* New York: St. Martin's, 1984.

The Medical Group: *The Mystery of Healing.* Wheaton, IL: Theosophical 1958. (Republished under authorship of the Theosophical Society 1983.)

*Meehan, T.C.: An Abstract of the Effect of Therapeutic Touch on the Experience of Acute Pain in Post-operative Patients. *Unpublished doctoral dissertation,* New York University 1985. (From Summary in: Lionberger, H.J.: An *Interpretive Study of Nurses' Practice of Therapeutic Touch.* San Francisco 1985.)

Meek, G.W.: *Healers and the Healing Process.* Wheaton, IL: Theosophical Publishing House 1977. (Quotes reprinted by permission of publisher. Copyright George W. Meek, 1977.)

Mesmer, Franz Anton: *Mesmerism: A Translation of the Original Medical and Scientific Writings of F.A. Mesmer, M.D.* (Trans. by Bloch, George J.). Los Altos, CA: William Kaufmann 1980.

*Metta, Louis (Pseud.): Psychokinesis on Lepidoptera larvae. *Journal of Parapsychology* 1972, 36, 213-221.

Mialowska, Zofia: Statistical assessment of Jerzy Rejmer's biotherapeutical activity at an Izis clinic in Warsaw. In: *Proceedings of the 6th International Conference on Psychotronic Research 1986,* 130-132.

Millar, B.: The observational theories: A primer. *European Journal of Parapsychology* 1978, 2, 304-332.

Miller, Casper J.: *Faith-Healers in the Himalayas.* Kathmandu, Nepal: Sahayogi 1979.

Miller, Lynn: An explanation of therapeutic touch using the science of unitary man. *Nursing Forum* 1979, 18(3), 278-287.

Miller, Paul: *Born to Heal: A Biography of Harry Edwards, the Spirit Healer.* London: Spiritualist Press 1969 (Orig. 1948).

*Miller, Robert N.: The Relationship Between the Energy State of Water and Its Physical Properties. *Research paper,* Ernest Holmes Research Foundation (undated).

Miller, Robert N.: Paraelectricity, a primary energy. *Human Dimensions* (undated) V.5(1 & 2), 22-26 (Also reported in: Miller, 1977).

Miller, Robert N.: The positive effect of prayer on plants. *Psychic* 1972, 3(5), 24-25.

*Miller, Robert: Methods of detecting and measuring healing energies. In: White, John/ Krippner, Stanley: *Future Science.* Garden City, NY: Anchor/Doubleday 1977.

* Miller, Robert N.: Study on the effectiveness of remote mental healing. *Medical Hypotheses* 1982, 8, 481-490. (Also reviewed briefly in: Maddock, Peter: International Parascience Institute: Toronto and London Conferences, 1981. *Parapsychology Review* 1982, 13(4), 7.)

Miller, Robert N./ Reinhart, Philip B./ Kern, Anita: Scientists register thought energy. *Science of Mind* 1974, July, 12-16.

Miller, Ronald N.: The Healing magic of crystals: An interview with Marcel Vogel. *Science of Mind,* 1984, August, 8-12.

Mills, Janet Melanie Ailsa: (Pseudonym Challoner), *The Path of Healing.* Wheaton IL: Quest/ Theosophical, 1976.

Mintz, Elizabeth E./ Schmeidler, Gertrude R.: *The*

Psychic Thread. New York: Human Sciences 1983.

Mir, Maria/ Vilenskaya, Larissa: *The Golden Chalice.* San Francisco, CA: H.S. Dakin.

*Mison, Karel: Statistical processing of diagnostics done by subject and by physician. In: *Proceedings of the 6th International Conference on Psychotronic Research 1986,* 137-138.

Montagno, Elson A. de: Clinical parapsychology: The spiritist model in Brazil. In: Weiner, Debra H./ Radin, Dean I. (Eds): *Research in Parapsychology 1985.* Metuchen, NJ, and London: Scarecrow 1986, 171-172.

Montgomery, Ruth: *Born to Heal.* New York: Popular Library 1973.

Moore, Marcia: *Hypersentience.* New York: Bantam 1976.

Morley, Peter/ Wallis, Roy (Eds): *Culture and Curing.* Pittsburgh, PA: University of Pittsburgh, 1978.

Morris, Robert L.: Book review: Alcock, James E., Parapsychology: Science or Magic? *Journal of the American Society for Psychical Research* 1982, 76(2), 177-185.

Moss, Richard: *The Black Butterfly: An Invitation to Radical Aliveness.* Berkeley, California: Celestial Arts 1986.

Moss, Thelma: *The Probability of the Impossible.* Bergenfield, NJ: New American Library 1974.

Moss, Thelma: *The Body Electric.* New York: St. Martin's 1979.

Moss, Vere: Non-physical factors in medical divination and treatment. *Journal of the British Society of Dowsers* 1968, 20, 288-292.

Motoyama, Hiroshi: *Science and the Evolution of Consciousness, Ki and Psi.* Autumn Press 1978.

Munson, R. J.: The effects of PK on rye seeds (Abstract). *Journal of Parapsychology* 1979, 43, 45.

Murphet, H.: *Sai Baba, Man of Miracles.* Avatar, India: Macmillan 1972.

Murphet, H.: *Sai Baba.* Avatar, India: Macmillan 1978.

Murphy, Gardner: *Challenge of Psychical Research: A Primer of Parapsychology.* New York: Harper/ Colophon 1970.

Murphy, Joseph: *How to Use Your Healing Power.* San Gabriel, CA: Willing, 1957.

Myers, A.T./ Myers, F.W.H.: Mind-cure, faith-cure and the miracles of Lourdes. *Proceedings of the Society for Psychical Research* 1894, 9, 160-209.

Nanko, Michael J.: A report on the case investigation of Natuzza Evolo. *Journal of the Southern California Society for Psychical Research* 1985, 3, 6-27.

Naranjo, Claudio/ Ornstein, Robert E.: *On the Psychology of Meditaton.* New York: Penguin 1977.

Nash, Carroll B.: Medical parapsychology. In: White, R. A.: *Surveys in Parapsychology.* Metuchen, NJ: Scarecrow 1976 (Orig. in: *Parapsychology Review* 1972, 3, 13-18).

Nash, Carroll B.: *Science of Psi: ESP and PK.* Springfield, IL: C.C. Thomas 1978. (See also Nash, 1986).

*Nash, Carroll B.: Psychokinetic control of bacterial growth. *Journal of the Society for Psychical Research* 1982, 51, 217-221.

*Nash, Carroll B.: Test of psychokinetic control of bacterial mutation. *Journal of the American Society for Psychical Research* 1984, 78(2), 145-152.

Nash, Carroll B.: *Parapsychology: The Science of Psiology.* Springfield, IL: Charles C. Thomas 1986. (See also Nash, 1978.)

Nash, Carroll B.: The possible detection of cervical cancer by ESP. *Journal of the Society for Psychical Research* 1987, 54, 143-144.

*Nash, C.B./ Nash, C.S.: The effect of paranormally conditioned solution on yeast fermentation. *Journal of Parapsychology* 967, 31, 314.

Nash, C.B./ Nash, C.S.: Psi-influenced movement of chicks and mice onto a visual cliff. In: Roll, W.G./ Beloff, J. (Eds): *Research in Parapsychology 1980* Metuchen, NJ: Scarecrow, 1981, 109-110.

Nash, June: The logic of behavior: Curing in a Maya Indian town. *Human Organization* 1967, 26(3), 132-140.

Neher, Andrew: *The Psychology of Transcendence.* Englewood Cliffs, New Jersey: Spectrum/ Prentice Hall 1980.

Neppe, Vernon Michael: Anomalous smells in the subjective paranormal experiment. *Psychoenergetics* 1983, 5, 11-28.

Neppe, Vernon M.: *The Psychology of Deja Vu: Have I Been Here Before?* Johannesburg, South Africa: Witwatersrand University Press 1983.

Nerem, Robert M./ Levesque, H.E./ Murina J./ Cornhill, J. Fedrick: Social environment as a factor in diet-induced atherosclerosis. *Science* 1980-208, 1475-1476.

Newton-Smith, W.H.: *The Structure of Time.* London: Routledge and Kegan Paul, 1984.

*Nicholas, Chris: The effects of loving attention on plant growth. *New England Journal of Parapsychology* 1977, 1, 19-24.

Nichols, Beverley: *Powers that Be.* New York: St. Martin's, 1966.

Nixon, F.: *Born to be Magnetic, Vol. 1.* Chemainus, British Columbia: Magnetic 1971.

Nolen, W.A.: *Healing: A Doctor in Search of a Miracle.* New York: Random House 1974.

*Null, Gary: Healers or hustlers? Part IV. *Self Help Update,* Spring 1981, p. 18.

Oakley, D.V./ MacKenna, G.W.: Safety of faith healing. *Lancet* 1986, (February 22) 444.

Omananda, Swami: *The Boy and the Brothers.* New York: Doubleday, 1960.

*Onetto, Brenio/ Elguin, Gita H.: Psychokinesis in experimental tumorgenesis. (Abstract of dissertation in psychology, University of Chile 1964.) *Journal of Parapsychology* 1966, 30, 220. (Also in Spanish, in: *Acta Psiquiatrica y Psicologia America Latina* 1968, 14, 47. See also brief comments of Campbell, Anthony, in: *Journal of the Society for Psychical Research* 1968, 44, 428).

Orsi, R.A.: The cult of the saints and the reimagination of the space and time of sickness in twentieth-century American Catholicism. *Literature and Medicine* 1989, 8, 63-77.

Osis, Karlis: A test of the occurrence of psi effect between man and cat. *Journal of Parapsychology* 1952, 16, 233-256.

Osis, Karlis/ Bokert, Edwin: ESP and changed states of consciousness induced by meditation. *Journal of the American Society for Psychical Research* 1971, 65, 17-65.

Ostrander, Sheila/ Schroeder, Lynn: *Psychic Discoveries Behind the Iron Curtain.* New York: Bantam 1970.

Osumi, Ikuko/ Ritchie, Malcolm: *The Shamanic Healer: The Healing World of Ikuko Osumi and the Traditional Art of Seiki-Jutsu.* London: Century 1987.

Oubre, Alondra: Shamanic trance and the placebo effect: The case for a study in psychobiological anthropology. *Psi Research* 1985, 5 (1/2),116-144.

Oursler, Will: *The Healing Power of Faith.* Hawthorn Books, New York 1957.

Owen, Iris M./ Sparrow, Margaret: *Conjuring Up Philip: An Adventure in Psychokinesis.* New York: Harper and Row 1976.

Oye, Robert/ Shapiro, Martin: Reporting results from chemotherapy trials. *Journal of the American Medical Association* 1984, 252, 2722-2725.

Packer, Rhonda: Sorcerers, Medicine-Men and Curing Doctors: A Study of Myth and Symbol in North American Shamanism. *Unpublished doctoral dissertation,* UCLA 1983.

Palmer, J.: Scoring in ESP tests as a function of belief in ESP: Part I. The sheep-goat effect. *Journal of the American Society for Psychical Research* 1971, 65, 373-408.

Palmer, John A./ Honorton, Charles/ Utts, Jessica: *Reply to the National Research Council Study on Parapsychology.* Research Triangle Park, NC:

Parapsychological Association 1988.

Parapsychology Foundation (Ed): *Proceedings of Four Conferences of Parapsychological Studies.* New York: Parapsychology Foundation 1957, 43-65. (Includes brief discussions of Bender, H., Booth, G., Eisenbud, J., Larcher, H., Moser, U., Saller, K., Servadio, E., Thouless, R. and Van Lennep, D., on the state of knowledge of healing at that date.)

*Parkes, Brenda Sue: Therapeutic Touch as an Intervention to Reduce Anxiety in Elderly Hospitalized Patients. *Unpublished doctoral dissertation,* University of Texas at Austin 1985.

Patrovsky, V.: On the bioactivation of water. *International Journal of Paraphysics* 1978, 12(5 & 6), 130-132.

Patrovsky, V.: Healers, water and force fields. In: *Proceedings of the 4th International Conference on Psychotronic Research, Sao Paulo, Brazil 1979,* 42- 43.

Patrovsky, V.: Effect of some force field on physical properties of water and some salt solutions. In: *Proceedings of the 5th International Conference on Psychotronic Research, Bratislava 1983,* 88-95.

Pattison, E. et al.: Faith healing. *Journal of Nervous and Mental Diseases* 1973, 156, 397-409.

*Pauli, Enrique Novillo: PK on living targets as related to sex, distance and time. In: Roll, W.G./ Morris, R.L./ Morris, J.D. (Eds): *Research in Parapsychology.* Metuchen, NJ: Scarecrow 1973, 68-70.

Pavlov, Ivan: *Conditioned Reflexes and Psychiatry.* New York: International Publishers 1941.

Pearson, K.: *The Life, Letters and Labours of Francis Galton.* Cambridge, UL: Cambridge University 1924-1930.

Pederson-Krag, Geraldine: Telepathy and repression. *Psychoanalytic Quarterly* 1947, 16, 61-68.

Persinger, Michael A.: Subjective telepathic experiences: Geomagnetic activity and the ELF hypothesis: Part II. Stimulus features and neural detection. *Psi Research* 1985, 4(2), 4-23.

Persinger, Michael A.: Spontaneous telepathic experiences from phantasms of the living and low global geomagnetic activity. *Journal of the American Society for Psychical Research* 1987, 81(1), 23-36.

Peterson, James W.: Extrasensory abilities of children: An ignored reality? *Learning* 1975 (December), 10-14.

Peterson, James W.: *The Secret Life of Kids: An Exploration into Their Psychic Senses.* Wheaton, IL: Quest/ Theosophical 1987.

Peters, Larry: *Ecstasy and Healing in Nepal.* Malibu, CA: Undena 1981.

Peters, Larry/ Price-Williams: Towards an experiential

analysis of shamanism. *American Ethnologist* 1980, 7 (3), 379-413.

Pfeiffer, Tomas: Personal communication about J. Zezulka, 1991.

Phoenix: New Directions in the Study of Man. Journal of the Association for Transpersonal Anthropology.

Pierrakos, John C.: *Human Energy Systems Theory: History and New Growth Perspectives.* New York: Institute For the New Age of Man 1976.

Pierrakos, John C.: *Core Energetics: Developing the Capacity to Love and Heal.* Mandocino, CA: LifeRhythm 1987.

Playfair, Guy Lyon: *The Unknown Power.* New York: Pocket 1975.

Playfair, Guy Lyon: Twenty years among the tables. *Psi Research,* 1985a, 4(1), 96-107.

Playfair, Guy Lyon: *If This Be Magic.* London: Jonathan Cape 1985b.

Playfair, Guy Lyon: *Medicine, Mind and Magic: The Power of the Mind-Body Connection in Hypnotism and Healing.* Wellingborough, Northamptonshire, England: Aquarian/ Thorsons 1987.

Playfair, Guy Lyon: Austria's medical shocker. *Fate* 1988 (Septembre), 41(9), 42-48.

*Pleass, C.M./ Dey, D.N.: Using the Doppler effect to study behavioral responses of motile algae to psi stimulus. In: Radin, D. I. (Ed): *Proceedings of Presented Papers: Parapsychological Association 28th Annual Convention.* Alexandria, VA: Parapsychological Association 1985, 373-405

*Pleass, C.M./ Dey, Dean: Conditions that appear to favor extrasensory interactions between Homo sapiens and microbes. *Journal of Scientific Exploration* 1990, 4(2) 213-231.

Podmore, Frank: Poltergeists. *Proceedings of the Society for Psychical Research* 1896, 12, 45-115.

Pollack, Jack Harrison: *Croiset: The Clairvoyant.* Garden City, NY: Doubleday 1964.

Polyakov, Vadim: *Extrasensory Praxis,* Translation of Russian booklets on work in St Petersburg - seeking publisher - and personal communication 1992.

Ponder, Catherine: *The Dynamic Laws of Healing.* Marina Del Rey, CA: De Vorss 1966.

Poulton, Kay: *Harvest of Light: A Pilgrimage of Healing.* London: Regency 1968.

Pratt, Gaither J.: *ESP Research Today: A Study of Developments in Parapsychology since 1960.* Metuchen, NJ: Scarecrow 1973.

Prince, Raymond: Fundamental differences of

psychoanalysis and faith healing. *International Journal of Psychiatry* 1972, 10(1), 125-128.

Puharich, Andrija: Pachita: Instant surgeon. *The Unexplained* 1983, 13 (154), 3074-3077.

Pulos, Lee: Evidence of macro-psychokinetic effects produced by Thomas of Brazil. *Psi Research* 1982, 1(3), 27-40.

*Purska-Rowinska, Ewa/ Rejmer, Jerzy: The effect of bio-energotherapy upon EEG tracings and on the clinical picture of epileptics. *Psychotronika* 1985, 10-12 (translated from Polish by Alexander Imich).

Puthoff, Harold/ Targ, Russell: PK experiments with Uri Geller and Ingo Swann. In: Roll, W.G./ Morris, R.L./ Morris, J.D. (Eds): *Research in Parapsychology 1973.* Metuchen, NJ: Scarecrow 1974, 125-128.

Puthoff, H.E./ Targ, R.A.: A perceptual channel for information transfer over kilometer distances: Historical perspective and Recent Research. In: *Proceedings of the IEEE* 1976, 64, 329-354 (cited in Schaut and Persinger).

Quinn, Janet F.: One nurse's evolution as a healer. *American Journal of Nursing* 1979 (April), 662-665.

*Quinn, Janet F.: An Investigation of the Effect of Therapeutic Touch Without Physical Contact on State Anxiety of Hospitalized Cardiovascular Patients. *Unpublished Ph.D. Thesis,* New York University 1982.

Quinn, Janet F.: Building a body of knowledge: Research on therapeutic touch 1974-1986. *Journal of Holistic Nursing* 1988, 6(1), 37-45.

*Quinn, Janet F.: Therapeutic touch as energy exchange: Replication and extension. *Nursing Science Quarterly* 1989(a), 2(2), 79-87.

Quinn, Janet F.: Future directions for therapeutic touch research. *Journal of Holistic Nursing* 1989(b), 7(1), 19-25.

*Randall, J.L.: An attempt to detect psi effects with protozoa. *Journal of the Society for Psychical Research* 1970, 45, 294-296.

Randi, James: "Be healed in the name of god!" An expose of the Reverend W.V. Grant. *Free Inquiry* 1986 (Spring), 8-19.

Randi, James: *The Faith Healers.* Buffalo, NY: Promethius 1987.

*Randolph, Gretchen Lay: The Differences in Physiological Response of Female College Students Exposed to Stressful Stimulus, when Simultaneously Treated by Either Therapeutic Touch or Casual Touch. *Unpublished Ph.D. dissertation,* New York University 1979. (Summary from Quinn 1982).

*Randolph, Gretchen Lay: Therapeutic and physical touch: Physiological response to stressful stimuli. *Nursing Research* 1984, 33(1), 33-36.

Rao, Kanthamani/ Puri, I.: Subsensory perception (SSP), extrasensory perception (ESP) and meditation. In: *Research in Parapsychology 1976*. Metuchen, NJ: Scarecrow 1977. p. 77-79.

Rao, Ramakrishna: On the nature of psi: An examination of some attempts to explain ESP and PK. *Journal of Parapsychology* 1977, 41, 294-351.

Raphaell, Katrina: *Crystal Healing Volume II*. New York: Aurora 1987.

Raucheisen, Mary L.: Therapeutic touch: Maybe there's something to it after all. *R.N.* 1984, 47(12), 49-51.

Rauscher, Elizabeth A.: The physics of psi phenomena in space and time: Part I. Major principles of physics, psychic phenomena and some physical models. *Psi Research* 1983, 2(2), 64-87; Part II. Multidimensional geometric models. *Psi Research* 1983, 2(3), 93-120.

Rauscher, Elizabeth: Psi applications: Alternative healing techniques in Brazil. *Psi Research* 1985, 4(1), 57-65.

* Rauscher, Elizabeth A./ Rubik, Beverly, A.: Effects on motility behavior and growth of Salmonella typhimurium in the presence of a psychic subject. In: *Research in Parapsychology 1979*. Metuchen, NJ: Scarecrow 1980.

Rauscher, Elisabeth A./ Rubik, Beverly A.: Human volitional effects on a model bacterial system. *Psi Research* 1983, 2(1), 38-48. (Also summarizes Rauscher and Rubik, 1979.)

Rawnsley, Marilyn M.: Health: A Rogerian perspective. *Journal of Holistic Nursing* 1985, 2, 25-29.

Ray, Barbara Weber: *The Reiki Factor*. Smithtown, NY: Exposition 1983.

Regan, Georgina/ Shapiro, Debbie: *The Healer's Handbook: A Step by Step Guide to Developing Your Latent Healing Abilities*. Dorset, England: Element 1988.

Regush, Nicholas M. (Ed): *Frontiers of Healing: New Dimensions in Parapsychology*. New York: Avon 1977.

Rehder, H.: Wunderheilungen, ein Experiment (German). *Hippokrates* 1, 26, 577- 580. (Quoted in: Frank, J.: *Persuasion and Healing*. New York: Schocken 1961.)

Reilly, Harold J./ Brod, Ruth Hagy: *The Edgar Cayce Handbook for Health Through Drugless Therapy*. New York: Jove 1979.

*Rein, Glen: An exosomatic effect on neurotransmitter metabolism in mice: A pilot study. *Second International Society for Parapsychological Research Conference*, Cambridge, England 1978.

*Rein, Glen: A psychokinetic effect of neurotransmitter metabolism: Alterations in the degradative enzyme monoamine oxidase. In: Weiner, Debra H./ Radin, Dean (Eds): *Research in Parapsychology 1985*. Metuchen, NJ and London: Scarecrow 1986, 77-80.

*Rein, Glen: Biological interactions with scalar energy: Cellular mechanisms of action. In: *Proceedings of the 7th International Association for Psychotronics Research, Georgia* 1988.

*Rein, Glen: Effect of non-Hertzian scalar waves on the immune system. *Journal of the U.S. Psychotronics Association* 1989, 15-17.

*Rein, Glen: Utilization of a cell culture bioassay for measuring quantum fields generated from a modified caduceus coil. *Proceedings of the 26th International Energy Conversion Engineering Conference*, Boston, MA 1991.

Rein, Glen: *Quantum Biology: Healing With Subtle Energy*. Quantum Biology Research Labs, P.O. Box 60653, Palo Alto, CA 94306, 1992.

Rein, Glen: Role of consciousness on holoenergetic healing: A new experimental approach. *Proceedings of International Society for the Study of Subtle Energies and Energy Medicine, Second Annual Conference*, Boulder, CO: June 1992 (b).

Rejmer, Jerzy: An attempt to measure the bioenergetic effect by nuclear magnetic resonance spectrometry. *Psychotronika* 1985, 86. (Translated from Polish by Alexander Imich.)

Rejmer, Jerzy: A test to measure bioenergetic influence with the aid of spectrometry by nuclear magnetic resonance. *Proceedings of the 6th International Conference on Psychotronic Research 1986*, 25.

Retallack, Dorothy: *The Sound of Music and Plants*. Santa Monica, CA: De Vorss 1973.

Rhine, J.B.: *Extrasensory Perception*. Boston: Branden 1964.

Rhine, J.B./ Feather, S. R.: The study of cases of 'psi-trailing' in animals. *Journal of Parapsychology* 1962, 26, 1-22.

Rhine, Louisa E.: *Hidden Channels of the Mind*. New York: William Morrow 1961.

Rhine, Louisa E.: *ESP in Life and Lab: Tracing Hidden Channels*. New York: MacMillan 1967.

Rhine, Louisa E.: *Mind Over Matter*. New York: Collier 1970.

Richards, John Thomas: *Sorrat: A History of the Neihardt Experiments in Rapport and Telekinesis (1961-1981)*. New Jersey: Scarecrow 1982.

Richmond, Kenneth: Experiments in the relief of pain. *Journal of the Society for Psychical Research* 1946, 33, 194-200.

*Richmond, Nigel: Two series of PK tests on paramecia. *Journal of the Society for Psychical Research* 1952, 36, 577-578.

Rindge, Jeane Pontius (Ed): Quote from *Human Dimensions* 1977, 5(1,2).

Riscalla, Louise Mead: A study of religious healers and healees. *Journal of the American Society for Psychosomatic Dentistry and Medicine* 1982, 29(3), 97-103.

Roberton, Jean: Spiritual healing in general practice. *Journal of Alternative and Complementary Medicine* 1991 (April), 9(4), 11-13; Part II (May), 9(5), 21- 23.

Roberts, C.A.: *Vic Coburn: Man with the Healing Touch.* New York: Thomas Nelson 1975.

Roberts, Estelle: *Fifty Years a Medium.* London: Corgi/ Transworld, 1969.

Roberts, Ursula: *Health, Healing and You.* London: Max Parrish, 1964.

Robinson, Diana: *To Stretch a Plank: A Survey of Psychokinesis.* Chicago, IL: Nelson-Hall 1981.

Rogers, Martha E.: *The Theoretical Basis of Nursing.* Philadelphia, PA: F.A.Davis 1970.

Rogers, Martha E.: Nursing: A science of unitary man. In: Riehl, J.P./ Roy, C. (Eds): *Conceptual Models for Nursing Practice;* 2nd Ed. New York: Appleton-Century-Crofts 1984, 329-337.

Rogo, D. Scott: Psychotherapy and the poltergeist. *Journal of the Society for Psychical Research* 1974, 47, 433-447.

Rogo, D. Scott: In pursuit of the healing force. In: *Fate Magazine. Exploring the Healing Miracle.* Highland Park, IL: Clark 1983(a) (Orig. *Fate Magazine*/March 1983).

Rogo, D. Scott: Psi and shamanism: A reconsideration. *Parapsychology Review* 1983(b), 14(6), 5-9.

Rogo, D. Scott: Can weather make you psychic? *Fate Magazine*/January 1986(a), 39(1), 65-69.

Rogo, D. Scott: The power of prayer. *Fate* (August) 1986(b), 43-50.

Rogo, D. Scott: Science debates therapeutic touch. *Fate* 1986(c), 39(12), 70-77.

Roland, C. G.: Does prayer preserve? *Archives of Internal Medicine* 1970, 125, 580-587. (Reprinted from Galton, F.: Statistical studies into the efficacy of prayer. *Fortnightly Review* 1872, 12, 125-135.)

Rolf, Ida: *Rolfing: The Integration of Human Structures.* Santa Monica, CA: Dennis-Landman 1977.

Roll, Wiliam: *The Poltergeist.* Garden City, New York: Nelson Doubleday 1972.

Roll, William/ Montagno, Elson/ Pulos, Lee/ Giovetti, Paola: Physical mediumship: Some recent claims. *Presentation at* 100th Society for Psychical Research and 25th Parapsychological Association Conference, August 1982.

Romanucci-Ross, L./ Moerman, D.E./ Taneredi, L.R. (Eds): *The Anthropology of Medicine: From Culture to Method.* South Hadley, MA: Bergin & Garvey 1983.

Rose, Louis: Some aspects of paranormal healing. *Journal of the Society for Psychical Research* 1955, 38, 105-120.

Rose, Louis: *Faith Healing.* London: Penguin 1971.

Rossi, Ernest L.: *The Psychobiology of Mind-Body Healing: New Concepts of Therapeutic Hypnosis.* New York, London: WW Norton 1986.

Roud, Paul C.: *Making Miracles: An Exploration Into the Dynamics of Self-Healing.* Wellingborough, England: Thorsons 1990.

Rowlands, D.: Therapeutic touch: Its effects on the depressed elderly. *Australia Nurses Journal* 1984, 13(11), 45-46, 52.

Rubik, B./ Rauscher, E.: Effects on motility behavior and growth rate of salmonella typhimurium in the presence of Olga Worrall. In: Roll, W.G. (Ed): *Research in Parapsychology* 1979, Metuchen, NJ: Scarecrow 1980.

Rush, James E.: *Toward a General Theory of Healing.* Washington, DC: University Press of America 1981.

Russell, Edward W.: *Design for Destiny.* London: Neville Spearman 1971.

*Russell, Edward W.: *Report On Radionics: Science of the Future, the Science Which Can Cure Where Orthodox Medicine Fails.* Suffolk, England: Neville Spearman 1973.

Safonov, Vladimir: Personal experience in psychic diagnostics and healing. In: Vilenskaya, Larissa: *Parapsychology in the USSR, Part III.* San Francisco: Washington Research Center 1981, 42-45.

St. Clair, David: Spiritism in Brazil. *Psychic* (December) 1970, 2(3), 8-14.

St. Clair, David: *Psychic Healers.* New York: Bantam/ Doubleday 1979. (Excerpts reprinted by permission of Doubleday & Co., Inc. Copyright David St. Clair 1974, 1976.)

*Saklani, Alok: Preliminary tests for psi-ability in shamans of Garhwal Himalaya. *Journal of the Society for Psychical Research* 1988, 55(81), 60-70.

*Saklani, Alok: Psychokinetic effects on plant growth: Further studies. In: Henkel, Linda A./ Palmer, John: *Research in Parapsychology* 1989, 1990, 37- 41.

Salmon, E.H.: *He Heals Today: Of a Healer's Case-Book.* Worcs., England: Arthur James 1951. [Cases, very brief]

Salmon, J. Warren (Ed): *Alternative Medicines: Popular and Policy Perspectives.* Metuchen, NJ, London: Tavistock 1984.

Sandner, Donald: Navaho symbolic healing. *Shaman's Drum* 1985, 1, 25-30.

Sandroff, Ronni: A skeptic's guide to therapeutic touch. *R.N.* 1980 (January), 25-30.

Sandweiss, Samuel H.: *Spirit and the Mind.* San Diego, CA: Birth Day 1985.

Sanford, Agnes: *The Healing Light.* St. Paul, MN: Macalester Park 1949.

Sauvin, Pierre Paul, in: Tompkins and Bird (see Burbank, Luther).

Scharfetter, C.: The shaman: Witness of an old culture - Is it revivable? (German with English abstract) *Schweiz. Arch. Neurol. Psychiatr.* 1985, 136(3), 81-95.

Schaut, George B./ Persinger, Michael A.: Subjective telepathic experiences, geomagnetic activity and the ELF hypothesis: Part I. Data analysis. *Psi Research* 1985, 4(1), 4-20.

*Schlitz, Marilyn J.: PK on living systems: Further studies with anesthetized mice. *Presentation at* Southeastern Regional Parapsychological Association, 1982, (Reviewed in: Weiner, Debra H.: Report of the 1982 SERPA Conference. *Parapsychology Review,* 1982, 13(4), 13.)

*Schlitz, Marilyn J./ Braud, William G.: Reiki plus natural healing: An ethnographic/experimental study. *Psi Research* 1985, 4(3/4), 100-123. (Also in: Weiner, Debra/ Radin, Dean (Eds): *Research in Parapsychology 1985.* Metuchen, NJ, and London: Scarecrow 1986, 17-18.)

Schlotfeldt, Rozella M.: Critique of the relationship of touch, with intent to help or heal to subjects' in-vivo hemoglobin values: A study in personalized interaction. *Paper presented at* American Nurses' Association 9th Nursing Research Conference, San Antonio, TX 1973.

Schmeidler, Gertrude: The relation between psychology and parasychology. In: Schmeidler, Gertrude R.: *Parapsychology: Its Relation to Physics, Biology, Psychology and Psychiatry,* Metuchen , New Jersey: Scarecrow 1976.

Schmeidler, Gertrude R./ Hess, Leslie B.: Review of Casdorph, H. Richard, *The Miracles.* In: *Journal of Parapsychology* 1986, 50(1), 75-79.

Schmeidler, Gertrude: Personal communication 1987.

Schmidt, Helmut: Comparison of PK action on two different random number generators. *Journal of Parapsychology* 1974, 38, 47-55.

Schmidt, Helmut: A logically consistent model of a world with psi interactions. In: Oteri, L. (Ed): *Quantum Physics and Parapsychology.* New York: Parapsychology Foundation 1975. 205-228.

Schmidt, Helmut: PK effect on pre-recorded targets. *Journal of the American Society for Psychical Research* 1976, 70, 267-291.

Schmitt, M./ Stanford, R.: Free response ESP during ganzfield stimulation: The possible influence of the menstrual cycle phase. *Journal of the American Society of Psychical Research* 1978, 72, 177.

Schouten, S.A.: Autonomic psychophysiological reactions to sensory and emotive stimuli in a psi experiment. *European Journal of Parapsychology* 1976, 1, 57-71.

Schul, Bill: *The Psychic Frontiers of Medicine.* Greenwich, CT: Fawcett 1977.

*Schutze, Barbara: Group counseling, with and without the addition of intercessory prayer, as a factor in self esteem. In: *Proceedings of the 4th International Conference on Psychotronic Research,* Sao Paulo, Brazil 1979, 330-331.

Schwartz, Stephan A.: *The Alexandria Project.* New York: Delta/ Eleanor Fried/ Dell 1983.

*Schwartz, Stephen: Infrared spectra alteration in water proximate to the palms of therapeutic practitioners. *Preliminary paper* presented at 29th Annual Parapsychological Association Meeting, August 1986; full paper: Los Angeles, CA: Mobius Society. Also in: *Subtle Energies* 1990, 1(1), 43-72.

Schwarz, Berthold E.: Possible telesomatic reactions. *Journal of the Medical Society of New Jersey,* 1967, 64, 600-603.

Scofield, Antony M./ Hodges, David R.: Demonstration of a healing effect in the laboratory using a simple plant model. *Journal of the Society for Psychical Research* 1991, 57, 321-343.

Sergeyev, Gennady: Biorhythms and the biosphere. (Translated from Russian). *Psi Research* 1982, 1(2), 29-31.

Servadio, E.: Unconscious and paranormal factors in healing and recovery. In: *15th Fredric WH Myers Memorial Lecture.* London: Society for Psychical Research 1963.

Setzer, J., Schoneberg: The God of Ambrose Worrall. *Spiritual Frontiers* 1983, 15(2), 15-22.

Shafer, Mark G.: PK metal bending in a semi-formal group. In: *Research in Parapsychology 1980.* Metuchen, NJ: Scarecrow 1981, 33-35.

Shallis, Michael: *On Time.* New York: Schocken, 1983.

Shallis, Michael: *The Electric Shock Book.* London: Souvenir 1988.

*Shealy, C. Norman: The role of psychics in medical diagnosis. In: Carlson, Rick (Ed): *Frontiers of Science and Medicine.* Chicago, IL: Contemporary 1975.

*Shealy, C. Norman: Clairvoyant diagnosis. In: Srinivasan, T.M.: *Energy Medicine Around the World.* Phoenix, AZ: Gabriel 1988, 291-303.

Shealy, C. Norman/ Freese, Arthur S.: *Occult Medicine Can Save Your Life.* New York: Bantam 1977.

Shealy, Norman/ Myss, Caroline: *AIDS: Passageway to Transformation.* Walpole, NH: Stillpoint 1987.

Sheldon, Michael: How Joan was cured at Lourdes. In: *Fate Magazine: Exploring the Healing Miracle.* Highland Park, IL: Clark 1983. (Orig. *Fate Magazine,* 1955/February.)

Shen, George J.: Study of mind-body effects and qigong in China. *Advances* 1986, 3(4), 134-142.

Shepard, Stephen Paul: *Healing Energies.* Provo, UT: Hawthorne, 1981.

Sheppard, J.M.: D'Angelo...Italy's great healer. In: *Fate Magazine: Exploring the Healing Miracle.* Highland Park, IL: Clark 1983 (Orig. *Fate Magazine,* 1953/July).

Sherman, Harold: *Your Power to Heal.* New York: Harper and Row 1972.

Shine, Betty: *Mind to Mind: The Secrets of Your Mind Energy Revealed.* London and New York: Bantam 1989.

Shubentsov, Yefim: Healing Seminar. Philadelphia, July 1982.

Siegel, Bernie S.: *Love, Medicine and Miracles: Lessons Learned about Self-Healing from a Surgeon's Experience with Exceptional Patients.* New York: Harper and Row 1986.

Siegel, Bernard S.: *Peace, Love and Healing.* London: Ryder 1990.

Sieveking, Paul: The strange world of twins. *The Unexplained* 1981, 5(57), 1121-1125.

Silbey, Uma: *The Complete Crystal Guidebook: A Practical Guide to Self Development, Empowerment and Healing.* San Francisco: U-Read 1986.

Singer, M. et al.: Indigenous treatment for alcoholism: The case of Puerto Rican spiritism. *Medical Anthropology* 1984, 8(4), 246-273.

Singer, Philip (Ed): *Traditional Healing: New Science or New Colonialism?* Buffalo, NY: Conch Magazine, 1977.

Skinner, B.F.: *Science and Human Behaviour.* New York: Macmillan 1953.

Slomoff, Danny: Ecstatic spirits: A West African healer at work. *Shaman's Drum* 1986(b), 5, 27-31.

Smith, Cyril W./ Best, Simon: *Electromagnetic Man: Health and Hazard in the Electrical Environment.* London: J.M. Pent and Sons 1989.

Smith, D.M.: Safety of faith healing. *Lancet* (March 15) 1986, 1(8481), 621.

Smith, Fritz Frederick: *Inner Bridges: A Guide to Energy Movement and Body Structure.* Atlanta, GA: Humanics New Age 1986.

Smith, Huston: *Forgotten Truth: The Primordial Tradition.* New York: Harper/ Colophon 1977.

*Smith, Justa: Paranormal effects on enzyme activity. *Human Dimensions* 1972, 1, 15-19.

Smith, Warren: *Strange and Miraculous Cures.* New York: Ace 1969.

*Snel, Frans W.J.J.: PK influence on malignant cell growth. *Research Letter of the University of Utrecht* 1980, 10, 19-27.

*Snel, Frans/ Hol, P.R.: Psychokinesis experiments in casein induced amyloidosis of the hamster. *European Journal of Parapsychology* 1983, 5(1), 51-76.

Snel, F./ Millar, B.: PK with the enzyme trypsin. *Unpublished manuscript,* 1982.

Snel, Frans/ Millar, Brian: The elements of so called 'paranormal healing:' Can these be identified from modern medical practice? *Nederlandse Tydschrift voor Integrale Geneeskunde* 1984, 1(3), 15-19.

*Solfvin, Gerald F.: Studies of the effects of mental healing and expectations on the growth of corn seedlings. *European Journal of Parapsychology* 1982(a), 4(3), 287-323.

*Solfvin, Gerald F.: Psi expectancy effects in psychic healing studies with malarial mice. *European Journal of Parapsychology* 1982(b), 4(2), 160-197.

Solfvin, Gerald F.: Towards a model for mental healing studies in real life settings. In: Roll, W.G./ Beloff, J./ White, R.A. (Eds): *Research in Parapsychology 1982.* Metuchen, NJ: Scarecrow 1983, 210-214.

Solfvin, Jerry: Mental healing. In: Krippner, Stanley (Ed): *Advances in Parapsychological Research.* Jefferson, NC: McFarland 1984, 31-63. [Reviews sketchily most of the studies in this bibliography, plus several unpublished studies not covered here, including studies of telepathic control over movements of animals.]

Spiritual Frontiers Editor: Research report: Setzer's sanctuary effect. *Spiritual Frontiers* 1980, 12(1), 20-23.

Spraggett, Allen: *Kathryn Kuhlman: The Woman who Believed in Miracles.* New York: World 1970.

Stanford, Rex G.: An experimentally testable model for spontaneous psi events: I. Extrasensory events. *Journal of the American Society for Psychical Research* 1974(a), 68(1), 34-57.

Stanford, Rex G.: An experimentally testable model for spontaneous psi events: II. Psychokinetic events. *Journal of the American Society for Psychical Research* 1974(b), 68(4), 321-356.

Stanford, Rex G.: The application of learning theory to ESP performance: A review of Dr. C.T. Tart's monograph. *Journal of the American Society for Psychical Research*

1977, 71, 55-80.

Stanford, Rex G.: Towards reinterpreting psi events. *Journal of the American Society for Psychical Research* 1978, 72, 197-214.

Stanford, R.G./ Fox, C.: An effect of release of effort in a psychokinetic task. In: Morris, J.D./ Roll, W.G./ Morris, R.L. (Eds): *Research in Parapsychology 1974*. Metuchen, NJ: Scarecrow 1975. 61-63.

Stanford, R.G., et al.: Psychokinesis as psi-mediated instrumental response. *Journal of the American Society for Psychical Research* 1975, 69, 127-133.

Steadman, Alice: *Who's the Matter With Me*. Marina del Rey, CA: De Vorss 1969.

Stearn, Jess: *Edgar Cayce: The Sleeping Prophet*. New York: Bantam 1967.

Stelter, Alfred: *Psi-Healing*. New York: Bantam 1976.

Stemman, Roy: New teeth for old. *The Unexplained* 1983, 12 (139), 2770-2773.

Stemman, Roy: Surgeon from the other side. *The Unexplained* 1983, 12(142), 2838-2840.

Stokes, Douglas M.: Promethian fire: The view from the other side. *Journal of Parapsychology* 1987, 51(3), 249-270.

Strauch, Inge: A contribution to the problem of "spiritual healing", Part II (German); Abstract. *Zeitschrift für Parapsychologie und Grenzgebiete der Psychologie* 1960, 4(1), 24-55. (Abstract translated in *Parapsychology Abstracts International* 1983, 1(2), No. 363.)

Strauch, Inge: Medical aspects of "mental" healing. *International Journal of Parapsychology* 1963, 5(2), 135-165. (Quotes with permission of Parapsychology Foundation, Inc.)

Sudre, Rene: *Treatise on Parapsychology*. Winchester, MA: Allen and Unwin 1960.

Sugrue, Thomas: *There is a River*. New York: Dell 1970.

Swan, Jim: When paranormal is normal: Psi in native American culture. *Psi Research* 1986, 5(1,2), 79-105.

Sykes, Pat: *You Don't Know John Cain?* Gerrard's Cross, England: Van Duren 1979.

Szymanski, Jan A.: Research on changes in the crystallization of copper chloride under the influence of bioenergotherapeutic interaction. *Proceedings of the 6th International Conference on Psychotronics* 1986(a), 145.

Szymanski, Jan A.: Application of electric field measurements in research of bioenergotherapeutic phenomena. In: *Proceedings of the 6th International Conference on Psychotronics* 1986(b), 68-71.

Taft, Adon (Religious Ed.): *Miami Herald/* May 4, 1968.

Takaguchi, Naoko: Miyako Shamanism: Shamans, Clients and Their Interactions. *Unpublished doctoral dissertation,* UCLA 1984.

Takahashi, Masaru/ Brown, Stephen: *Qigong for Health: Chinese Traditional Exercise for Cure and Prevention*. New York: Japan 1986.

Targ, Russell/ Harary, Keith: *The Mind Race: Understanding and Using Psychic Abilities*. New York: Villard 1984.

Targ, Russell/ Puthoff, H.: Information transmission under conditions of sensory shielding. *Nature* 1974, 251, 602-607.

Targ, Russell/ Tart, Charles T.: Pure clairvoyance and the necessity of feedback. *Journal of the Society for Psychical Research* 1985, 79, 485-492.

Tart, Charles T.: Physiological correlates of psi cognition. *International Journal of Parapsychology*. 1963, 5, 375-386.

Tart, Charles: States of consciousness and state-specific sciences. *Science* 1972, 176, 1203-1210.

Tart, Charles T.: The Application of Learning Theory to ESP Performance. *Parapsychological Monographs*. New York: Parapsychology Foundation 1975, 15.

Tart, Charles: Acknowledging and dealing with the fear of psi. *Journal of the American Society for Psychical Research* 1984, 78(2), 133-143.

Tart, Charles T.: Psychics' fears of psychic powers. *Journal of the American Society for Psychical Research* 1986a, 80(3), 279-292.

Tart, Charles T.: *Waking Up*. Boston: New Science/ Shambhala 1986b.

Taylor, Allegra: *I Fly Out with Bright Feathers: The Quest of a Novice Healer*. London: Fontana/ Collins 1987.

Taylor, John: *Superminds: An Investigation into the Supernatural*. London: Picador/ Pan/ Macmillan 1975.

Taylor, J.G./ Balanovski, E.: Is there any scientific explanation for the paranormal? *Nature* 1979, 279, 631-633.

Tebecis, Andris K.: *Mahikari: Thank God for the Answers at Last*. Tokyo, Japan: L.H. Yoko Shuppan 1982.

*Tedder, William H./ Monty, Melissa L.: Exploration of long-distance PK: A conceptual replication of the influence on a biological system. In: Roll, W.G., et al. (Eds): *Research in Parapsychology 1980*. Metuchen, NJ: Scarecrow 1981. 90-93.

Teschler, Wilfried: *The Polarity Healing Handbook: A Practical Introduction to the Healing Therapy of Energy Balancing*. San Leandro, CA: Interbook 1986.

Tester, M.H.: *The Healing Touch*. London: Psychic 1982 (Orig. 1970).

Theosophical Research Center: *The Mystery of Healing*. Wheaton, IL: Theosophical 1980. (Also published under the authorship of 'The Medical Group'.)

Thompson, C.J.S.: *Magic and Healing.* London: Rider, 1946.

Thorley, Kevan: Disappearing gallstones. *Lancet* 1984 (June 2), 1(8388), 1247- 1248.

Thornton, Francis Beauchesne: *Catholic Shrines in the United States and Canada.* New York: Wilfred Funk 1954.

Thurston, Herbert: *The Physical Phenomena of Mysticism.* London: Burns Oates 1952.

Thurston, Herbert: *Ghosts and Poltergeists.* Chicago: Henry Regnery, 1954.

Timosenko, Alexander: Contributions to the investigation of the "Backster effect". *Proceedings of the 6th International Conference on Psychotronics* 1986, 160-163.

Tinworth, Jane: Dynamic healing. *Caduceus* 1989 (No. 7), 10-11.

Tompkins, Peter/ Bird, Christopher: *The Secret Life of Plants.* New York: Harper and Row 1972.

Torrey, E. Fuller: *The Mind Game: Witchdoctors and Psychiatrists.* New York: Bantam 1972.

Tunnell, Gilbert B.: Three dimensions of naturalness: An expanded definition of field research. *Psychological Bulletin* 1977, 84(3), 426-437.

Tunyi, I. et al.: The Influence of geomagnetic activity upon the psychotronical diagnosis and therapy. *Proceedings of the 6th International Conference on Psychotronic Research* 1986, 118-119.

Turner, Gordon: What power is transmitted in treatment? (Part 1 of 4-Part Series). *Two Worlds* 1969 (July), 199-201.

Turner, Gordon: I treated plants, not patients (Part 2 of 4-Part Series). *Two Worlds* 1969 (Aug.), 232-234.

Turner, Gordon: I experiment in absent treatment (Part 3 of 4-Part Series). *Two Worlds* 1969 (Sept.), 281-283.

Turner, Gordon: Psychic energy is the power of life (Part 4 of 4-Part Series). *Two Worlds* 1969 (Oct.), 302-303.

Turner, Gordon: *An Outline of Spiritual Healing.* London: Psychic Press 1970.

Turner, Gordon: *A Time to Heal: The Autobiography of an Extraordinary Healer.* London: Talmy, Franklin 1974.

Ullman, Montague: Symposium: Psychokinesis on stable systems: Work in progress. In: Roll, W.G./ Morris, R.L./ Morris, J.D. (Eds): *Research in Parapsychology 1973.* Metuchen, NJ: Scarecrow 1974(a), 120-125.

Ullman, Montague: Parapsychology and psychiatry Chapter 52.2a; in: Freedman, A./ Kaplan, H./ Saddock, B. (Eds): *Comprehensive Textbook of Psychiatry,* 2nd Ed. Baltimore: Williams and Wilkins 1974(b), p. 2552-2561.

Ullrich, Ann Christine: Traditional healing in the Third World. *Journal of Holistic Medicine* 1984, 6(2), 200-212.

Uphoff, Walter, H./ Uri Geller: *New Frontiers* 1987, Nos. 22/23, 8-9.

Uphoff, Walter/ Uphoff, Mary Jo: *Mind Over Matter: Implications of Masuaki Kiyota's PK Feats with Metal and Film for: Healing, Physics, Psychiatry, War and Peace, Et Cetera.* Oregon, WI: New Frontiers Center 1980.

Uphoff, Walter/ Uphoff, Mary Jo: *New Psychic Frontiers: Your Key to New Worlds.* Gerrards Cross, England: Colin Smythe 1980.

Upledger, John/ Vredevoogd, Jon D.: *Craniosacral Therapy.* Chicago: Eastland 1983.

van der Post, Laurens: *The Lost World of the Kalahari.* Aylesbury, England: Hazell, Watson and Viney 1973.

Vasiliev, Leonid L.: *Mysterious Phenomena of the Human Psyche* (translated from Russian). New Hyde Park, NY: University Books 1965.

Vasiliev, L.L.: *Experiments in Distant Influence: Discoveries by Russia's Foremost Parapsychologist.* New York: Dutton 1976. (Previously published as *Experiments in Mental Suggestion; Rev. Ed.* Hampshire, England: Gally Hill Press/ Institute for the Study of Mental Images 1963. [See also review of the latter by Rush, J.H.]

*Vaughan, A.: Investigation of Silva Mind Control claims. In: *Research in Parapsychology 1973.* Metuchen, NJ: Scarecrow 1974, 51.

Vilenskaya, Larissa V.: Optimal period for biofield activity. *International Journal of Paraphysics* 1976(a), 19(1 & 2), 9-12.

Vilenskaya, Larissa: A scientific approach to some aspects of psychic healing. *International Journal of Paraphysics* 1976(b), 10(3), 74-79.

Vilenskaya, Larissa: On PK and related subjects' research in the USSR. In: Uphoff, Walter/ Uphoff, Mary Jo: *Mind over Matter.* Oregon, WI: New Frontiers Center 1980.

Vilenskaya, Larissa: Psychoregualtion and psychic healing. In: *Parapsychology in the USSR, Part I.* San Francisco: Washington Research Center 1981, 26-33.

Vilenskaya, Larissa: Development of abilities of remote diagnostics and psychic healing (of Barbara Ivanova). In: Vilenskaya, Larissa (Translator and Editor): *Parapsychology in the USSR, Part III.* San Francisco: Washington Research Center 1981, 46-51.

Vilenskaya, Larissa: Bioelectronics in Leningrad and Alma-Ata. *Psi Research* 1982, 1(4), 27-35.

Vilenskaya, Larissa: Psi and qigong in China: Interview with Paul Dong. *Psi Research* 1985(a), 4(1), 81-95.

Vilenskaya, Larissa (Ed): Soviet "accumulators" of healing energies. *Psi Research* 1985(b), 4(1), 68-78.

Vilenskaya, Larissa: Qigong, psi, healing and human potential in the People's Republic of China. *Psi Research* 1985(c), 4(3/4), 124-133.

Vilenskaya, Larissa: "Extraordinary" Israelis. *Psi Research* 1985(d), 4(3/4), 148-163.

Vilenskaya, Larissa: Around Italy in search of "miracles": The healers who work with animals. *Psi Research* 1985(e), 4(3/4), 164-180.

Vilenskaya, Larissa: Firewalking and beyond. *Psi Research* 1985(f), 4(2), 89-109.

Vilenskaya, Larissa: Understanding and healing animals: Interview with Penelope Smith, animal consultant. *Psi Research* 1986, 5(1,2), 208-213.

Villoldo, Alberto/ Krippner, Stanley: *Healing States: A Journey into the World of Spiritual Healing and Shamanism.* New York: Fireside/ Simon and Schuster 1987.

Vogel, M.: Man-plant communication. In: Mitchell, E.D./ White, J. (Eds): *Psychic Exploration.* New York: G.P. Putnam's Sons 1974.

Vu, Alexander: Determining blood pressure at a distance. In: Vilenskaya, Larissa (Translator and Editor): *Parapsychology in the USSR, Part III.* San Francisco: Washington Research Center 1981, 61-62.

Wallace, Amy/ Henkin, Bill: *The Psychic Healing Book.* New York: Delacorte 1978.

*Wallack, Joseph Michael: Testing for the Psychokinetic Effect on Plants: Effect of a Laying-on of Hands on Germinating Corn Seed. *M.S. thesis,* West Georgia College 1982; summarized in *Psychological Reports* 1984, 55, 15-18.

Watkins, Graham K.: Psychic healing: The experimental viewpoint. In: Roll, W.G. (Ed) *Research in Parapsychology 1978.* Metuchen, NJ: Scarecrow 1979, 21-23.

*Watkins, G.K./ Watkins, A.M.: Possible PK influence on the resuscitation of anesthetized mice. *Journal of Parapsychology* 1971, 35(4), 257-272.

Watkins, G.K./ Watkins, Anita: Apparent psychokinesis on static objects by a "gifted" subject: A laboratory demonstration. In: Roll, W.G., et al. (Eds): *Research in Parapsychology 1973.* Metuchen, NJ: Scarecrow 1974.

*Watkins, G.K./ Watkins, A.M./ Wells, R.A.: Further studies on the resuscetation of anesthetized mice. In: Roll, W.G./ Morris, R.L./ Morris, J.D. (Eds): *Research in Parapsychology 1972.* Metuchen, NJ: Scarecrow 1973, 157-159.

Watson, Lyall: *The Romeo Error.* Garden City, New York: Anchor/ Doubleday 1975.

Watson, Lyall: *Lifetide.* New York: Bantam 1979.

Webster, H.: *Taboo, A Sociological Study.* Stanford, CA: Stanford University Press 1942.

*Wells, Roger/ Klein, Judith: A replication of a "psychic healing" paradigm. *Journal of Parapsychology* 1972, 36, 144-147.

*Wells, Roger/ Watkins, Graham: Linger effects in several PK experiments. In: Morris, J.D./ Roll, W.G./ Morris, R.L. (Eds). *Research in Parapsychology 1974.* Metuchen, NJ: Scarecrow 1975, 143-147.

West, D.J.: The investigation of spontaneous cases. *Proceedings of the Society for Psychical Research* 1948(b), 264-300.

West, D.J.: *Eleven Lourdes Miracles.* London: Helix 1957.

Westerbeke, Patricia/ Gover, John/ Krippner, Stanley: Subjective reactions to the Phillipino "healers:" A questionnaire study. In: Morris, J.D./ Roll, W.G./ Morris, R.L. (Eds): *Research in Parapsychology 1976.* Metuchen, NJ: Scarecrow 1977, 70-71.

Westlake, Aubrey T.: *The Pattern of Health: A Search For a Greater Understanding of the Life Force in Health and Disease.* New York: Devin-Adair 1961.

Westlake, A.: *The Pattern of Health: A Search for a Greater Understanding of the Life Force in Health and Disease.* Berkeley, CA: Shambala 1973.

Wetzel, Wendy S.: Reiki healing: A physiologic perspective. *Journal of Holistic Nursing* 1989, 7(1), 47-54

Wharton, Richard/ Lewith, George: Complementary medicine and the general practitioner. *British Medical Journal* 1986, 292.

White, John/ Krippner, Stanley (Eds): *Future Science.* Garden City, NY: Anchor/ Doubleday 1977.

White, Rhea: A comparison of old and new methods of response to targets in ESP experiments. *Journal of the Society for Psychical Research* 1964, 58(1), 21-56.

White, Ruth/ Swainson, Mary: *The Healing Spectrum.* Suffolk, England: Neville Spearman, 1979.

Wilbur, Ken: Eye to eye. *Science and Transpersonal Psychology,* Revision, 1979, 2(1).

Wilson, Colin: The horrors of healing. *The Unexplained* 1983, 12(137), 2734-2737.

Wilson, Sheryl C./ Barber, Theodore X.: The fantasy-prone personality: Implications for understanding imagery, hypnosis and parapsychological phenomena. *Psi Research* 1982, 1(3), 94-116.

Winkelman, Michael James: A Cross-cultural Study of Magico-Religious Practitioners. *Unpublished doctoral dissertation,* University of CA, Irvine 1984.

Winn, Godfrey: *The Quest for Healing.* London: Frederick Muller 1956.

*Winston, Shirley: Research in Psychic Healing: A Multivariate Experiment. *Unpublished doctoral dissertation,* Union Graduate School, Yellow Springs, OH 1975.

Wirkus, Mieczyslaw: Personal communications 1987, 1-2-1.

*Wirth, Daniel P.: Unorthodox healing: The effect of noncontact therapeutic touch on the healing rate of full thickness dermal wounds. *M.A. thesis,* JFK University. (Summarized in: Henkel, Linda/ Palmer, John: *Research in Parapsychology 1989, 1990,* 190, 47-52. Also in: *Subtle Energies* 1990, 1(1), 1-20.

Witt, J.: Relieving chronic pain. *Nurse Pract* 1984, 9(1), 36-38.

Wolman, Benjamin B. (Ed): *Handbook of Parapsychology.* New York: Van Nostrand 1977, 547-556.

Wolpe, J.: *Psychotherapy by Reciprocal Inhibition.* Palo Alto, California: Stanford University Press 1958.

Wooding, Valerie: *John Cain Healing Guide.* England: Van Duren 1980.

Worrall, Ambrose A.: A philosophy of spiritual healing. *Spiritual Frontiers* 1983, 15(2), 23.

Worrall, Ambrose A./ Worrall, Olga N.: *The Gift of Healing.* New York: Harper and Row 1965.

Worrall, Ambrose A./ Worrall, Olga N./ Oursler, Will: *Explore Your Psychic World.* New York: Harper and Row 1970. (Quotes reprinted by permission of the publishers.)

Worrall, Olga: *Presentation at* Healing in Our Time Conference, Washington, DC, November 1981.

Worrall, Olga N.: Personal communication 1982.

Wright, Susan M.: The use of therapeutic touch in the management of pain. *Nursing Clinics of North America* 1987, 22(3), 705-714.

Yan, Naihau: Sensational qigong feats. *China Reconstructs* 1985 (July) 34(7), 60-61.

Young, Alan: Some implications of medical beliefs and practices for social anthropology. *American Anthropologist* 1976, 78(1), 5-24.

Young, Alan: *Spiritual Healing: Miracle or Mirage.* Marina del Rey, CA: De Vorss 1981.

Zeng Qing-nan: Qigong - Ancient way to good health. *China Reconstructs* 1985, 34(7), 56-57. (Cited in *Psi Research* 1985, 4(3/4), 139.)

Zezulka, J.: Biotronic healing, *Psychoenergetic Systems* 1976, 1, 145-147. [One healer's view and updates of Tomas Pfeiffer (1992).]

*Zhukoborsky, Savely: An experimental approach to the study of psychic healing. In: Vilenskaya, Larissa (Translator and Editor): *Parapsychology in the USSR, Part III.* San Francisco: Washington Research Center 1981, 52-54.

Zimmels, H.J.: *Magicians, Theologians and Doctors.* London: Edward Goldston and Sons 1952.

Zukav, Gary: *The Dancing Wu Li Masters.* New York: William Morrow 1979.

GLOSSARY

Akasha   The cosmic light from which all consciousness is said (by Eastern mysticism) to derive. Some healers claim their diagnoses and prescriptions derive from 'Akashic' records.

Aura   Halo of color around objects, especially living things perceived by psychics and correlated by them with physical, mental, emotional and spiritual states of the individual. This perception may not occur through the ordinary visual processes, as some psychics report they can see auras with their eyes closed.

BUN (Blood Urea Nitrogen)   A laboratory measure of kidney function.

Clairvoyance   The knowing of information about an animate or inanimate object without sensory cues. (*See also* Psychometry.)

Controls   *In research:* Comparison groups receiving either no treatment or a treatment of known effect which is used as a contrast with groups of patients receiving a new treatment of unknown effects, designated the 'experimental group'. *In mediumistic parlance:* Spirit entities which speak through (control the mind of) the medium, usually in a trance state.

Creatinine   Blood chemistry test reflecting kidney function.

Cushingoid   Bloated appearance from treatment with steroids.

Diastolic   The lower of the pair of numbers used to define blood pressure, reflecting arterial and coronary disease when permanently elevated.

Double Blind Study   Research in which neither the treating physician(s) nor the patients know who received active treatment and who received control (or placebo) treatment.

Dowsing   *see* Radiesthesia and Radionics.

Dyspnea   Shortness of breath.

ECG   Electrocardiogram; an electronic recording of voltages produced by contractions of the heart.

EDA   Electrodermal activity; *see* GSR.

EEG   Electroencephalogram; an electronic recording of voltages between points on the scalp, reflecting in a very rough way some of the electrical activity of the brain, especially at the surface of the cortex. Various wave frequencies have been correlated with different states of consciousness.

EM   Electromagnetic.

EMG   Electromyogram, measuring muscle function, indicating whether certain muscular diseases are present.

EOG   Electro-oculogram, recording of eye movements.

Errors   *see* Research.
Experimenter effect (Rosenthal effect)
Suggestion on the part of an experimenter which leads his subjects to demonstrate the behaviors the experimenter expects to find.
Extra Sensory Perception (ESP)   The obtaining of information by telepathy, clairvoyance, precognition and/or retrocognition, without cues from the 'normal' senses (sight, sound, taste, smell, touch, kinesthesia, etc.).
ESPer   *see* Sensitive.

Faraday cage   Cage of wire mesh which excludes electromagnetic radiations.
Frontalis muscle   Forehead muscle.

Ganzfeld   Standard bland visual and auditory stimuli which are commonly imposed on subjects in order to enhance the occurrence of psi phenomena.
'Goats'   Non-believers in psi (contrasted with 'sheep').
GSR   Galvanic Skin Response, an electric measure of resistance, correlating roughly with states of physical and emotional tension.

Healing   Any systematic, purposeful intervention by a person purporting to help another living thing (person, animal, plant, or other living system or part thereof) to change via the sole process of focused intention or via hand contact or 'passes'. *Type 1 (distant, or absent healing):* The direction of healing solely through   efforts of the mind of the healer to the healee. *Type 2 (touch; near-the-body; or laying-on of hands healing):* The direction of healing through the body of the healer to the healee. This may involve various 'passes' of the hands of the healer around the body.
'Hit'   A successful attmept to produce psi effects; derived from visual 'target' pictures

for psi perception in the laboratory; opposite to 'miss'.
Hypotonic   More dilute.

Iatrogenic   Caused by a medical intervention.
In vitro   In the laboratory.
In vivo   In life outside the laboratory.
IR   Infrared.

(Applied) Kinesiology   Testing of muscle strength to determine allergies and food/medicine sensitives (*described in Chapter II-2*).
Kirlian photography   Methods utilizing a small electrical charge in conjunction with photography to produce photographs of objects with an aura of color around them. Used in East-European countries extensively for diagnosis of disease states in plants, animals and humans.

Manometer   Instrument measuring gas production in cultures of microorganisms.
'Miss'   A failed attempt to produce psi effects; opposite to 'hit'.

NaCl   Chemical designation for table salt or saline, as in body fluids.
Noetic   Having properties which derive from inner experiences which are difficult to describe in linear terms.

Obsession   Used interchangeably with *(see)* Possession.
Oscilloscope   Instrument displaying electromagnetic vibrational patterns on a screen.
Osmotic stress (pressure)   Pressure created within living cells which are placed in solutions that are hypotonic (more dilute than normal body fluids).

Passes   Movements of the hands of a healer

around the body of a healee, either following a prescribed or ritualistic pattern or dictated by the healer's psi or intuitive senses.

PK   *see* Psychokinesis.

PKMB (warm forming)   Bending metal or softening it so that it can be bent via psi effects.

Plumial   Leaflet emerging from seed.

Poltergeist effects (*also designated* **Random Spontaneous Psychokinesis, or RSPK)** Apparently random, spontaneous Psychokinesis, usually associated with the presence of one particular individual who is presumed to be the unconscious agent producing these events.

Possession   The alleged taking over of a person's behavior by a discarnate spirit.

Precognition   Knowing about a future event prior to its occurrence.

Psi   Abbreviation for 'parapsychological', connoting ESP (telepathy, clairvoyance, precognition and retrocognition) and PK; taken from the Greek letter ψ (spoken 'psi').

Psychokinesis (PK)   Moving or transforming an object without use of physical means, commonly referred to as 'mind over matter'. *(See also* PKMB, RSPK, Healing and PS, which seem to be more specific forms of PK.)

Psychic surgery (PS)   Surgery performed with the hands or with a knife, in which very rapid healing occurs, often even instantaneously, usually without pain or excessive bleeding and with no subsequent infection (despite the fact that sterile techniques are not utilized). *PS I:* Healer manipulates aura; *PS II:* Healer manipulates physical body; *PS III:* A combination of I and II.

Psychometry   Clairvoyance focused on a specific object. Psychics report that when a person handles an object, especially over prolonged periods, he leaves an impression

upon that object which sensitives can pick up.

Radicle   Root.

Radiesthesia (Dowsing)   The use of a device (e.g. pendulum, forked tree branch, etc.) to obtain clairvoyant information.

Radionics   The use of more complex devices (usually calibrated, often with dials) to obtain clairsentient information and to project effects psychokinetically (e.g. healing).

Research errors   *Type 1:* Accepting as true something which is not. *Type 2:* Rejecting as invalid an effect which actually has some substance.

Retrocognition   Perceptions of events occurring prior to the time of their perception by the sensitive.

Rosenthal effect   *see* Experimenter effect.

Sensitive (ESPer)   Noun designating a person who has psi abilities.

Shaman   In non-western societies, a person serving as healer, herbalist, and ritual leader for a group of people.

'Sheep'   Believer/s in psi (contrasted with 'goats').

'Sheep-goat' effect   Believers ('sheep') perform significantly better than chance, while disbelievers ('goats') score significantly poorer than chance expectancy on psi tasks.

Sleight-of-hand   'Magic tricks', i.e., clever deceptions which mislead the perceiver to believe that something paranormal might have occurred, when in fact it did not.

Stigmata   Wounds appearing spontaneously, without outside cause for injury, often in the places Christ was wounded.

Subcutaneous   Under the skin, as with injections given at this site.

Super-ESP   Using psi powers to scan the environment for meaningful information which then leads to PK influence over the environment to the benefit of the individual.

Synchronicity   A coincidence which is meaningful to a perceiver or participant in the component events.

Synesthesia   A crossed-sensory perception, such as hearing color.

Systolic   The higher of the pair of numbers used to designate blood pressure, often rising transiently with states of anxiety.

Tachycardia   Excessively rapid heart rate.

Telepathy   The transfer of thoughts, images or commands from one living thing to another, without use of sensory cues.

Thaumaturgy   Sleight-of-hand.

Thoughtography   Production of photographic images by PK.

UV   Ultraviolet.

Visual analog scale (VAS)   Series of numbers (e.g. 1/2/3/4/5) for rating degrees of presence of absence of symptoms such as pain, anxiety, etc. before and after treatments.

(In) vitro   In laboratory culture (contrasted with *in vivo*).

(In) vivo   In the natural living state (contrasted with *in vitro*).

Witness   Object used by dowsers to 'connect' with that which is being dowsed. For instance, in tracing to a missing person, clothing belonging to such people helps the dowser to locate them. A blood or sputum sample may likewise help a dowser connect with a healee for diagnosis and treatment.

Xenoglossy   Speaking a language which was not learned by any known normal means.

LIST OF TABLES

INDEX OF NAMES

INDEX OF SUBJECTS